ORGANIC PROTECTIVE COATINGS

edited by

WILLIAM von FISCHER

Head, Department of Chemistry and Chemical Engineering
Case Institute of Technology

and

EDWARD G. BOBALEK

Associate Professor of Chemistry
Case Institute of Technology

BOOK DIVISION

REINHOLD PUBLISHING CORPORATION

Also Publishers of Chemical Engineering Catalog, Chemical Materials Catalog, Materials & Methods, Progressive Architecture, Advertising Management for American Chemical Society

330 West Forty-Second Street   New York 36, N.Y.

1953

Printed in U. S. A.

Contributing Authors

EDWARD G. BOBALEK
Case Institute of Technology

EDMOND C. BOTTI
E. I. du Pont de Nemours & Co., Inc.

F. L. BROWNE
Forest Products Laboratory, Forest Service, U. S. Department of Agriculture

J. R. DEVORE
The New Jersey Zinc Company (of Pennsylvania)

ARNOLD J. EICKHOFF
National Lead Company Research Laboratories

D. M. GANS
The Arco Company

H. GRINSFELDER
Rohn and Haas Company

FRANK J. HAHN
Monsanto Chemical Company

MYRON KIN
Dow Corning Corporation

R. E. LALLY
The Ferro Chemical Corporation

E. E. MCSWEENEY
Battelle Memorial Institute

CHARLES H. PARKER
Monsanto Chemical Company

F. E. PIECH
Hercules Powder Company

R. W. QUARLES
Mellon Institute

J. L. SAUNDERSON
The Dow Chemical Company

A. J. SHERBURNE
General Electric Company

WILLIAM VON FISCHER
Case Institute of Technology

R. F. WINT
Hercules Powder Company

Preface

Through its Organic Coatings Division, Case Institute of Technology sponsors a number of lecture series, symposia, and conferences in the field of organic coatings. These activities are always planned and scheduled in cooperation with the technical men in the paint and varnish industries in northern Ohio and they are held primarily for the benefit of the employees of these industries and for the students and faculty at Case. Through these activities the technical men and our students and faculty are kept abreast of the advances in the coatings field.

The present volume, like the earlier volume, "Paint and Varnish Technology," is an outgrowth of one of these lecture series. The very large demand for copies of the earlier volume and the many requests which have been received for copies of the lectures of the present series have made the editors decide to issue this series in book form in order that anyone who wishes may obtain the information.

The material in this book serves as a complement to the material in "Paint and Varnish Technology." In this volume greater emphasis is placed on the problems of coatings formulation from the viewpoint of paint as an engineering material.

In the main, coatings research and development are motivated by several objectives:

1. Given a particular problem for protective coatings, attempt to find materials or methods which satisfy the needs proposed by fixed engineering requirements.

2. Beginning with new raw materials which may have possibilities in organic coatings, derive the method of use and determine the range of utility of such materials.

3. Extend the utility of traditional materials by developing new methods for their use.

4. Solve any problems of chemistry or physics required to promote any of the above objectives.

A separate series of lectures could be planned to cover each of these aspects of coatings research. However, such an organization of material, while seemingly more logical, would not really present the varied viewpoints of coatings technology as it exists today. The selection of material in this volume was intended to show by example how all of these divergent

ideas contribute to the development of the coatings art. That is, examples
are presented to show the direction of coatings development as it is
influenced by engineers in other technical arts, by suppliers of raw materials, by coatings and corrosion engineers, and by scientists who
provide the practical engineer with fundamental research.

Where alternate choices needed to be made to illustrate the same
viewpoint, the selection was presented which at the time seemed most
complete. Throughout, emphasis was placed on demonstrating the new
technical and economic problems which arise when formulation is based
on new synthetic raw materials.

W v F
E G B

Cleveland, Ohio
September 8, 1953

Contents

viii   CONTENTS

1 : Paint as an Engineering Material

W. von FISCHER

Case Institute of Technology
Cleveland, Ohio

It seems as though the phrase "paint as an engineering material" is becoming as much used today as the old advertising slogan "Save the surface and you save all." Except to those who are actively engaged in organic protective coatings work the full import of the former phrase may not be obvious. Therefore, some consideration may well be given to the phrase as such, and to its importance to those who are concerned with the technology of paint and its application.

Paint is not a simple material or even an easily defined class of materials such as steel, wood, glass, or other engineering materials. It is extremely difficult to define it at all in terms of composition. It can be composed of few or many of literally thousands of natural and synthetic chemicals, both inorganic and organic. Any definition of a paint in terms of composition would have to be indirect; for example, "Paint is a material of at least partially organic nature which can be used to coat surfaces with films that protect and decorate." The preparation of films which perform the desired functions can involve the manipulation of a great variety of important techniques using a large number of materials. The way in which this is done is still very much of an art—an art which today uses many techniques of other fields of science, but which, nevertheless, still remains difficult to formalize.

To a paint technologist, the expression "paint as an engineering material" has special emphasis, since his mind contrasts it immediately with the infrequently stated but more readily appreciated fact of "paint as an artistic material." To understand this it would be well to review the history of paint.

From the early history of man we find that it was the artist who accumulated the materials and devised the methods which made it possible to make a paint. Since scientists were not involved in the development, naturally the approach was quite different from that used in a modern science, in which objective data are accumulated and analyzed. Through centuries, the sole guide for progress was an aesthetic concept of what an artist wanted after a brush stroke. The gauge of the brush stroke solved the enormous complexity of the engineering problems and left us with an art of paint. For example, to this day we still have not advanced the new science of rheology to such a state that we can make an engineering analysis of the brush stroke which was the guide to all the early development.

When did this art of paint manufacture develop? Very long ago. It is necessarily as old as painting itself, and we find primitive cave drawings nearly as old as the archaeological history of man. A very advanced stage of color knowledge is shown in surviving examples of some Aegean frescoes, some of which go as far back as 1500 B.C. In the period 200 B.C.– 600 A.D. an even greater maturity of the art of color formulation is demonstrated in the frescoes preserved in the dry caves at Ajanta (near Bombay, India). By the time of Botticelli in the fifteenth century, the painting art and the art of paint-making had reached a perfection which has never been surpassed from the viewpoint of manipulation of color.

Insofar as decorative properties are concerned, paint-making on a limited scale was an old art before European civilization began, and certainly it has not been improved very much as a decorative medium in the age of modern engineering. However, some important improvements were made in other respects as much as 500 years ago.

(1) Development of better varnish binders that made the colors more durable. Though accomplished in a limited way, this was done so well that it made possible the first nondecorative use of paint, namely, as a protective medium.

(2) Coincident with the development of paints for protective purposes was the widespread commercial use of coatings. Paint-making expanded to a large production basis—gallons instead of the artist's ounces. The basic techniques, however, were essentially the same. A stone mill replaced the mortar and pestle as a grinding medium; 50- to 500-gallon varnish pots replaced the cook-stove kettle; mechanical presses replaced hand mulling for extraction of linseed oil from the flax seed, and the world was searched for substitute resins which in some instances were not better than the artists' materials, but which could be obtained in commercial quantities. This manufacturing history is old, compared with the machine age, but it is a comparatively recent development in the centuries-old history of paint-making. For example, the first varnish and paint factories were established in the industrial nations of England, the United States, France, the Netherlands, and Germany in the late eighteenth

and nineteenth centuries. In some lands where paint probably originated, such as India, China, and other nations of the Orient, there still is very little of a commercial paint industry as we know it. In the United States the paint industry as measured by dollar volume of sales now represents close to a one and one-half billion dollar operation.

Just how good was the ancient art of paint? We must admit that it was very good. The industrial era, which from the very start had to develop engineering skills for the preparation of other engineering materials, was able to ignore paint advances for nearly a century: painting of a machine, apparatus, or manufactured articles was an afterthought in engineering design. In protective and decorative properties, existing paints were good enough and cheap enough to be taken for granted. It is only within recent years that other industrial arts have begun to be concerned with the quality of paint, its composition, and with methods of its application. Engineers began to worry about coatings in their original design calculations instead of regarding the coatings problem as inconsequential— something to be taken for granted, and no more deserving of special engineering attention than affixing a label to a product. At this time, paint men began to turn their thoughts toward integrating their activities with other engineers, and other engineers began to examine the paint art to see what could be done to satisfy their increasingly involved needs. This was the time when paint had to forsake its status as an isolated art and find a means of joint communication and cooperative research with other fields of engineering. This reorientation in thinking is the fact that gives point to the phrase "paint as an engineering material." Some consideration of how far this has gone and what remains to be done to make the change in viewpoint complete will now be considered.

Although in its basic principles paint technology is very old, more research progress has been made in the past 30 years than during the previous five centuries. Some indication of the growth of this field of scientific endeavor can be estimated by noting the part played in it by the chemist and chemical engineer. Prior to 1910, the number of scientists working in paints was so small that almost any one of them could name all his colleagues in the field. By 1950, about one chemist in 25 was engaged directly in the design or manufacture of coatings. Only very few other engineering sciences, such as petroleum technology, have required this much technical talent. Today at least six high-quality technical journals in the English language are devoted largely to coatings. The Paint, Plastic, and Printing Ink Division of the American Chemical Society is one of the largest divisions of the Society. None of the industrial arts or crafts that are of a comparable age with paint has been given as much attention by modern scientists. There must be some important reason why this one among the many ancient craft-arts should be receiving so much scientific attention.

The reason is not difficult to find: it is the fact that modern technology is based on steel and on nonferrous metals. A fact implicitly known by many and well appreciated by too few is that metals are among the more easily perishable forms of matter. Metals are subject to chemical decomposition in a variety of environments and for a variety of causes. The whole problem of preserving them is known as corrosion control. Corrosion, if it were not at least partially controlled, would make our present mechanical age virtually impossible.

A great deal of research has been carried on for the purpose of minimizing corrosion losses by alloying, metal coating, and chemical treatment. This type of research is difficult, since there is not just one corrosion problem, from the viewpoint of the why and the how of its occurrence, but hundreds of chemical variations of the process, all of which produce the same disastrous end result. This fact has greatly hampered research on the problem of corrosion inhibition; and many remedies, even when found, fit only special circumstances and frequently are too costly. The most economic and most general attack on the corrosion problem is through the use of organic protective coatings which exclude all varieties of chemical environments. Had there been no early and universal solution to this difficult corrosion problem it is probable that our industrial age could not have developed in its present directions.

The industrial era began in the nineteenth century; however, as we have pointed out, paint technology has received extensive scientific attention only in the past three decades of the twentieth century. It is only fair to ask why a paint art that served the industrial age for nearly a century in providing corrosion protection should suddenly become inadequate and require an army of scientists for its modernization.

The answer to this question is that within recent years the industrial age has brought forth many new developments, which have made new demands on paint. While coatings of medieval origin were able to satisfy the more modest demands of the nineteenth century industrial era, with respect to protective properties, they were not good enough for the twentieth, as most of them were not originally adapted for protection of metals. Where protection could be obtained, decorative properties had to be sacrificed, as for example in the use of asphalt coatings. Where decoration was important, as in the attempt to use colored coach paints of the old varnish type on automobiles, the paint would not withstand drastic service conditions. These coach paints, which were our direct ʰᵃge from the medieval artists, *look* the same when first applied as ᵕn modern automobiles. In contrast, however, a service exposure of two or three months would deteriorate these coach paints more than would five to ten years of similar exposure in the case of modern automotive finishes.

Prior to the twentieth century the old finishes were satisfactory only because frequent repainting was accepted as a necessity. When the quantity of metal equipment was relatively small and labor was cheap, these finishes served the need. When the use of metals became more widespread, economic necessity demanded improvements in coatings. This became all the more important as capital costs of equipment increased because of its greater complexity. For example, a metal ship hull had to be dry-docked for repainting more often than a wood hull. If a ship is expected to spend ten per cent of its life in dry dock for repainting, an extra ship must be purchased at costs running into millions if ten must be kept in continuous operation. Continuous process chemical plants or other manufacturing plants are costly to shut down for maintenance; hence better coatings which allow for better corrosion protection and fewer shutdowns are an economic necessity. Our old industrial economy was largely a batch or piecework process; hence the losses due to inferior protection and more frequent maintenance work were not as costly as they would be on modern operations.

Many new situations also arose; for example, the introduction of the light metals, for which medieval paints were totally unsuited.

Another example is provided by oil-drilling rigs which are to be used in ever less favorable situations, for example, in marine tidelands. In this last instance the equipment can be given only the initial protective coating, since maintenance of underwater structures would require disassembling and removal to paint shops. If coatings had not been produced of a quality such that the first and only coating would last through the service life, many such a multimillion dollar installation of marine oil-drilling rigs or other marine construction projects could not have been undertaken.

Examples like these could be multiplied endlessly, and all would confirm the point that coatings design had to keep pace with other engineering projects which used metals; otherwise many modern engineering developments would not have been feasible. The existence of these complicated engineering developments indicates that at least passable solutions have been found for their critical corrosion protection problems. This progress in coatings is the result of the work of several thousand coatings technologists, who have revolutionized the paint art; they have done so largely by adapting the art to the use of synthetic resins, which are the product of the last 30 years of research in plastics. During this period the technologies of plastics and paint have become so intimately related that they are now hard to separate into distinct classifications. Table 1.1 lists some popular paint-vehicle systems that are based on synthetic resins.

TABLE 1.1.　SYNTHETIC RESINS FOR MODERN COATINGS

Class I. Systems containing alkyd resins
   A. Alkyd resins, oil-modified
      1. oxidizing (air-drying types)
      2. nondrying types
   B. Resin mixtures containing alkyds
      a. Two component mixtures
         1. alkyds plus aminoplasts
         2. alkyds plus nitrocellulose
         3. alkyds plus phenoplasts
         4. alkyds plus chlorinated rubber
      b. Three component mixtures
         1. alkyds plus epichlorohydrin resin plus aminoplasts
         2. alkyds plus vinyl resins plus aminoplasts
   C. Alkyds modified by chemical reaction with other resins
      1. styrenated alkyds (air-drying or baking, with or without aminoplasts)
      2. silicone alkyds
Class II. Resin systems containing no drying oil or alkyd
   A. Curing (or thermosetting) types
      1. phenoplasts
      2. aminoplasts
      3. epichlorohydrin resins
      4. allyl and other polyester resins
      5. silicone resins
   B. Noncuring (or thermoplastic) types
      1. resins derived from cellulose
      2. synthetic rubber types
      3. vinyl resin types
      4. acrylic resins
      5. nylon

Besides making possible modern automotive, marine, machinery, and other coatings of outstanding corrosion protection properties, this use of synthetic materials has permitted the achievement of decorative properties equal to and even superior in some respects to those of the art of the ancient painters. These modern finishes which we take for granted on our automobiles, home appliances, ships, machinery, and interior decoration are almost entirely based on new resins and new pigments that did not exist 30 years ago. Only three types of paints have failed, in part, to find a modern synthetic replacement, namely, exterior house paints, red-lead oil paints for structural steel, and asphaltic coatings; and even these have been modified substantially and improved by synthetic chemistry.

Quality improvement for better decorative properties and better protection brought under control the corrosion problem in a technical sense. Another accomplishment of great importance was to adapt these improved paints to the continuous production line. If this had not been done the finishing problem would have been a bottleneck to modern production rates, which largely determine the economics of the industrial age. Coatings of 50 years ago, even if they had been adequate from the standpoint of protection, took too long to apply and to dry. For example, it took days or even weeks to apply a satisfactory finish to an automobile. Coating engineers, besides solving the quality problem of finishes by using synthetic materials, also discovered how to apply finishes rapidly. To apply and dry a modern industrial finish on a home appliance, automobile or furniture now requires only minutes or at most a few hours.

In a general way, the foregoing discussion brings the history of paint up to date. Much that is interesting could be added to describe the details of modern paint technology. At least we have seen how advancement of other engineering technologies has brought about the development of paints which have modernized the old art. The purpose of this review, however, is not only to relate the story of the past but also to speak about the future of paint engineering research. From what we have said so far, one might be left with the impression that the paint art has been rapidly modernized to such an extent that it is ready to serve the next 100 years of industrial engineering development, just as the heritage we received from the artists was able to take care of the first century of service to the mass production age. This is far from true. As the paint technologist looks at the new requirements proposed by other engineers, he realizes that his position is even more critical today than it was 30 years ago, and that some of the greatest problems remain to be solved.

Let us concern ourselves now with some of the details of this research challenge. It must be met if our industrial development is to progress; when it is met, very probably in retrospect the whole accomplishment in coatings research of the last 30 years may be as obsolete as are now the nineteenth century coach paints. In fact, when we set up our research objective, we will realize that this supposedly golden era of research actually contains less novelty than has been supposed, and that it really has been only an elaboration and complication of an ancient art with new materials.

As we have seen, the advances in paint technology in the last 30 years involved these two features:

(1) Improving the corrosion protection properties of paints without

sacrificing any of the decorative or color properties of the ancient art.

(2) Solving the problem of rapid application of coatings so that painting would not be a critical limitation to mass production. In a large measure this was accomplished by the discovery and use of synthetic resins and pigments and by outstanding engineering developments in paint application, especially the use of spray-painting and baking techniques suitably adjusted to give a continuous process.

In only a few years the old "white lead and oil," "black-japan," and oil-varnish era of paint did not become obsolete, but rather seemed to be absorbed into and to become a small part of a greatly expanded technology based on plastics or synthetic resins.

It would be pleasant if we could report that in the course of this expansion by chemistry of synthetics the empirical paint art had been changed entirely into a branch of engineering governed by well understood scientific principles. Unfortunately this is not the case. The old paint art did not vanish, nor did new engineering principles take over. The effort was all in the reverse direction—new materials were adapted only if their properties could be altered so as to make them similar to the old and so that old techniques, with some modern refinements, could still be used to put a paint together. It is certainly surprising that the old art was sufficiently versatile to absorb such a tremendous wealth of detail in new materials when the need arose without essentially changing its nature with respect to its working rules. Among many other things this required such expedients as developing chemical alterations of the surfaces of new pigments so that they could be wet properly and thus be suspended in such vehicles as linseed oil. Conversely, when a synthetic resin was used, some oil was incorporated as a part of the chemical structure of the resin so that lyophilic or oil-loving pigments could be compounded properly into the resins.

Today paint manufacturing finds itself in a position such that, in order to progress further, it cannot merely adapt old ideas, but must start more or less from the beginning and build new practices on a foundation of basic scientific and engineering principles. It would be impractical to suggest that we should or could forget all that has come before, and start out to develop a paint technology from the beginning as was done, for example, with plastics and titanium metal. Rather, it is now necessary to perform some critical research to explain the reasons why the old art was successful before the requirements demanded of it became too severe. Having achieved such understanding, then we might apply such scientific knowledge to solve or to by-pass existing critical problems in coatings development.

We might refer briefly to a few of the research problems which face the coatings industry.

1. The Dispersion Problem

A problem of both the old and new paint technology is that of dispersing solids (i.e., pigments) in liquids (vehicles) so as to achieve two conditions:

(a) A stable pigment dispersion with a pigment of the proper fineness for optimum decorative properties.

(b) Proper consistency properties in the paint.

The ancients hit upon a combination where nature solved this problem. Earth pigments (mostly oxide types) are naturally complementary to the dispersion-promoting (surface-active) agents in natural vegetable oils. Because of this fortunate and natural coincidence, it was possible to make paints of very high quality with comparatively little difficulty. As long as paint technology used these natural materials, the art was adequate. However, modern demands on the technology to produce paints that are of consistent quality, which are more durable, and which possess superior decorative properties, require a departure from the use of traditional materials. Alternate materials of potentially superior properties were the new synthetic pigments and vehicles. To the extent that the physical (or surface chemistry) properties of the new synthetics resembled the old, they could be used; for example, synthetic oxide pigments resembled the natural earths, and oil-modified alkyds in some degree resembled oleoresinous varnishes.

However, there is a limit to the ease with which we can develop materials that are better in some respect than the traditional standards but which resemble the old in their fundamental surface chemistry. The technology is straining these limits now—for example, if we require durable blue and green pigments of high tinctorial strength and excellent color purity (e.g., phthalocyanines and other insoluble organic dyes), we can no longer duplicate the surface properties of natural earths or clays without sacrificing some of the desirable features potentially in the new pigment. The unsolved dispersion problems limit the effective use of these new materials. Also, synthetic resins, which produce protective films that are superior to drying oil films, may no longer have dispersion agents in their composition which are complementary to even standard pigments, and these agents must be introduced synthetically. There are many new and potentially useful synthetic pigments and vehicles which cannot prove their worth until we learn enough about the physicochemical mechanisms of dispersion to guide chemical engineering in producing practical coatings from such materials. A schematic illustration of the dispersion problem is shown in Figure 1.1.

2. The Solubility Problem

The primitive paints contained very little volatile material. When varnishes displaced simple drying oils as vehicles, the use of rather simple solvents became necessary in order to control the working consistency of the paint and to establish optimum rates of film formation. When

DISPERSION vs. AGGREGATION

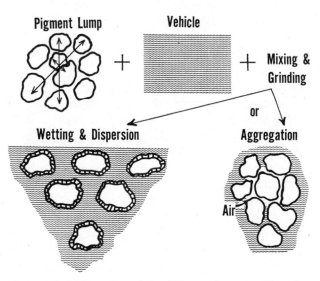

Figure 1.1.   A simplified illustration of the difference between dispersion and aggregation. The latter situation may prevail if the surface chemistry of pigment and vehicle are not complementary.

synthetic resins were introduced, the need for a greater variety of more active solvents became evident. Extensive developments in solvent technology made possible a great variety of synthetic resin-containing paint vehicles. This greatly enhanced the design capacity of coatings technology. Eventually, however, the rate of progress in these directions became slow. If better synthetic resins than those now available are desired, we are faced with the dilemma that synthetic resins become less soluble as their physical and chemical properties are improved. For the better resins it is even now necessary to heat the paint in order to establish a workable consistency with satisfactory application properties even when thinners of maximum solvency power are used. If we must rely on soluble binders, it then seems as if paint technology cannot progress far beyond the present in the use of improved resins. Fortunately, this problem has been recognized at least implicitly, and during the last few years considerable effort has been made to by-pass the solubility or solvent problem for improved types of thermoplastic resins. This has been largely through two developments which in the next decade may do much to revolutionize paint technology:

(a) **Dispersion Resins.** Resins are treated, more or less, as if they were insoluble pigments and are dispersed, but not dissolved, in a liquid vehicle; for example, emulsions (if the resin particles are dispersed in water) or organosols (if dispersed in organic liquids). The theory of film formation from such dispersion resin systems can be very complicated, and will be described later in this text.

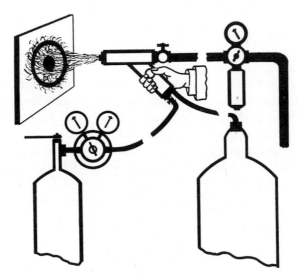

Figure 1.2.   Flame spraying—a hot melt technique for applying coatings of insoluble synthetic resins. A cloud of powdered resin suspended in air is provided to the special gun from the feed tank on the right. The resin is melted on being blown through the flame shrouded nozzle of the gun and freezes to a continuous film on the target area.

(b) **Hot Melt Techniques.** These are useful if the resins are stable above their melting points. Where the stability period may be of very short duration, a technique of flame-spraying has been developed; a resin is liquefied for only a fraction of a second while it passes from a spray gun, and then solidifies on the work. Even many unstable resins can be handled in this manner providing that the induction period of the decomposition reaction at melt temperatures is appreciable. Chemical engineering research is devoting considerable attention to this valuable technique (Figure 1.2). Plastics derived from ethylene polysulfides, polytetrafluoroethylene, polyethylene and many others might be handled in this manner.

(c) **Reactive Solvents.** In these, a relatively low molecular weight resin is dissolved in a solvent. However, in response to special conditions, such as would be induced by heat or the addition of catalysts, the solvent can react with the resin so as to create a new type of resin film of increased molecular weight and superior properties.

A large number of systems of this kind have been tried. Many have today become useful in adhesives technology. Very few have as yet shown much promise as protective coatings; however, it can be anticipated that this interesting principle will not be neglected in coatings research.

3. The Adhesion Problem

No matter how great the chemical resistance of a coating, it is of little value for corrosion protection unless it is held to the metal surface by strong attractive forces. If the film is not held firmly and if a corrosive material enters underneath it because of microscopic flaws in the film, the metal can corrode freely and possibly even at an accelerated rate underneath the film. In the old paint art, adhesion was not much of a problem. The paint contained oil. Metal surfaces ordinarily have an oxide film. Oils wet oxide films to form an adherent bond in the same way in which oils wet the surface of natural iron oxide pigments. Hence the dispersion problem and adhesion problem have much in common. However, oil-containing films, no matter how adherent they are, can deteriorate chemically so that eventually protection is lost. If we replace oils with chemically resistant resins, such resins are hard to pigment and they are even less adherent to the oxidized surface of metals. Whatever is done to change the resin so as to make it more adherent usually reduces its chemical resistance; hence we cancel some of the advantages of using the synthetic resin.

There is very little hope for an easy solution to this difficult problem. It is certain, however, that the study of metal surface preparations must receive greater emphasis in our research in coatings. Some specialized metal treatments should be possible for surfaces, which, with respect to adhesion, are favorably complementary to each particular type of organic film. The benefit of a process that favors this approach is illustrated by the success of metal treatments in improving the durability of automotive paints. The proper surface preparation (here phosphate treatments) produces a tremendous improvement in promoting lasting adherence of paint film. In the painting of ship bottoms, a resin-bonded phosphate treatment has been found for metal surfaces which promotes adherence of such synthetic resins as would normally not adhere at all to untreated metal. Without the adhesion-promoting treatment, the synthetic resin paint system would probably not withstand a few days of service. With the treatment, the same finish may be durable and protect the ship bottom for years.

For attaching some resins to glass, a treatment with vinyl silane has been found which produces a surface that locks an organic resin chemically to a glass surface when the monomer of the subsequently adherent resin is polymerized on that surface.

The modest successes illustrated by these examples with respect to the means of bridging the antipathy between inorganic and organic surfaces have shown the way. If further use is made of synthetic resins and plastics to obtain even better protective coatings, the greatest progress must be made first in developing adhesion-promoting treatments for various metals.

OTHER FUNCTIONAL PROPERTIES OF PAINT

In referring to the functional properties of paint we often tend to think exclusively of corrosion protection. Without a doubt this is most important; but paints have other functions also, many of which are not trivial. These are rather novel and are the subject matter for current and future research.

Radiation Protection

Originally this problem was a simple one, namely, to reflect the sun's rays so as to prevent overheating of buildings, or especially structures, such as gas and petroleum storage tanks, to reduce danger of built-up pressure or losses from volatilization.

The future demands of aeronautical engineering promise to pose even more serious problems of this nature for aircraft designed for stratosphere flight. In the upper reaches of the earth's atmosphere radiations are very intense, particularly in the ultraviolet, while the ambient temperature of the atmosphere is subzero. A surface that reflects too well will make it difficult to maintain warmth in a ship, whereas if the surface is too absorbing, overheating may become a problem. Design for optimum reflectance or absorption requires good engineering data regarding the reflectance properties of coatings.

Electrical Insulation

Organic coatings are used extensively on electrical insulation. The design problems here are very complicated. Not only must materials have proper electrical properties, such as dielectric strength, power factor, etc. but frequently must be able to withstand elevated temperatures for extended periods. In some cases, as in wire enamels, insulating coatings are subject to a great deal of mechanical shock on machines which wind coils. In motors, the insulation on high-speed rotors must withstand centrifugal shearing or flow. Nearly all the properties of protective coatings in general are required for insulation materials, in addition to a great number of additional demands for special mechanical and electrical properties.

In this field also some of the more recent advances have come through the use of synthetic resins. In general, the resins which have the best insulation properties are also the most difficult to apply. The electrical properties are generally the poorest for the kinds of coatings which are easiest to produce and which are among the class that gives the poorest corrosion protection when used as protective coatings. While the fields of coatings and insulation research are apparently dissimilar, most of the problems are common to both, since in each the manifestations of particular advantages or disadvantages of a particular material are frequently related to the same causes.

Antibiotic Properties

The design of paints containing biological poisons is an important problem for the painting of ships for salt water exposure, where marine growths are severe. In addition to damaging the paint film and thereby aggravating metal corrosion, these growths roughen the bottom of a ship so that friction is increased; excess power is thus required to propel ships or flying-boat hulls at rated speed. Coatings must be designed to meet anti-fouling requirements, that is, to inhibit marine growth. While much has already been done, this aspect of protection is still an important research field in coatings.

A problem which is less common in our temperate climate is the protection of organic materials, such as cloth, wood, or electrical insulation, from deterioration by fungi or bacteria. This problem will be a severe one as the industrial development of tropical countries is accelerated. There is no doubt that much present and future paint research must use the services of the biological scientists, who have much to discover regarding the classification of destructive organisms and the specificity of poisons to limit their growth. The Committee on Deterioration of

Materials of the National Research Council has been very active in this field of investigation.

Aeronautical Engineering

In addition to protection from a number of novel and serious corrosion conditions, the aeronautical engineer is concerned also with the resistance of paint films to air friction. As the speed of aircraft continues to be increased, a greater premium is placed on minimizing even micro-roughness of surfaces, which does slightly reduce speed; much effort will be directed in an attempt to accomplish this economically with coatings rather than by the alternative of polishing operations.

Jet engine design puts a new premium on high temperature-resistant coatings which also give corrosion protection under novel and very serious conditions of exposure. Coatings research for the special problems of aeronautical engineering is relatively recent, and not much has yet been done to solve the new problems that have come as a result of progress in aircraft design during the last few years.

Other Novel Functions

Coatings have been used to indicate temperatures; for instance, thermally unstable pigments can indicate a record of peak temperature by undergoing color changes that vary with the temperature. An even more modern approach is to use special types of phosphors as pigments where the luminescence depends on the temperature.

Engineering Data for Paint

We have enumerated the functional properties of coatings, namely, decorative properties, corrosion protection, radiation absorption or reflectance, antibiotic properties, smoothness, and electrical insulation. Naturally, not all of these are important for every coating. The required combination of properties for a given coating is determined in every case by the special nature of the coatings problem. There are countless variations of coating needs and any particular need may have a variety of solutions in terms of materials and coating methods. A solution to a specific problem can be arrived at only by a cooperative effort by both the user and the supplier of coatings, that is, a meeting of minds between coatings engineers and other engineers who need the coating. This implies also some agreement in test methods.

Decorative properties, as represented by color, luster and smoothness, are rather easily controlled by visual inspection. Up to now, precise specification of decorative properties has largely escaped control through engineering data. This is not to say that attempts to do so have not been made. Complicated and expensive instruments have been developed for color and reflectance measurements, for example, the automatic recording spectrophotometer used to measure the spectral distribution of reflected light (Figure 1.3). Such instruments are very successful for measuring the reproducibility of a particular color obtained in a particular way. Unfortunately, color is not that simple. To a spectrophotometer, every spectral curve is a different color. To the eye, any color can

Figure 1.3.   G. E. recording spectrophotometer.

be matched by pigment combinations that give a great number, possibly an infinite number, of different spectral curves. From the viewpoint of batch-wise quality control, all these elaborate optical apparatus are useful. From the viewpoint of an engineer who wishes to define precisely the particular visual decorative properties in terms of color and reflectance, the equipment is of little use, since a standard spectral curve represents only one of a great number of ways of accomplishing exactly what he wants. If, however, the issue is one of design for radiation protection, data showing reflectances for different wavelengths of light then become precise engineering data for evaluating the quality of finishes.

It can be determined more or less exactly whether a paint film has decorative, electrical, radiation reflectance, and antibiotic properties. These are the immediate objectives of coatings design and frequently, whichever are needed can be obtained in the required degree in a variety of coatings. For example, if the object is an automotive or washing machine or marine finish, a number of sample coatings can be prepared which differ greatly in cost and are entirely different in the materials from which they are made, but which seem to be identical in appearance and physical properties. Only at this point, in a practical sense, does one read the term quality into specifications. The greater part of engineering concerned with quality is not with the attainment of initially desirable properties, but rather with the question of how long such properties can be maintained during the actual service life of a coating.

All organic films decay and lose their properties on aging in their service environment. The loss of decorative, reflectance, and electrical properties is relatively easy to measure. This is not true of the way a film will function in corrosion protection. Corrosion can occur when the film becomes sufficiently damaged so that it ceases to provide inhibition to the electrochemical corrosion processes. This rate of damage can be followed quantitatively only by quantitative measurements of the mechanical properties of films. In this field of engineering testing our greatest difficulties occur; consequently the greatest amount of research has been expended in it.

The mechanical properties of greatest interest are hardness, elongation, and adhesion. The original testing method for mechanical properties was simple. Throughout a test exposure an experienced paint man would scratch the paint with a fingernail or knife, and would judge the rate of deterioration of the mechanical properties by "feel." The ancient artist, who was concerned solely with color, devised a whole art of paint-making by the measure of looking at the effect of a brush stroke. His modern successor, an artist who is concerned with film testing, has developed a sensitive perception through the feel of scratching a film. In each case, the individual judgments were highly accurate and years ahead of science in cutting through a multitude of variables to accomplish a practical result. However, such an approach is not conducive to systematizing an engineering science. Quantitative data are impossible by such procedures; and as paint technology became more complicated in terms of numerous materials, a lifetime would be insufficient to learn to know them all well enough to make even qualitatively accurate judgments by the scratch test. This fact has been long appreciated, and great effort has been expended in developing methods for measuring physical properties. We can take time to illustrate only a few.

Properties such as elongation present no serious problems. Coated panels can be punched to a measured depth with a standard die until the film ruptures under stress, or the panel can be struck with a hammer to measure breakability under impact extrusion conditions. Still more simply, the panel can be bent over mandrels of a variety of diameters until an angle of bending is found which is sufficiently severe to crack the film.

Hardness can be estimated by a variety of devices. A popular method is provided by the Sward rocker (Figure 1.4) which, when set into motion under controlled conditions in the standard gravitational field, will rock back and forth until it is stopped by expending its energy through frictional resistance. The frictional loss of energy is greater for softer surfaces; hence the fewer cycles the rocker executes, the softer the film.

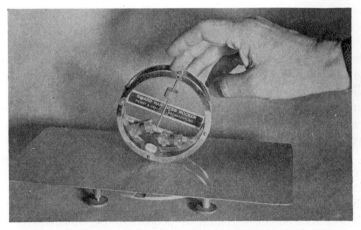

Figure 1.4. Sward rocker for measuring hardness of coatings films.

The hardness of films is usually compared to glass. It is not too difficult for any engineer to visualize the principle of the method and the numerous difficulties of obtaining thereby consistent and precise measurements in different laboratories.

Measurements of hardness and elongation deserve much greater attention. The importance of these measurements has been neglected, however, because there seems to be little point in fussing with them until the major problem has been solved, namely, that of measuring the adherence of films to metal substrates. If the film separates or loses adherence to its surface under exposure conditions, it doesn't matter much what its hardness and elongation are, because corrosion protection is lost even though the film otherwise retains good properties. In fact, practically speaking, the measurement of adherence involves a composite of the forces of adhesions referred to in the earlier part of this discussion, and also the mechanical properties of the film. In general, it is this composite of properties that the paint man measures with his fingernail or pen knife. In seeking a quantitative expression of this complex variable, it is not surprising that the first attempts took the form of mechanizing and metering the scratch test. Two outstanding examples of this effort are represented by two commercial instruments.

The first of these is the Arco Micro-Knife (Figure 1.5) which measures both hardness and a property related to adherence. A diamond point is weighted until it can penetrate a film to a metal in two retracing scratch strokes. The weight necessary to get this cutting force for films of standard thickness is a measure of hardness. The panel is advanced

Courtesy The Gardner Laboratory, Inc., Bethesda, Md.

Figure 1.5. Arco microknife for measuring adherence of paint films to metal.

past the stroking diamond point so as to accomplish a series of parallel scratches, the measured distance between scratches decreasing with each successive advance of the knife. Ultimately two scratches come so close together that the film between the scratches tears. The closer one can get the parallel scratches together without tearing the film between them, the greater is the adherence rating of the film.

The other machine is the Interchemical Adherometer (Figure 1.6), designed to measure the stripping force in dynes required to remove a paint film from the surface of a test panel. The test panel is moved slowly under a hard, ivory-cutting tool 4 mm wide. The ivory tool is held by a lever arm which is weighted to hold the cutting edge firmly against the metal surface of the panel. The lever arm, mounted on a practically frictionless roller bearing, is connected to a weighted pendulum, causing it to swing outward to an extent proportional to the force being utilized in stripping the 4-mm band of paint film. The amount of pendulum swing is read on the Ames gauge operating through an accurately machined cam attached to the pendulum at its axis.

A greater number of testing devices of varying utility have been designed for assaying mechanical properties of films than we have time to mention. All these tools have been directed to the study of durability, particularly in accelerated testing. The index of quality is not expressed

Courtesy The Gardner Laboratory, Inc., Bethesda, Md.

Figure 1.6. Interchemical adherometer for measuring adherence of paint films to metal.

ordinarily as the time required for total failure, but rather as a rate function where the slow deterioration of mechanical properties is followed under exposure conditions, such as weathering, immersion in salt or fresh water, or soaking in acids or alkalies.

Thus far we have discussed only methods of following the course of deterioration under service conditions. To many paint experts this problem is of less concern than the more difficult one of establishing significant exposure conditions for testing. For chemical resistance, for example alkali and acid tests, the problem is less severe. Tests can be accelerated in general by using increased concentrations of the chemical to be tested. While this procedure is by no means clear-cut, in general it has given satisfactory predictions. Much more treacherous is the attempt to evaluate the lasting quality of protection under long-term, mild conditions of deterioration, such as weathering or water immersion at mild temperatures.

We are inclined to call this exposure to normal weathering. However, the term "normal weathering" can be very misleading. There is no variable more difficult to control or to duplicate than the weather. From the viewpoint of paint durability, climatic differences are not trivial.

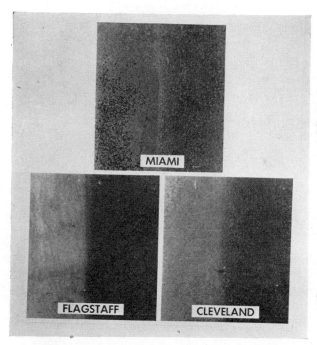

Figure 1.7. Film deterioration after one year of weathering in different climates.

Different climates vary considerably in critical deteriorating factors, such as intensity of radiation, schedule of temperature changes, and the quantity and periodicity of precipitation of snow, rain or dew. Possibly exposures such as 45° south (Miami, Florida) are the most severe; hence many paint testers specify this condition for routine testing. However, as compared to other locations, the Miami exposure is in a sense an accelerated test, and if the engineer specifying paints is considering Cleveland, or any other location, he would have to have an extensive amount of correlation data in order to reduce Miami exposure experiments to practical information (Figure 1.7). However, even Miami exposure takes at least six months to give satisfactory results. For research and development purposes, much greater testing speed is necessary. For years efforts have been made to use accelerated testing apparatus such as is represented by the Weatherometer, which provides adjustable cycles of water spray, strong ultraviolet, and fluctuating temperature (Figure 1.8). When used without good judgment, such

Figure 1.8. Atlas Type X1A—weathering unit for accelerating film deterioration by exposure to intense ultraviolet and cyclic changes in temperature and water-spray.

accelerated aging machines give very erroneous results. If, however, care is taken to standardize the condition of the paint films, much can be done to correlate this accelerated testing with some standard test area of real weathering. Accelerated testing can be applied fairly when paints are entered into test only after they have reached an optimum state of cure; that is to say, if the initial processes of film formation, such as drying of the film or solvent evaporation, are not interfered with by premature exposure to the Weatherometer.

The problem of judging what is a proper stage of film maturity is complicated, but important, since accelerated testing is designed to

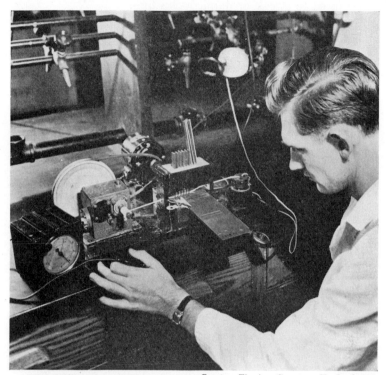

Courtesy The Arco Company, Cleveland, Ohio

Figure 1.9. A device for measuring the chemical and solvent resistance of paint films. A liquid-saturated string is drawn across the panel at a constant rate, and held against the panel by a series of removable weights. The weights are lifted by the operator one at a time at regular intervals and mild tension holds the unweighted segment of the string off the panel. The exposure is most severe under the last weight lifted. Inspection of the time-abrasion trace provides a quantitative measure of the chemical or solvent resistance of the film under controlled test conditions.

compare healthy films rather than to test the influence of adverse conditions on film formation. Since the curing of films varies in properties, such as hardness, flexibility, and adhesion, it is obvious that these measurements can be used to judge when a film is ready for exposure. Maturity is reached when these properties remain nearly constant for several days. Since cure of films usually renders them more insoluble, further standardizations can be made by measuring solubility of films in some precise manner. This can be done, for example, with devices such as the Arco Proofometer (Figure 1.9) which drags a solvent-saturated string across the film under constant abrasive conditions for varying periods of time. The solvent resistance can be expressed in units of time required to streak or damage the film.

When care is taken to standardize the condition of films to be tested, a high degree of correlation can be found between film failures produced

Courtesy Frankford Arsenal, U. S. Ordnance Dept.

Figure 1.10.   View looking east at paint panels exposed in the jungle.

by a 21-day cycle in the laboratory Weatherometer and a six-month exposure in Florida. This represents an advance in precise specification of weathering data. Of course, for effective engineering use of weathering data, further correlations between Miami and other regions are necessary. Such studies, following in general the lines of approach indicated here, are in progress both in the United States and Great Britain. Test fences are being established for long-term observation in many diverse locations (Figures 1.10 and 1.11). In the next decade this subject should achieve a high degree of systematization. Laboratory testing of weathering durability is in considerable disrepute at the moment because engineers are not quite aware of the magnitude of the problem. It is true that such tests are imperfect; it is unjust, however, to assume that they are totally false. When applied judiciously, such methods can be of considerable value to engineers even in their present rather limited stage of development. The greatest caution that must be exercised is not to extend experience correlations to type-classes of coatings materials for which data are unknown. For example, accelerated data for vinyl resins should not be judged by experience tables derived for alkyd enamels.

Apart from weathering testing, no issue is more controversial than testing for marine exposure or for water immersion in general. We know

Courtesy Frankford Arsenal, U. S. Ordnance Dept.

Figure 1.11. View of marine exposure rack.

that one of the most severe exposure conditions is immersion in deionized water, since this quickly shows up all faults of adhesion and poor metal preparation by inducing blistering. Fortunately, most water, such as sea water, contains electrolytes; hence blistering failure is ordinarily not as severe as can be induced, for example, by repeated condensations of deionized dew on paint surfaces. However, sea water is very corrosive and protection is quickly lost if the paint film develops any faults during exposure.

Up to now, laboratory testing of water-immersion conditions has not been correlated sufficiently with field experience to have much value. One principal source of trouble is the fact that the highly important temperature changes are very difficult to record in extensive periods of field testing, and are nearly impossible to reproduce in the laboratory. Most valid immersion studies are still long-term projects on field testing stations—for example, marine testing stations—which provide for both continuous immersion and periodic exposure to air and water at the tide line. Because exposure periods, temperature cycles, water velocity and composition of electrolytes and abrasive materials vary so greatly, precise data for particular environments must be tested specifically on the job location for all conditions that differ from the more regular marine exposure. However, by judicious use of laboratory and marine data it is possible to select the more probable coatings for many applications. The main point to remember is that caution should be exercised in using such data—what may seem to be insignificant variables to an engineer may be very significant to the paint film.

Possibly the best measure of the extent to which coatings are becoming established as a branch of engineering is to be seen in the emphasis of the past ten years on methods of testing for measuring quantitative data on film properties. The foregoing comments regarding the accomplishments of testing were somewhat critical in emphasizing the limitations. This does not imply that paint evaluation is any less precise or less scientific than testing of other materials. The dissatisfaction arises from the fact that because of the complex nature of coatings, it is not feasible to freeze arbitrarily the methods and standards of testing, since in coatings we are less satisfied with approximate test methods. Here testing has less importance in respect to quality control, and much more importance in predicting engineering design data in selection of coatings. At the present time, it is impossible for economic or technical reasons to apply safety factors. Unlike most materials, coatings have to be extended to the limits of their design capacity, and uncertainties of testing cannot be masked or minimized by traditional devices of using more material. This sort of use of testing data requires high precision and accuracy.

The field of paint testing is unique in that its standards of quality for test data are more severe than those for most other types of materials. The testing problem is made more difficult by the fact that developments in new materials and new uses for paints change so fast that testing methods which seem to cover a situation adequately become obsolescent almost as fast as developed. If paint technology were to remain relatively static for ten years, it is probable that the methods of testing and evaluation would become a model for other engineering sciences. At the present, however, that is the last thing we would like to see happen.

The critical questioning and research into all phases of the properties of organic films is a healthy condition that already has had and will continue to have a stimulating effect on research. This present and future research is becoming less and less a monopoly of any single group of scientists or engineers. It is likely that in the next decade an awareness of the coatings problem will have pervaded all engineering sciences to such an extent that paint design will no longer be regarded as an isolated activity, existing apart from the main current of engineering activity. Research activity is now approaching so many attractive crossroads that it is virtually impossible to prophesy just what will be the dominant form of coatings science ten or twenty years hence, when it will have reached the status of a mature field of engineering.

Bibliography

1. Mattiello, Joseph J., "Protective Organic Coatings As Engineering Materials," *Proc. Am. Soc. Testing Materials,* **46,** 1–100 (1946).
2. Kienle, Roy H., "Physical Chemical Research in the Protective Coatings Industry," *Official Digest Federation Paint & Varnish Production Clubs* (Jan. 1950).

2 : Principles of Paint Formulation

EDWARD G. BOBALEK

Case Institute of Technology
Cleveland, Ohio

Commercial paint formulation is the practical art of controlling the numerous variables which determine the properties of a coating. Economics is just as important as technology; indeed, the two considerations are inseparable, because the objective must be a satisfactory coating that can be produced economically in large volume. Let us first concentrate on technology.

FORMULATION TECHNOLOGY

In general, any project of formulation requires well-considered judgments regarding three related problems, (1) selection of proper raw materials, (2) selection of methods for their combination, and (3) selection of the proportions required to give a useful product. Subsequent chapters will describe some of the details of these considerations for various aspects of coatings technology.

Selection of Raw Materials

A paint formulator has an enormous number of raw materials at his command. At first sight some may seem to be wasteful duplications; however, they usually prove to be contraries with respect to one or more important physical or chemical properties. Careful analysis will disclose that actually no two items are exact equivalents if fine enough lines of comparison are drawn. However, if the specifications are too sharply defined, the formulator is confronted with such a number of choices that a lifetime would be required to make an optimum selection. On the other hand, if the classification is too coarse, the formulator will have too few choices to allow him to face with confidence a great diversity of end-use specifications.

Where should one draw the line? This is difficult to say, since so much depends on individual artistic and scientific capacity. A pigment classification which groups pigments by approximate color (red, blue, green, etc.) is obviously inadequate, for reasons soon to be made clear. On the other hand, it is useless to maintain a long list of mineral spirits that differ from one another only by a few units in Kauri-Butanol value. The extent of a formulator's skill will depend on what kind of classifications he establishes. They should be neither too loose nor too restrictive, and each compromise will depend to a certain extent on the individual.

In general, the materials selection problem involves a choice of pigments and a vehicle. Each can be quite complicated with respect to the number of ingredients involved. The vehicle is frequently classified with respect to its content of nonvolatile, film-forming material (the *binder*) and a volatile component (the *thinner*). This classification is by general functions; actually, the pigment, binder, and thinner each may contain a variety of materials.

Selection of a Vehicle. The vehicle is a fluid consisting of a solution or mixture of a binder with a thinner (solvent). The binder is the primary constituent because it cements pigment particles together and fixes the whole mass to the substrate being coated.

The first problem is to choose a suitable binder. We can operate more skillfully if we know something of the chemistry of the resinous (or resin-forming) materials that can be used as binders. Frequently, if we know the specifications for the finished coating, we can predict which type of binder may be useful and which may not be adequate for some particular function. For example, if the specification calls for a strongly alkali-resistant film, binders that are drying oils, alkyds, or other polyesters would not be suitable, as they all contain ester linkages which are susceptible to saponification by alkalies. Where resistance to oxidation at high temperatures is required, resins containing a considerable proportion of certain types of high molecular weight hydrocarbons should be avoided. If they must be used, those low in olefinic content are preferable, since unsaturates promote decomposition or discoloration.

The problem of selection cannot always be decided by the chemical resistance properties of the resin, however. For example, in considering a problem such as corrosion protection for a ship bottom, one must balance the greater stability advantages of the hydrocarbon resins against their disadvantage of poor adhesion. In this instance it may be preferable to use oleoresinous varnishes of lesser chemical resistance but good adhesion instead of hydrocarbon resins or vinyl resins, where the reverse situation prevails. When the former are used, the deterioration of the film is uniform, but rapid (possibly six months are compared to years for the synthetic resins) ; however, while oleoresinous varnishes last they may give more uniform protection. On the other hand, where adhesion is poor, severe creep-corrosion at faults in a very durable film will rapidly dislodge the film and very little benefit is gained from its potentially greater chemical resistance. The problem of developing superior adhesion in the chemically resistant films is difficult. Chemical resistance and adhesion-developing properties are contraries—the same structures that tend to promote good adhesion are frequently the cause of inferior chemical resistance. Hence, in choosing a particular type of binder, a judgment must be made regarding how much of the potentially available chemical resistance of the resin need be sacrificed in order to accomplish adequate adhesion. In the oil and varnish art of the older coatings technology, the direction of the compromise was reversed; namely, how to improve the chemical resistance of the film without sacrificing too much of the adhesion that was possible with oils or ester types of resins.

Apart from considerations of adhesion and chemical resistance, it is necessary to make a useful choice of one of several possible methods of film formation.

Film Formation by Chemical Reactions. At the time the paint is applied, the binder is not in a condition to form a hard protective film, but must undergo chemical reactions which convert it from a mobile liquid into a hard, gel-like structure. These may be either oxidation-promoted, as in the case of drying oils, or polymerization reactions that occur during subsequent baking. In most of these instances, the vehicle contains some thinner; however, its evaporation alone is inadequate to cause formation of a stable film. Included in this class of binders of the thermosetting or curing type are the drying oils (including drying oil-modified alkyds, varnishes, epichlorohydrin resins, etc.) ; the formaldehyde condensation resins (phenolic, urea, and triazine resins) ; the allyl resins; and the polyurethanes. Sometimes the curing process must be accelerated by the use of catalysts, high baking temperatures, or both.

Film Formation with Solvent-Type Resins. This class of binders consists of stable, resinous materials, which are thermoplastic, soluble in some solvents, and chemically stable during film formation. The resin is deposited from solution and film formation is completed when the last of the thinner has evaporated. This group includes resins such as nitrocellulose and most other cellulose ethers or esters; many vinyl resins; the polyacrylates or polymethacrylates; the styrene resins; the rubber derivatives (cyclized rubber, chlorinated rubber) ; and some polyester or polyamide resins. This class of binders, while relatively new to paint technology, has become very important, particularly for coating applications where high-temperature baking of the finish is not feasible. In this class we find also some of the most chemically resistant binders, e.g., polyethylene, polytetrafluoroethylene, polyvinyl esters, etc.

Almost any of this class of resins can be manufactured to varying molecular weight specifications. Ordinarily it is the lower molecular weight resins which have the greatest solubility in solvents. Unfortunately, these more soluble resins yield films that have inferior physical properties and chemical resistance. As the resins are improved with respect to film properties they become less and less soluble, and lacquer formulation becomes less practical. If these least soluble and more durable thermoplastic resins are to be used, then new principles of film formation must be devised.

Film Formation by Congelation. Many sparingly soluble thermoplastic resins can be melted; sometimes a solvent or plasticizer is used to lower the melting point, and a hot solution is obtained. Cooling will cause these molten resins or hot solutions to coagulate to a film of hard, coherent gel. In this method of film formation a thinner is either unnecessary, or it functions in a minor role by lowering the melting point: the primary process is coagulation or "freezing." Theoretically this method differs in degree, rather than in kind, from room-temperature lacquer deposition; however, with respect to techniques and end results in the finished film, it is sufficiently different to merit at least a subclassification of its own. For example, this method is employed in the dipping application of molten lacquers for electrical insulation; hot-solution deposition of polyethylene by roller coating; dipping application of gelled lacquers; and flame-spraying of resins such as polyethylene. Some types of film-forming resins applied by these methods provide nearly the ultimate in chemically resistant coatings. The only feature which restricts their more general use is the yet unsolved adhesion problem.

Film Formation with Dispersion Resins. This method does not eliminate the use of a thinner, but it makes unnecessary the restriction that the thinner should dissolve the resin. Rather, the principle of the method is to use a volatile nonsolvent and to disperse therein the insoluble resin particles so that a condition is obtained which is similar to the dispersion of pigments in ordinary vehicles. That is to say, the binder, together with the pigment, is a part of the dispersed phase and is really not a part of the vehicle at all. Here all of the vehicle is volatile.

If the binder is dispersed in water, a latex or emulsion results; if the thinner is an organic liquid such as toluene, an organosol is formed. The resin particles are concentrated and deposited by evaporation of the dispersing medium. If the particles have a tendency to coalesce or at least to cement together, a continuous film will form. For some applications, the film can be made uniform by fusion; thus a dispersion resin method of application is sometimes followed by a hot-melt method for completing film formation. In any event, the solubility problem has been by-passed, and it is now possible to use the more chemically resistant types of thermoplastic resins, for example, the high molecular weight vinyls, polytetrafluoroethylene, and insoluble synthetic rubbers. This dispersion resin mode of film formation is one of the more important fundamental developments of paint technology in the past half-century.

Selection of Pigments. In pigment selection, paint technology most closely approximates a pure art. Color perceptions involve subjective reaction of varying intensity and acuteness to certain physical stimuli. Though physics can describe the nature of the light waves that cause the impression of color, the sensory and psychological responses are still only vaguely defined. Specific spectral lines give the visual impression of red, orange, green, blue, etc.; but any particular impression, for an individual, can be matched not by some one spectral combination, but frequently by a large number of combinations. Moreover, the idea of effective color is associated intimately with such impressions as luster or gloss, about which, as a psychophysical phenomenon, we know even less than we do about color. In view of this complex situation, the formulator must still proceed by experience and artistic sense regarding color formulation, i.e., choice of pigments for color matching or for creation of new colors. Some have a greater natural aptitude for this than others. Rarely do two individuals have the same sense of composition; hence two formulators may make entirely different selections of materials, proportions, and methods to achieve an apparently similar result.

Apart from the subjective feature of color, the paint formulator must be very conversant with the chemical properties of the pigments he chooses. For example, he would not use an acid-sensitive pigment such as ultramarine for maintenance painting near a hydrochloric acid plant, nor would he use an alkali-sensitive pigment, such as Iron Blue, for a wall paint that will almost certainly be washed with alkaline cleaners. A lead-containing pigment is obviously unsuited for an industrial area where sulfur compounds foul the atmosphere, and a bleeding type of organic red pigment should not be used to paint bicycle fenders which will be striped with white lacquer. Certain titanium pigments which catalyze the photochemical decomposition of the binder (and hence produce chalking) are not suited for an automotive finish. A strongly basic pigment such as zinc oxide is not suited for use in alkyd resins having a high acid value; nor are pigments such as Iron Blue, which contain water-soluble acid salts, suited for latex paints where the medium requires an alkaline condition for stability. In addition to all these considerations, pigments which have identical composition and identical chemical properties may differ greatly in hiding power, tinting strength, or even color, because they differ in particle size. Pigments which have the same light absorption characteristics may look very different in a paint, because the index of refraction and particle size distribution are different.

In addition to being used for their decorative properties, there are some pigments that are used for functional properties, for example:

(1) Zinc oxide sometimes inhibits the yellowing, and frequently promotes hardening or embrittlement, of oil-containing binders. Antimony trioxide, white lead, and other pigments perform similar functions for some synthetic resins. This selection is determined by knowledge of chemical properties.

(2) Certain pigments have selective reflectance or absorption properties for different portions of the invisible spectrum; e.g., zinc oxide is black to the same range of ultraviolet at which carbon black is a white pigment, and certain antimony sulfide pigments have specific reflectance properties to infrared. Features of this sort should be known if one is searching, for example, for a reflecting coating to cut down evaporation losses of gasoline storage tanks or for camouflage colors against infrared photography.

(3) Some pigments modify for better or for worse the electrochemical mechanism of corrosion, e.g., metallic pigments, zinc yellow, and red lead. These pigments must be selected carefully for use in corrosion-resistant paints.

Methods of Combining Pigments and Vehicles

Let us presume that a formulator selects the pigment and vehicle combination which, in accord with a sound knowledge of chemistry and physics, seems to be an optimum choice for a given specification. Now he is faced with the last selection problem—that of a method for combining them into a paint that has good application characteristics, while still retaining the specified decorative and protective properties. At this point he may have to revise his original selections of materials and proportions. There are certain combinations which cannot be mixed to give a useful paint. This possible dilemma we can call the *dispersion problem*.

The subject of dispersion has been referred to as a problem only in recent years. The old paint technology was developed on the basis of natural materials, mixtures of which possess good paint properties. This is particularly true of the natural earths or synthetic oxide pigments in combination with vehicles containing unsaturated vegetable oils. These natural vehicles, either because of their major chemical composition, or because they contain certain surface-active impurities, such as free oil acids or lecithin, have the ability to form with pigments a heterogeneous dispersion of adequate stability and desirable flow characteristics.

As one departs from natural materials the dispersion problem becomes more difficult to solve. For example, to disperse pigments in some of the more durable synthetic resins, a synthetic equivalent for the dispersion-promoting, surface-active agents that occur naturally in linseed oil is essential. To find one is not easy. Some agents give good dispersion stability with respect to settling, but do not supply the proper fluidity characteristics and vice versa.

There is also the important matter of equipment to be considered. What may be an excellent combination of pigment, vehicle, and surface-active agent for dispersion in one type of mechanical mixer (e.g., the Baker-Perkins mill), may give entirely inadequate results in another type (e.g., a colloid mill or roller mill). For this reason, as well as others, there is a great variety of paint mills. If a formulator is restricted to a certain type of milling equipment, he may require entirely different materials from those he would have selected if he had a free choice of all available types. For example, his optimum choice for chemical reasons may be a combination of phthalocyanine pigments and vinyl resins. Unless he has a two-roll rubber mill or a Banbury mill suited for preparing chip-dispersions, he will have to revise his decision or else abandon the project. Although much is still unknown regarding the limits of utility of any particular type of milling equipment, a little experience shows that some mills are inadequate for certain materials and proportions. For example, a roller mill is impractical for dispersing some Iron Blue pigments or some organic toners even in oil-containing vehicles; or, even apart from discoloration effects, a ball mill is not the most efficient way to disperse titanium dioxide. As we proceed to more complicated pigments and binders, the selection of a method becomes increasingly difficult. Indeed, for some combinations of materials, no method is known that can effect a satisfactory mixture.

Proportions in Pigment-Vehicle Combinations

Granting the fact that the pigments and vehicles selected can be compounded into a stable paint by some suitable combination of chemical and physical dispersion methods, the formulator must choose the proper proportions. This choice involves largely an optimum volume concentration of pigment. This in turn depends entirely on what sort of coating is desired; for example, the object of formulation may be (1) a primer, where adhesion is the most desired property, and where other features, such as easy sanding characteristics, durability, and adequate hold-out to topcoats, are essential; (2) a surfacer where the principal service function will be to provide a smooth, regular surface that enhances the decorative value of the topcoats, and where good adhesion to topcoat and primer is essential (frequently, combination primer-surfacers are used); and (3) a gloss or semi-gloss topcoat (enamel or lacquer).

In general, glossy finishes must contain a volume concentration of pigment that is less than some critical value, which depends on the nature of the vehicle and on the nature and surface area of the pigment. This property is related to what is called the vehicle-absorption limit of the pigment. To explain briefly, if a vehicle is added to a fixed quantity of pigment, the pigment will adsorb or absorb it without losing its characteristic of a powdered solid. It may become more or less wet, but nevertheless, even though it contains a considerable quantity of vehicle, it still remains a crumbly solid, and in no way resembles a fluid paint, irrespective of the degree of grinding. As more vehicle is added, a concentration is eventually attained at which a reasonable grinding force will change the system into a fluid dispersion of vehicle-saturated pigment in an excess of vehicle. This is the *vehicle absorption limit*. It is not an absolute physical constant, for it is related to the practical physical methods of dispersing pigments in paint vehicles. (We have only an imperfect knowledge of what might be the influence of much greater shearing stresses on this vehicle absorption value.)

As a practical phenomenon, the fact that this limit exists has been recognized for many years; it finds its expression in the published values wherein this absorption property of pigments is standardized in relation to their absorption value for linseed oil. This is called the *oil absorption value*, for which there are numerous and controversial methods of determination. In general, pigments having large surface area (fine-ground) have greater oil-absorption values than those of less surface area (coarse). Involved also is the question of the nature of the flocculation of the pigment in air and in the paint vehicle. But if one is not too precise about exact values, most pigments can be placed in a regular order in terms of their oil-absorption values. This same order is preserved in other common vehicles, with few exceptions; but the significant fact is that the magnitude of the values changes from one vehicle to another.

The question of why this difference is important may now be asked. To understand the reason requires some knowledge of the effect of the volume concentration of pigment on the properties of paint, and the realization that vehicle absorption is an important measurable variable that can be used at least qualitatively to predict this effect to some degree.

First of all, if the specified volume concentration of pigment is greater than the concentration that characterizes the end point of the vehicle-absorption value (that is, the solid-liquid transition point), it is impossible to prepare a fluid paint. If only a slight excess of vehicle were present, fluid paint would result. It would have excellent hiding properties, would be "easy-sanding," and would fill scratches in a surface; however, it would have no appreciable gloss, and would be excessively permeable to water. Hence its protective functions would be very limited. Its only possible use would be as a surfacer, where best adhesion to bare metal, for example, is not required, but where the optimum in filling and sanding properties is desired. (The latter is due to the brittleness of the film.)

As the excess of vehicle over pigment is increased somewhat, the film becomes more flexible and less permeable; its sanding and fill-in properties become poorer; and it may begin to develop a sheen. It is customary to formulate most primers or primer-surfacers within the range of pigment volume concentrations between the vehicle-absorption value and the point where a semi-gloss or eggshell luster appears. If the excess of vehicle is increased still further, the film tends to develop more gloss, greater impermeability to water, and in general improved protective and decorative functions. Sanding and filling properties disappear; the tendency for lifting by additional topcoats is increased; the mechanical properties (elongation, flexibility, mar-resistance) improve; but frequently the adhesion becomes less. Often there is a critical point in volume concentration of pigment where the loss of adhesive properties balances the gains achieved by the improvement of a number of other properties; this is most likely to occur at some pigment-vehicle ratio near the semi-gloss point. This fact, of course, implies that, if a combination of protective and decorative properties in a single-coat finish is required, some sacrifice of gloss or luster is inevitable. Hence, if the ultimate in both protective and decorative properties is desired, a one-coat system is inadequate; adhesion and filling properties must be secured by undercoats, and luster and protective properties by topcoats. In general, most topcoats have good adhesion to other paint films, if they have reasonably porous or roughened surfaces, as do most primers and surfacers. Depending on the nature of the topcoat, one must select the vehicle and pigmentation for undercoats so as to provide good primer and surfacer properties and still have "hold-out" for the topcoats, without any tendency to "lift." Such multi-coat design is called a "balanced" paint system.

We cannot identify all the variables that determine gloss in a pigmented film. We do know that glossy pigmented films are most likely to be attained with vehicle-pigment combinations that have vehicle-absorption values, under the practical conditions of mechanical grinding, which are neither too low nor excessively high. These values are hard to determine precisely; but if a particular reference pigment, for example, titanium dioxide, is selected, and paints of various gloss properties are prepared, a curve of gloss rating versus pigment concentration could be plotted for each system. If the values of pigment concentration that correspond to the first appearance of luster were selected from the curves, the vehicles could be ordered in a series, which, for all practical purposes, is related to the vehicle-absorption values of the different binders for this particular pigment. Near the top of such a list would be the drying oils. Near the bottom of the list would be many of the synthetic resins. In fact, for many synthetic resin vehicles, the gloss point may be at a pigment concentration so low that the film would have insufficient opacity at any reasonable thickness. To improve this situation we might compound the binder with other ingredients (plasticizers, modifying resins, etc.) so as to increase the vehicle-absorption value and hence make possible an increase in the pigment concentration at the gloss point.

In summary, it can be emphasized that the formulator cannot concentrate his attention on a single paint, but nearly always must deal with a multi-coat paint system. This involves careful selection of pigments and vehicles for each coat in order to establish (1) optimum chemical resistance of the whole system, and (2) optimum pigment concentration in each layer, to permit building up the proper protective and decorative properties through multiple coats. The choice of the materials and proportions which accomplish these two objectives simultaneously is the major technological problem of coatings formulation.

THE ECONOMICS OF FORMULATION

When the paint technologist is confronted with a particular coatings problem, his aim is to devise the best possible coating within the cost tolerance permitted him. However, it is almost never true that the "best possible" and the "best practical" can be obtained together; indeed, the gap that exists between them is the measure of the research field in formulation. Hence the formulator must work out a compromise between cost and quality that meets the specifications and is consistent with good engineering judgment. This comprises formulation economics.

In considering cost, the following considerations should always be borne in mind:

(1) Cost differences between raw materials are not always marginal;

for example, a silicone resin or some colored pigments may be more than twenty times as costly as other reasonable alternates.

(2) The sales cost of a can of paint that must satisfy unusually severe specifications may have to absorb the cost of rejected batches, since it is not always possible to manufacture to conformity with the more rigid specifications on *every* production trail.

(3) The best of coatings are frequently the most difficult to apply correctly, and the cost of rejected finished articles must be taken into account. Moreover, inspection costs can greatly add to the expense.

(4) Use of the best coatings usually requires more time and effort on the part of a greater number of more skilled personnel in the painting shop.

(5) Some of the best coatings from the film formation viewpoint have limited package stability and involve the added cost of precise maintenance of inventory to assure that no overage paint reaches the job.

(6) Some coatings that are "best" require special or costly equipment to apply, for example, special spraying equipment or special ovens for baking.

The fact that formulation is so dependent upon practical economics explains why new raw materials cannot always replace the old. Many new materials may be superior to the old in only one or two properties, which may be unimportant for some already established end-use. If the new products are more costly, either directly or because reformulation costs may be involved, they will not be used for such an application, even though in other cases they might satisfy a critical need. In ways both important and trivial, the economic factor does much to add to the complexity of formulation practice.

Assuming that the formulator has a high degree of technical aptitude, the cost of a coating is largely determined when a starting specification is drawn. The more exacting the specification, the more strongly will economic factors force independent formulators to almost identical solutions to the problem. The less exacting the specification, the more varied is the number of possible solutions in terms of materials, proportions, and methods, and the less costly will be the attainment of a useful product.

A specification is usually defined as a set of properties and performance characteristics required by the purchaser of a manufactured product. In the somewhat lesser terminology of paint technology it is merely a description of a material in terms of some of its properties. The subject matter and form of a specification are determined by the purpose for which it is written. Most frequently we tend to equate specifications with the objectives of quality control. However, this is not the only reason for writing specifications. Quality control is concerned primarily with measuring deviations from previously determined property standards. Where the definition of such standards is obvious, e.g., data on allowable contamination of a pure chemical, the limited objective of quality control may indeed be the major purpose of a specification. However, for complicated technologies such as coatings the possible quality control standards for a given material usually are not at all obvious. Consequently, specifications become a means of communication between the individuals involved in the design, manufacture, distribution, application, and testing of protective coatings.

Unfortunately, the operations involved in these processes are diverse and complicated; different parts of the problem are carried out by different specialists who understand their own work very well, but rarely are conversant with the over-all situation. Each specialist recognizes his own technical and economic limitations, and he attempts to minimize these by specifying optimum conditions on phases of the operation over which he has no direct control. As a result, conflicts frequently arise. For example, the optimum conditions for application of a paint may conflict with the paint designer's ability to formulate a paint of adequate film properties. A compromise between these two may result in a paint that is difficult to manufacture or to package, or that is too flammable. In short, it is obvious that a specification will rarely please everyone who must deal with the material, and that the best compromise must be sought.

To attain such a compromise, it is necessary to review the opinions (or specifications) of all the specialists. These preliminary specifications must be presented in such a way that all concerned will have a clear idea of the various properties desired. *Good presentation of data depends on precision, accuracy, and lack of ambiguity.*

Accuracy versus Clarity

The definition of a specification previously given does not restrict one's choice of details for describing a product. However, the details must be selected in such a way that the description will be accurate and clearly understood by everyone for whom it is intended. In writing a specification, the requirement of *accuracy* is easily fulfilled, since it involves mostly matters of scientific fact. The necessity that the specification be *understandable* and *unambiguous* becomes more difficult as the number of persons to whom the specification is directed increases. For example, there is a minimum of ambiguity when a specification originates in a laboratory and is written for laboratory personnel. However, when a specification is intended for laboratory, factory, sales, and customer, much greater simplicity of presentation is necessary, and ambiguity is more difficult to avoid.

Even a simple specification, to be fully explained to all concerned, necessarily includes reservations and qualifications. For example, it is easy to write the simple statement that a certain paint has adequate opacity or "full hiding power" in one brushed-coat. However, to be accurate, this statement must be qualified by the secondary fact that the wet-film thickness should be at least 3 to 4 mils, and that this is true only if the packaged paint is thinned no more than 10 per cent by volume with a thinner such as a low-solvency mineral spirits. If it is thinned with turpentine, the consistency may be changed so that it is impossible to apply a coat of more than 1 to 2 mils without sagging, and a 1- to 2-mil film will not have full hiding. Or it may be necessary to explain that the term "full hiding" does not mean that the paint, when spread over a black and white checkerboard, will totally obscure the background pattern, but rather that light reflection determined by a particular method of measurement is no more than 1, 2, 3, or 5 per cent less in the black areas than in the white. The term may be further qualified by explaining that it means that one coat of this paint will satisfactorily cover a solid white or pastel background, but that two coats will be necessary if the surface is part dark and part white.

All these qualifications may be implicitly understood by paint formulators in a particular laboratory; to others who lack understanding of the qualifying factors, they must be explained. The more explanation that is necessary, the more complicated the specification becomes; at the expense of clarity, it becomes more accurate. Since the attainment of accuracy detracts from clarity, and vice versa, one must usually compromise between the most literally truthful and the most readily comprehensible statement. Sufficient accuracy must be retained to permit the statement to be used as a working rule by the uninitiated without resulting in serious errors of judgment.

Accuracy versus Precision

Whatever be the form, nature, or purpose of a specification, above all it must be *accurate*. Accuracy can be defined as a truthful statement regarding some property or properties of a material. Properties must be measured, and it is unfortunate that identical measurements do not give identical results even on the same sample. In general, in defining a property that is characteristic of a particular type of material, our determination is limited by the uncertainties of measurement and by the ordinary differences between the samples selected for measurement. To obtain a single datum for a particular property, it is customary to

make a number of measurements on a number of samples and then calculate an *average* result. The expression of an average value is accurate
only if one includes information that defines the precision of the measurement, i.e., the possible range of values for that property. The narrower the range or, to put it another way, the less the expected deviation
of any particular value from the average, the better is the precision
with which that property is defined.

This manner of expressing an experimental result is easy to understand.
A feature that is frequently overlooked, however, is that high precision
of measurement does not guarantee an accurate result. Precision limits
are an estimate of the reproducibility of a measurement, and if a measurement is faulty in principle, the greatest possible reproducibility does
not give a correct conclusion. For example, much faith is placed in
certain optical devices that measure the gloss of paint films. Some of
the methods can be applied to some films so as to give data of a very high
degree of reproducibility and excellent accuracy, if we judge accuracy by
the extent to which they provide a sensitive, quantitative discrimination
among several films which obviously vary in gloss insofar as visual
observation is concerned. If, however, these same measurements are
applied to other surfaces whose reflection properties are such that this
precise measuring technique fails to interpret visual differences, the
method is faulty, because it fails to serve the purpose for which it is
intended.

The "Best Compromise" Specification

In principle, we have made the point that specifications are a means
of communication between technologists in various operations of coating
production. As such they need special consideration in their writing with
respect to achieving a happy mean between the sometimes conflicting
requirements of clarity and accuracy. A properly written specification
provides the subject matter that is to be searched by different specialists
who hope to arrive at the best compromise solution to a particular coatings problem. Let us assume that here only the supplier and the user are
involved. Ordinarily, the first tentative specification originates with the
user of the coating. The more prudent this is, and the more clearly it is
recognized that it is tentative, the less will be the labor and misunder-
standing involved in the search for the "best compromise."

The most naive approach to the writing of an original specification is
to list all desirable properties of coatings in general and then to require
that the specified coating should be optimum with respect to *each* property. The optimum is judged by a case where a particular property occurs
at its best in *some* existing coating. Very little experience is necessary

to demonstrate that all possible perfections cannot be achieved in one type of coating. A more subtle error can be made by requiring that a specified coating come as close to encompassing general perfection as technology allows. In a sense, such a specification represents a compromise with the facts of science and technology. It calls for a demonstration of what can and what cannot be accomplished with respect to approaching perfection in a single product. However, this sort of compromise is not necessarily practical because it neglects one of the most significant problems, namely, *cost*. Any particular ultimate property in a coating must be attained with a certain minimum cost. Unfortunately, if the ultimate in more than one property in a single coating material is desired, the costs are not necessarily additive. The more technologically possible ultimates one achieves within a single coating, the more disproportionate is the increase in cost with regard to the added value. This fact can be illustrated best with some examples.

Table 2.1 represents such an example, somewhat oversimplified, in detail. Here are listed some properties of several formulations of a white baking enamel for home appliances. The example is oversimplified in that it assumes a constant application cost to produce enamel films of the same thickness, and that pigmentation, solvents, etc., are on a comparable cost level in each case—that is, the cost variations depend largely on the type of the synthetic resin used in the vehicle. If all these simplifying assumptions are not made, the analysis would require more details, and hence might result in somewhat different conclusions; but the procedure of analysis would be similar in principle. The table lists certain properties which the coatings user and designer agreed were important, and it is assumed that both had agreed on what test methods should be used for evaluating the various properties. The rating scale is such that zero means complete failure in this property, while ten represents the best rating that present technology can achieve with respect to this property in any existing coating. The last two columns list respectively a *quality index* obtained by totaling the score (giving each property listed an equal weight), and a *cost index*, where the most expensive coating in the list is given a rating of 100. (In this case, the most expensive coating would cost about $38.00 a gallon.)

One might say that such a procedure of analysis sets a cost-quality index for several possible solutions to a particular coatings problem. Ordinarily, for practical problems each property is not given equal weighting; for example, for a washing machine finish, hot soap resistance is more important than resistance to food stains, while the converse may be true for kitchen appliances. Once the properties of interest are listed, it is not difficult to agree how to weigh the ratings for particular proper-

TABLE 2.1. WHITE BAKING ENAMELS FOR HOME APPLIANCE APPLICATION*

Resin Type	Hardness	Alkali Resistance	Acid Resistance	Yellowing Moderate Temp. (300° F)	Yellowing High Temp. (300–500° F)	Weathering Durability	Flexibility	Staining	Net Rating (Good avg. properties)	Cost Index
Alkyd (A)	2	2	3	4	0	7	8	0	26	3.4
Alkyd Urea (B)	7	4	4	5	0	7	7	3	37	4.5
Alkyd Melamine (C)	9	6	7	7	4	7	7	5	52	5.5
Epoxy Melamine (D)	9	9	9	5	2	8	9	9	60	6.0
Vinyl (E)	6	7	8	1	0	6	3	3	34	5.7
Methacrylate (F)	4	4	3	10	7	6	8	3	44	11.5
Silicone (G)	8	9	9	10	9	8	7	6	64	100

*These data (and also the data of Table 2.2) while derived from testing of real paints, nevertheless represent the limited experience of one coatings designer in conference with an imaginary customer for a coating. No implication is here intended that these results represent the best possible formulations for the materials that are indicated, and that comparisons which favor one material versus another are scientifically absolute. In practical formulation work, minor changes in variables can effect drastic changes in properties.

ties with respect to the total score. Assuming that this example is adequate in its detail, the analysis justifies certain conclusions. For example, coating G best demonstrates how well one can accomplish the objective of developing nearly the best ratings with respect to all desirable properties in one material. The quality index is the highest, and so is the cost index.

Coating D has the next best quality index, but the cost is only 6.0 per cent of that for the best coating (G). Coating D is obviously the best compromise from the economic and quality viewpoint, providing that one can sacrifice some quality on the specifications for resistance to discoloration at high temperature. Obviously such a sacrifice could be made readily for a washing machine finish, but possibly not for a coating that will be applied to certain hot zones of a stove or water heater. Assuming that the latter situation demands better color retention than can be obtained with coating D, some sacrifice may be allowed with respect to the high standards of coating G. Here one might select coating F for a cost of 11.5 per cent of coating G; however, in striving for better yellowing resistance at a lower cost, it is necessary to sacrifice the high ratings for chemical resistance that can be had in either coating D or G.

Table 2.1 shows that the best coating is also the most expensive. This is generally true. However, it is frequently true also that for any particular list of properties, there is no regular relationship between cost and the over-all index of quality. Coating F is nearly twice as expensive as coating D, although the latter has a far better quality index. Similarly, coatings C, D, and E are competitive with respect to cost, but their quality varies considerably.

The principle of evaluating specifications in terms of a cost-quality index can be illustrated also by the example where a search is made for the best compromise selection of a pigment system for a red baking enamel. In this instance, possibly as a result of an analysis as in the preceding example, the selection of the binder has already been agreed upon. The user of the paint may specify that the proper vehicle system should be used and that the paint should come as close as possible to matching a color for which the merchandizing department may have indicated a preference. Ordinarily there is a tendency to overlook details of specifications for color, when in fact this may be of even greater importance than the binder. In this instance, assume that the designer and user of the coating have agreed that certain properties are important. For example:

(1) Chemical resistance to dilute acids and alkali, and also resistance to discoloration in an atmosphere fouled by sulfur compounds. The

enamel will be exposed to a variety of environments and it is anticipated that it may be washed with alkaline cleansers.

(2) Since the enamel may be applied over a primer of a variety of colors, the opacity of the paint should be as high as possible at the anticipated film thickness.

(3) Over the enamel will be printed lettering and designs, possibly with white enamel, or preferably with lacquer, by the silk screen process. Hence, the red paint should resist bleeding, or the white design may become stained.

(4) Several colors may be applied in sequence to the same metal part, and each color will be baked in turn; hence, if red is the first color to be applied, the pigment should resist fading or color change on repeated exposure to high temperatures.

(5) The color should be light-fast on exposure to direct sunlight.

(6) The color should match as closely as possible the standard selected by the advertising department.

Armed with this information, the color formulator tried a color match with various pigment combinations, and each system was evaluated in terms of the requirements enumerated above. The data are summarized in Table 2.2.

It is obvious that a color match of a particular type has a variety of solutions. Each pigment formulation can be defined by specifications with respect to those properties that are regarded as important. The comparative specification table does not indicate obviously what is the best compromise: this depends on the direction in which one wishes to compromise. If the purity of the color (absence of either chalkiness or grayness) is the all-important feature, organic colors must be used and a considerable sacrifice in some other properties accepted. If one hopes for a minimum sacrifice in durability properties, one must yield to some extent as regards the color match specification. In this instance cadmium red could be selected. With respect to over-all excellence, this is the preferred system, but the cost is excessive. Should one choose to revise the "color-match" specification so as to make the Ferrite-BON system acceptable, a pigmentation of a durability rating comparable to the cadmium red system could be obtained for less than 20 per cent of the cost of the most expensive system. Between the extremes of emphasizing durability versus color match, a variety of compromises can be agreed upon at a variety of cost ratings, all of which cost less than the cadmium red system.

The foregoing examples illustrate the point that there is no unequivocal answer to the very popular question "What is the best coating I can use?" Even the question "What is the optimum selection I

TABLE 2.2. SPECIFICATIONS FOR PIGMENT PROPERTIES FOR SEVERAL APPROXIMATIONS OF A STANDARD COLOR CHIP

No.*	Chemical Resistance			Bleeding Resistance to Solvents			Resistance to High Temp. (300° F)	Fading Resistance (Weathering and Ultra Violet)	Opacity	Color Match	Rating	
	Alkali	Acid	Sulfur Compounds	Aliphatic	Aromatic	Lacquer					Point† Score	Cost Index
I	2	6	10	10	9	7	3	3	7	9	66	23
II	6	10	10	6	0	0	6	8	10	10	66	29
III	10	7	10	10	10	10	10	9	5	7 (chalky)	88	100
IV	6	5	10	0	0	0	3	5	10	9	54	23
V	4	7	0	10	10	8	5	7	7	7	65	31
VI	7	7	10	10	10	8	6	8	10	2 (too gray)	78	18
VII	7	0	0	10	10	8	5	7	5	6	58	25
VIII	7	7	10	10	10	7	4	7	9	7	78	52

*No.	Pigment System	Wt % per Gal
I	Lithol Red	10
II	Toluidine Red	8
III	Cadmium Red (lithopone type)	20
IV	Para Red	10
V	57%-Molybdate Orange 43%-BON Red	9.3

*No.	Pigment System	Wt % per Gal
VI	68%-Ferrite 32%-BON Red	11
VII	72%-Chrome Orange 28%-BON Red	10.5
VIII	BON-Red	8 to 10

† Perfect score = 100, maximum rating for each property = 10.
Index of 100 here corresponds to about $5.00/gal for pigment cost in paint.

can make at a reasonable cost?" may not have an obvious answer. In fact, such questions only by rare accident can have the same meaning to both the questioner and respondent. It is virtually impossible for both coatings designer and user to explain clearly the fine details of their respective technological and economic necessities in their original tentative specifications. If, however, both are aware of this difficulty, and proceed in some manner similar to that indicated in the foregoing examples, the situation may become clearer. By this procedure, the inquirer (here the paint user) has expressed the desire to purchase the most possible of certain desirable properties that are technologically available for a certain dollar value. The respondent replies with a cost-quality table of specifications for a variety of possible coatings. If the original "probing-specification" and the "reply-specification" are accurate, the data which are to be searched for the compromise solution are then available in terms that are comprehensible to both parties. The possible solutions to the coatings problem are demonstrated, and the technological difficulties associated with each solution are reflected in a summary form by the cost index.

Bibliography

1. Asbeck, W. K., and Van Loo, Maurice, "Critical Pigment Volume Relationship," *Ind. Eng. Chem.*, **41**, 1470–5 (1949).
2. Barnett, C. E., "Physics and Chemistry of Pigments," *Ind. Eng. Chem.*, **41**, 272–279 (1949).
3. Blom, A. V., "Organic Coatings in Theory and Practice," Chapter IV, Elsevier Publishing Co., New York, 1949.
4. Cooper, A. C., "The Refractive Index of Organic Pigments," *J. Oil & Colour Chemists' Assoc.*, **31**, 343–357 (1948).
5. Fuller, C. S., "Contribution of Polymer Chemistry to Coating Industry," *Ind. Eng. Chem.*, **41**, 259–266 (1949).
6. Jarrett, M. E. D., "Consistency in Relation to the Storage, Application, and Levelling of Paints," *J. Oil & Colour Chemists' Assoc.*, **31**, 357–378 (1948); see also Mills, H., *Ibid.* **29**, 128–145 (1946).
7. Weed, F. G., "Principles of Formulation," *Am. Paint J.*, **32** (38), 69 (1948).

3 : Pigment Dispersion in Paint Formulation

DAVID M. GANS

The Arco Company
Cleveland, Ohio

The Microscopic Structure of Paint Systems

Pigmented finishes, being heterogeneous systems, allow for examination of their physical structure with the ordinary microscope. The differences which the microscope reveals between the various types of coatings shed considerable light on their behavior, particularly in the package and during application. These differences have also been intensively studied by rheological methods. It is the purpose of the present discussion to review some of the basic relationships.

When a sample of high-gloss enamel is examined under the microscope, it is found that the pigment particles generally are thoroughly and quite uniformly scattered in the vehicle. There is no clumping of the pigment and each pigment particle is individually suspended at a distance from its neighbors. In other words, the pigment is *deflocculated* in this system.

Specimens of some primers show a different picture. The pigment particles form cross-linked networks. Hardly a particle can be found which is not physically associated with some of its neighbors. Such a system is *flocculated*. The flocculates, however, are not permanent in identity. If a specimen is disturbed and re-examined, the flocculates which are now observed are different from the original in shape and membership.

Comparatively permanent groups of pigment particles can be found in some finishing materials. These types of *aggregates* owe their stability to the fact that the constituent particles are cemented together. The aggregates already exist in the original dry pigment or extender, and the grinding process of paint manufacture is not vigorous enough to effect their comminution. The origin of many such aggregates is explained by the fact that the great majority of pigments or extenders are either precipitated in aqueous systems or are wet-milled during some point in their manufacture. The aqueous medium contains at least traces of soluble

48

salts which occur as by-products of the precipitation, or which are leached out in the wet-milling operation, or which are added deliberately for some desired effect on the product. In the subsequent drying process which converts the powder to a marketable form, these soluble materials function undesirably as cementing agents to bind one particle to another. Pulverizing the dried product destroys many of these bonds but, despite mechanical screening, some remain as aggregates. Attempts have been made to avoid the possibility of this type of aggregation by eliminating the drying process and transferring the pigment directly from the aqueous phase into a usable oil phase (the flushing process); but this has met with only limited commercial acceptance.

Should we expect these hard aggregates to be destroyed in the grinding processes of a paint factory? The diameter of the average pigment particle is of the order of 0.1 micron (0.004 mil). When a roll mill is set for a fairly tight grind, its rolls are spread about 10 microns apart. This means that a column of one hundred pigment particles long could march abreast between the rolls without mishap. There are exceptions to this generalization, for an occasional aggregate or a pigment crystal may tangle too strenuously with the roll surface and be fractured. By and large, the same geometry exists in all conventional grinding equipment. We may therefore conclude that any hard aggregates that are left in a batch of pigment are already too small to be broken down.

We may also conclude that whatever the mechanism that is responsible for the effectiveness of pigment dispersion on a commercial scale, it is not one of attrition of pigment clusters by the roll surfaces. If the several types of mills which are today in use do not, in general, serve to crack up aggregates, they must act primarily as more or less intensive mixers. In their mechanical contribution to the mixing operation they are aided by the physicochemical energy contribution made in varying degree by the pigment-vehicle interface. For completely deflocculated systems which are not starved for vehicle, the mildest sort of mechanical action readily results in a uniform free-flowing mixture of solid and liquid ingredients. But the greater the degree of flocculation in the mixture we propose to create, the greater is the relative mechanical effort required, especially for viscous liquids. In any event, dry powder is dispersed in a viscous liquid in conventional equipment by a sort of taffy-pulling effect, and if the powder tends to flocculate in the liquid—that is, is not readily wetted by it—the job becomes more difficult.

A given pigment may become completely deflocculated when ground in one vehicle but may show extensive flocculation in another. This difference can be traced to the nature of the pigment-vehicle interface in each case. The motivating influence in the phenomenon is the free interfacial energy of the system. Thermodynamically, each system will tend to assume the state possessing the minimum free interfacial energy. If two pigment particles immersed in a vehicle achieve that minimum by staying away from each other, then they assume the deflocculated state. If, on the other hand, the two pigment particles release free energy by mutual physical contact, they then tend to form a flocculated structure.

In more common paint parlance, if the two pigment particles are preferentially wetted by the vehicle, deflocculation results. If, on the other hand, they prefer each other's company and would rather set up an interface with each other than be individually surrounded by the vehicle, flocculation occurs. In extreme cases, two particles may not only back up to each other to squeeze out the undesired vehicle but in the attempt to leave behind them as much of the vehicle as possible they may actually come to the surface of the system.

Since the extent of flocculation or deflocculation is thus governed by the constitution of the interface between the solid particles and the vehicle, we find that surface-active agents, which by their nature concentrate in the interface, exercise a marked influence on flocculation by modifying the free interfacial energy relationships.

Crowding should not be mistaken for flocculation. In a system which is vehicle-hungry, the solid particles in it may rub elbows with one another, not because they have any thermodynamic desire to do so but only because they do not have the space in which to separate from each other as they would like.

Flocculation creates a physical structure within a paint. It is not surprising, therefore, to find that flocculation is intimately tied up with the flow properties of the paint. There are degrees of flocculation, for the structure may in some cases be loose and even nonexistent, and in others firm and extensive. Some materials pour readily and flow out to mirror-like surfaces; others just fall out of their containers and resist flow.

Furthermore (and this point cannot be overemphasized), the extent of flocculation is not necessarily the same throughout the life history of manufacture and use of pigmented vehicles. In great part, the art of paint formulation is based on the skillful selection of such ingredients as will maintain the most desirable state of flocculation in each period through the history of the finish. For example, it may be desired that those ingredients which form a deflocculated system should be premixed first, for deflocculation often promotes good mixing. Subsequently, in order to promote a more efficient ball-milling operation the system can be moderately flocculated by addition of a well-chosen diluent. It may be desired that the finished paint in the package be decidedly flocculated, since this is best for nonsettling characteristics. During or just after the application of the paint, it would be desirable for it to lose some of its flocculated structure (which could happen as a result of the evaporation of a flocculating constituent of the solvent combination), since this would result in greater fluidity and hence better leveling of the film.

A moderately flocculated product does not necessarily represent a poorer grind or poorer dispersion than one which is completely deflocculated. High-gloss enamels show very little flocculation. Primers are formulated to possess at least a moderate degree of flocculation. House paints as a rule are decidedly flocculated. A gloss enamel which is highly flocculated or a house paint which is totally deflocculated is poorly formulated, for neither has the flow properties required of its class. Thus what would seem a poor dispersion for one job, if flocculation is the yardstick, becomes a good dispersion for another. Further, occasional dry pigment clusters may hide out in the nooks of a dough mixer or the crannies of a ball mill, escape disintegration, and show up unwanted in the finished paint. The dough mixer, to continue with that example, is so apt to miss a cluster here and there that steps must be taken to remove them afterward. Yet the paste-product of a dough mixer is considered an excellent dispersion, despite the fact that it contains a minute weight fraction of these undesirable clusters. Many paints retain such poorly mixed agglomerates because they cannot be ground for any prolonged period, for fear that some other fragile constituents will be crushed. Some flat wall finishes which contain flatting extenders whose particles are needle-shaped are a case in point. These are well enough dispersed for their intended use after only a gentle grind, and such would be considered a very inadequate dispersion if judged by criteria for other uses. It is necessary therefore to qualify the adjectives "good" and "poor" as applied to dispersions or avoid them altogether.

The forces between suspended particles that give rise to flocculation are not the only ones that operate in a pigment dispersion. Other mutual influences exist that cause such effects as thixotropy, but these are not quite as well understood today as those discussed above.

The Measurement of Structure

Since the microscopic structure of a paint system is related to many of its physical properties, we should have a method for measuring that structure. Examination of the material with the microscope is not a method sufficiently sensitive for our purposes, although gross differences between specimens can be detected by the techniques of microscopy. We have seen that flocculation and flow are interrelated. It is not surprising therefore, that the measurement of the flow characteristics of a system, which is the business of the science of rheology, is the method we seek.

However, when we say "measurement of flow characteristics," we do not mean such simple approaches as the use of a Ford cup. Consider two samples, one a primer and the second a high-gloss enamel; the one moderately flocculated, the other almost completely deflocculated, as seen under the microscope. Only by accident will these two give the same Ford cup

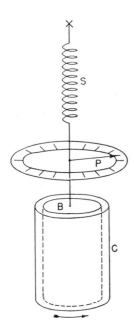

reading, but one or the other can be reduced with a suitably chosen thinner that does not affect the degree of flocculation to any extent, until both have exactly the same Ford cup "viscosity." The two samples are now still quite different in microscopic structural differences.

Either of the samples runs through the orifice of the cup because of the gravitational pull on the contents. If the experiment could be transported to the moon, where the gravitational factor is lower, both readings would be higher but they would no longer be equal; the "viscosity" reading for the primer would be higher than that for the enamel. So long as flow measurements are made under a single set of flow-inducing conditions—for example, in one Ford cup and only under the earth's gravitation pull—there is not enough information for a picture of the structure of the sample examined. In other words, single-point flow methods are inadequate to determine rheological characteristics.

Figure 3.1. Schematic diagram of a rotational viscosimeter.

One instrument which is adequate for our problem is the rotational viscometer, available in several forms. An idealized version of such an instrument is shown in Figure 3.1. From a fixed point above is suspended a spring S to the bottom of which is attached a solid cylindrical bob B. Around the bob is a cup C which may be rotated at various rates about the vertical axis of the assembly. A pointer P is attached near the bottom of the spring. With a viscous material in the annular space between the cup and the bob, any continued rotation of the cup imparts a twist to the bob which is registered as a deflection by the pointer. When the rate of rotation of the cylinder is kept at some constant value, the pointer holds a single deflected position. If the rate goes up, the deflection is increased. When the motion of the cylinder stops, the pointer returns to its zero position.

Let us put a liquid such as an oil into the cup, and make a series of pointer readings for a number of rotational rates. The results in graphical form are shown in Figure 3.2. In this graph we choose to plot the revolutions per minute (rpm)* of the cup, as ordinates, against the twist or torque* which the pointer registers, as abscissae. The result is a straight line through the origin. All true liquids, which rheologists have come to call Newtonian liquids, give similar graphs. The one difference lies in the slope of the line. The more viscous the liquid, the greater the twist or torque which we should expect the cylinder to transfer to the bob at some one value for rpm, and thus the lower the slope. In fact, the cotangent of the angle alpha is directly proportional to the true viscosity of the liquid, and a numerical factor can be calculated from the physical dimensions of the apparatus which will convert the cotangent of the

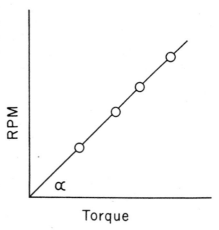

Figure 3.2. Flow curve for a Newtonian liquid.

angle into the viscosity in poises.
    Now let us replace the oil in the viscometer with flat wall finish. The picture becomes more complicated. Again the data fall along a straight line, as in Figure 3.3, but no longer through the origin. Rather, the line cuts the torque axis at an intercept whose magnitude is F.

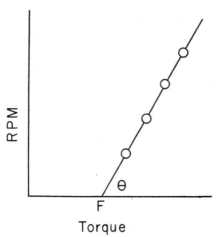

Figure 3.3. Flow curve for a plastic material.

    What is the significance of this intercept? The oil originally in the viscometer flowed under the slightest mechanical stress, a property characteristic of true liquids. But the flat paint, because of the loose chains of flocculated particles in it, resists flow, and it is not until this is overcome that the paint starts to flow. The point F, as is clearly seen from Figure 3.3 represents the down payment in torque, so to speak, that must be made before any rpm or any flow motion results. The point F is the threshold value that must be exceeded before the system yields
* Units for rpm are t^{-1}; for torque, ml^2t^{-2}.

to the torque. When the value F is recast into a slightly different function (from a threshold value for torque into a threshold value for shearing stress, the two differing merely by a volume factor) which is independent of the physical dimensions of the cup and bob and therefore more useful, we have the value f, which is called the *yield value*.* The greater the degree of flocculation of the system, the larger is the yield value, which thus becomes a measure of flocculation. The yield value of a completely deflocculated system is zero.

The similarity between the angle alpha of Figure 3.2 and the angle theta of Figure 3.3 suggests that theta measures a sort of viscosity, and indeed it does. Its cotangent, converted by the same numerical factor as for alpha, gives a value in poises, which is distinguished from the true viscosity of liquids by the designation *plastic viscosity*,† for which the symbol is U. Again, the steeper the slope of the line, the lower is the value of the plastic viscosity.

It is possible to select two paints, one having a lower yield value but a higher plastic viscosity than the other, so that their flow curves cross

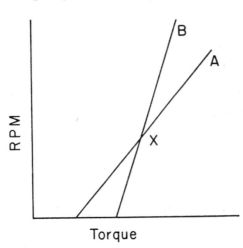

as at X in Figure 3.4. At the rpm and torque represented by point X, both paints have equal flow. At higher torques, paint B is the more fluid of the two; at torques below X, paint A flows the more readily. If a Ford cup were designed of such dimensions that the gravitational pull on the stream leaving the orifice exerted the same stress as for the torque at point X in the rotational viscometer, then both paints would flow out of this Ford cup in the same time interval. But for Ford

Figure 3.4. Flow curves for two plastic materials showing the same flow at one point X.

cups of other dimensions, one of the paints would leave the cup more rapidly, and which of the two that would be, would depend on the design of the cup. We must again conclude that the Ford cup and similar instruments for measuring "viscosity" which all share the single-point drawback do not give us a true rheological picture of a finishing material, such as is presented by

* Its units are $ml^{-1}t^{-2}$.
† Its units are $ml^{-1}t^{-1}$.

the multipoint flow curves (or consistency curves, as they are sometimes called) of Figures 3.2 to 3.4.

This does not deny the usefulness of the Ford cup in practical applications. Once a formula for a product has been set up, successive batches in manufacture will not vary much from each other in their flow curves. If the consistency of the batch is controlled by a single point measurement, as with a Ford or Zahn cup, the likelihood is great, although by no means certain, that the flow curves, coincident at one point, will fall close to each other throughout.

If, then, single-point measurements are satisfactory from the practical viewpoint of paint manufacture, why bother with yield value and plastic viscosity? For the simple reason that the consistency of a paint depends on a number of factors, and if we are to study or modify it intelligently, particularly for new types of formulation, we must appreciate the existence of these factors and be able when necessary to measure them separately instead of remaining content with a Ford cup composite.

It would no doubt greatly simplify the problems of the rheologist if the consistency characteristics of a mixture like paint could be fully described in terms of the two factors so far mentioned, plastic viscosity and yield value. However, there are such phenomena as *pseudoplasticity, dilatancy, thixotropy* and others that must be considered. In our elementary discussion we shall have to be content with only a short description of the first two, and a discussion of thixotropy.

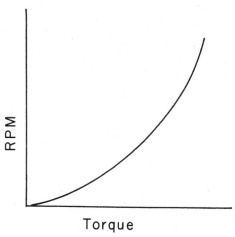

Figure 3.5. Flow curve for a pseudoplastic material.

Not all finishing materials give the linear flow curves of Figure 3.3. Some have flow curves that are concave upward, as in Figure 3.5. These are called pseudoplastics. Nitrocellulose solutions are prone to give such curves. They pass through the origin and continue from the first to bend upward. In other words, pseudoplastics, unlike plastics, flow even under infinitesimal stress, and under increasing stress they appear relatively thinner in consistency than if they were true liquids.

Dilatant bodies, on the other hand, give consistency curves that are concave downward, as in Figure 3.6. They too show flow under low stress, but act thicker than would the corresponding true liquid, as the stress increases. Some deflocculated systems that are overcrowded with the solid dispersed phase are dilatant in behavior.

Thixotropy is a phenomenon that the protective coatings technician meets very frequently. When a flow curve is determined for a plastic

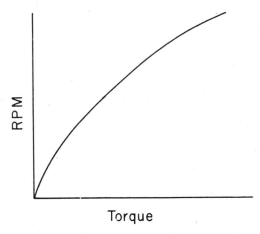

Figure 3.6.   Flow curve for a dilatant material.

body, the experimental points fall on the line regardless of what the rpm was for previous measurements. A graph like Figure 3.3 results whether the sequence of measurements is made with increasing or decreasing values of rpm. But for thixotropic bodies, this is not the case. The curve taken with increasing speeds, that is, the "up-curve," falls below the "down-curve," and it is only the down-curve which has the straight-line characteristic of a plastic, as depicted in Figure 3.7. The up-curve mimics that for a pseudoplastic, but a pseudoplastic, like a plastic, also follows a single curve, up and down. In a thixotropic body, there is apparently another type of force in addition to the force of flocculation manifested in the yield value. When the thixotropic attraction between two particles is broken by agitation, it does not reappear instantaneously but requires time for reconstitution. Under moderate agitation, the thixotropic system becomes thinner and thinner in consistency as the agitation continues, to a limit. If it is desired to break the consistency down further, past this limit, more violent agitation is required, which in turn determines another lower limit to the consistency. Still more drastic mechanical action creates a third limit. However, if agitation is stopped at any point and a down-curve is run in a reasonably short time, the straight line for a plastic results. But any number of such lines exists for the same sample, the uppermost point of each line being determined by the most violent agitation to which the sample is submitted just before starting the down-curve measurements.

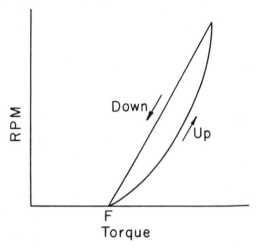

Figure 3.7.   Flow curve for a thixotropic plastic material.

A considerable amount of investigation has been carried out on thixotropic systems. This work has demonstrated that the amount of thixotrophy can be measured, and that its measure is the area of the loop between the up- and the down-curves. For the material represented in Figure 3.8, the thixotropy was broken down to one extent, *C*, by stirring, using the rotational viscometer itself as the stirring device, and to a second and greater extent by repeating the experiment but carrying the rotation up to the higher value *D*.

If a thixotropic paint which has had its structure broken down to a certain extent is allowed to stand, the material increases in consistency until it may regain its original stiffness. The fact that there

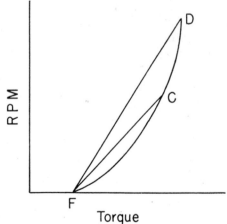

Figure 3.8.   Flow curves for a thixotropic material at two levels of thixotropic breakdown *C* and *D*.

is a time lag involved gives the paint formulator a powerful tool, for by adjusting the thixotropy through proper selection of the ingredients he can formulate a finish with considerable fluidity at the instant of application.

inasmuch as brushing or spraying will break down thixotropy, thereby allowing a short period of low consistency when the paint can spread and level. Because of thixotropic reconstitution, fluidity will diminish after work is stopped and the film will not sag. The yield value factor also operates in favor of flow during application and against it afterward, but the time component is missing, which detracts from its usefulness as a formulation tool.

Only flocculated systems seem to be thixotropic. It may therefore be argued that all plastics are thixotropic, as in Figure 3.8, but that for some the degree of thixotropy is vanishingly small or zero, as in Figure 3.3.

As has already been mentioned, the problem of thixotropic breakdown has received the attention of rheologists. But at least as important as thixotropic breakdown for the paint formulator is thixotropic reconstitution, and this aspect of the problem is almost a virgin field for exploration.

Some Practical Aspects

The numerical rheological characteristics of some types of commercial paints ready for application are given in Table 3.1.[3] In view of the fact that the plastic viscosity of some printing inks is as high as a thousand poises and their yield value is over several thousand dynes per sq cm,

TABLE 3.1. RHEOLOGICAL DATA ON COMMERCIAL PAINTS[3]

Product	Plastic Viscosity (poises)	Yield Value (dynes/cm^2)	Thixotropy Rating
Enamels, gloss	1.4–3.9	0–30	Nil to slight
Enamel, semigloss	1.0–3.5	50–120	Slight
Flat or matte paints	0.6–1	20–100	Slight to marked
Wall, water-dispersible	0.2–1.4	10–100	Slight to marked
Primers, metal	0.3–1.2	0–100	Nil to marked
Varnishes	0.9–2.9	0	Nil

the range of values for the paints listed may seem rather narrow. However, even this narrow range is sufficient to account for the wide differences in application and leveling properties of these materials. While there is very little variation in plastic viscosity from one paint type to another, the differences in yield value and thixotropy are enough to give each finish its character.

Throughout it must be kept in mind that the figures in the table give the initial rheological values only. Once the paint is on the work, its flow behavior is characterized by new and continually changing values that come from changes of composition caused largely by solvent evaporation and sometimes by chemical changes in the vehicle.

Because varnishes and most high-gloss enamels have a plastic viscosity in the neighborhood of a poise or two and show either no or a very slight yield value or thixotropy, they are applied with ease and level beautifully. For plastic viscosities not very much higher than those tabulated, these two classes of product would drag when applied by brush or atomize poorly when sprayed with conventional equipment, and in neither case would they level rapidly enough.

If it were not for the immediate build-up in consistency due to solvent evaporation, enamels with no appreciable yield value would not stay put over sharp edges. Hence compromises must be evolved which couple the lower yield values with the use of faster evaporating solvents and the higher yield values with the slower evaporating solvents. In no instance should yield values or solvent evaporation rates be so high that the leveling characteristics of high-gloss enamels are lost.

Deflocculation and gloss are interrelated. Other factors being equal, the finish which has little or no yield value when applied and which maintains little, if any, yield value as it sets up, whether by air-dry or baking, will give the highest gloss.

Completely deflocculated systems, that is, those with zero yield value, show very slow settling, but the type of settling is the kind least desired in a paint. The sediment is low in vehicle content, heavy in body, and is stirred back in again with difficulty. Flocculated systems settle rapidly to the extent that they will settle, but they do not settle far, and the sediment is soft and easily reincorporated by moderate agitation. Very often the supernatant liquid for a flocculated system is quite clear, but the sediment volume and vehicle content of the settled layer is high as compared to that of deflocculated systems.

The rate at which thixotropy rebuilds itself after the mechanical agitation of the application process has reduced it to a low level, is generally so slow that it is a negligible factor in overcoming excessive flow. But marked thixotropy is beneficial, as is also higher yield value, in minimizing hard settling in storage. If a high degree of flow is desired but accompanied by very little settling in the package, then advantage must be taken of at least moderate thixotropy rather than yield value.

From this brief discussion it is evident that while a single-point consistency measurement, as with a Ford cup, may suffice for batch control in production (provided no changes are involved in proportions or in raw material quality), the formulator, particularly in dealing with new formulations, works under a handicap without some understanding and often some actual measurements of the several factors that control the consistency and flow of the compositions which he creates.

The Future

The protective coatings industry is faced with a number of critical problems and the order in which these are solved may determine the future of paint technology. When lead in oil served as the basis of protective coatings for generations, one could practice the art of paint formulation at leisure. But today nearly every month brings some novel development, particularly among vehicles. Each new resin gives rise to problems in pigment grinding, in flow, or in settling. If these are not solved with haste, the utility of the new resin may remain unrecognized, for the attention of the formulator is drawn away to the next resin development.

Not only are these different paint systems competing with one another, but they also face competition from new directions. One example is the flame-spraying of mixtures of pigment and powder plastic, an application method that by-passes many of the rheological problems encountered in conventional paints.

For the greatest possible service to the protective coatings industry, then, the empirical method must be replaced wherever possible with a more scientific approach. Nowhere is the opportunity for benefit greater than in the application of the techniques and findings of rheology and surface chemistry. Some progress has been made, but here as elsewhere inertia preponderates. As a positive program, let us hope that the next several years will achieve the following:

(1) Extension of our basic knowledge of the fundamentals of the rheology of heterogeneous systems.

(2) Development of our understanding of the rheology of paint systems as related to their surface chemistry, the physical and the chemical cross sections of the same problem.

(3) Translation of the findings of rheology as coupled with surface chemistry into terms that have meaning and utility for practical technological personnel, including formulators, factory supervisors, and engineers responsible for the development of new manufacturing and application processes.

References

1. Fischer, E. K., and Gans, D. M., "Dispersions of Finely Divided Solids in Liquid Media," Chapter 14 in Alexander, "Colloid Chemistry," Vol. **VI**, Reinhold Publishing Corporation, New York, 1946.
2. Green, Henry, "Industrial Rheology and Rheological Structure," John Wiley and Sons, New York, 1949.
3. Fischer, Earl K., "Colloidal Dispersions," John Wiley and Sons, New York, 1950.

4 : Anticorrosive Pigments

ARNOLD J. EICKHOFF

*National Lead Company Research Laboratories
Brooklyn, New York*

Corrosion surrounds our very existence and gnaws at practically every metal that man has been able to isolate. It never takes a holiday. Measured in dollars, the total annual damage due to corrosion in the United States alone is estimated to be over five and one half billions.[1]

A recent survey of corrosion damage to railroad[2] rolling stock "indicates that the ratio of corrosion damage repair to total repair costs on selected types" may vary from 8 to 64 per cent with an average cost of 33.5 per cent on freight cars and 28.9 per cent on passenger equipment cars. It is suspected that similar maintenance losses are encountered in other industries. Within the past few years one of the large oil refining companies has concentrated its efforts in better surface preparation of the metal prior to painting and is attempting to find paints which give longer and better protection under the particular environment.

It may be possible to reduce some of these corrosion losses by improved plant or equipment design, proper maintenance, cathodic protection, and the more appropriate choice of vehicles and anticorrosive pigments. In spite of its tendency to corrode, steel is still one of the most commonly used metals.

In general, corrosion is an electrochemical phenomenon. At times some of our observations and conclusions seem to be contradictory. However, on closer examination there is usually some explanation for this apparent contradiction. Specifically, corrosion is the result of one or more factors and is understood as a tendency of the metal to revert to its original state; e.g., iron tends to revert to the oxide. In other words, corrosion is a gradual disappearance or disintegration of a metal.

MECHANISM OF CORROSION

During the past fifty years or more various and sundry theories have been proposed to explain the mechanism of corrosion. For practical reasons only four will be considered in this discussion.

Peroxide Theory.[3] Some investigators[4] claimed they found evidences of hydrogen peroxide during the corrosion of copper, mercury, lead, zinc, and certain other metals. Traube[5] reported it as present when iron corrodes. For purposes of illustration the following chemical equations use iron to describe the reactions:

$$Fe° + 2H_2O \longrightarrow Fe(OH)_2 + 2H^+$$
$$2H^+ + O_2 \longrightarrow H_2O_2$$
$$2Fe(OH)_2 + H_2O_2 \longrightarrow 2Fe(OH)_3$$
$$Fe° + H_2O_2 \longrightarrow Fe(OH)_2$$

However, Dunstan *et al.* failed to find hydrogen peroxide on corroded iron, as have many other investigators. Such inconsistent data effectively weakened this hypothesis.

Oxygen Attack Theory. In 1922 Bengough and Stuart[6] emphasized the direct oxidation of a metal by dissolved oxygen. Their theory expressed in equation form is:

$$2Fe° + 2H_2O + O_2 \longrightarrow 2Fe(OH)_2$$

They failed to explain hydrogen evolution and localized corrosion. Hence, this theory, too, soon lost favor.

Alkaline Theory.[7] It is well known that acid solutions corrode most metals rapidly and also that alkaline solutions provide some slight protection. According to the equation $H_2O + CO_2 \rightarrow H_2CO_3$, natural waters could be considered acid. If iron is present, corrosion proceeds as follows:

$$Fe + H_2CO_3 \longrightarrow FeCO_3 + H_2$$

If the conditions are favorable, carbonic acid is readily regenerated by

$$4FeCO_3 + 10H_2O + O_2 \longrightarrow 4Fe(OH)_3 + 4H_2CO_3$$

and the cycle repeats itself.

Some of the more widely used metal-protective pigments produce alkaline aqueous slurries—red lead gives a pH of approximately 8.0. Thus, it could be deduced from the alkaline theory that protection was due to the alkalinity of the pigment. Walker[8] and his co-workers showed that even in the absence of carbon dioxide, corrosion can proceed in an alkaline media. Work done by Shaw and Hawke[9] shows that there is an initial high acidity with a pH of 4.8 which gradually increases to a pH of 6.2 in about two months when pigmented paint films are in contact with distilled water. In spite of the fact that the water passing through the paint film is acid, the metal was protected from corrosion by the paint film (see Figure 4.1). Thus, it can be observed that an alkaline condition is not necessary for the prevention of corrosion.

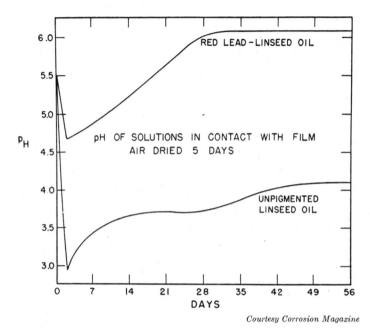

Courtesy Corrosion Magazine

Figure 4.1. Time versus pH of water in contact with paint film.

Electrochemical Theory. In 1903 Whitney[10] proposed a theory which has steadily gained in recognition. Its most notable champion is Bancroft.[11] In 1924 he published a classic which is worthy of study and thought for any investigator working on the subject of corrosion. Further proof that corrosion is electrochemical was provided by Hoar,[12] Thornhill,[13] and Mears.[14] The theory states that the corroding metal consists of anodic and cathodic areas. Where iron is concerned, these poles act like a network of short-circuit electrolytic cells on the metal surface. Figure 4.2 illustrates the electrochemical theory of corrosion.

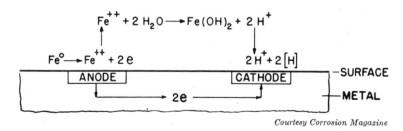

Courtesy Corrosion Magazine

Figure 4.2. Electrochemical concept of corrosion of iron.

Briefly, when iron loses two electrons it goes into solution as ferrous iron. These electrons convert the hydrogen ion to nascent hydrogen which may form hydrogen gas or combine with the oxygen to produce water.

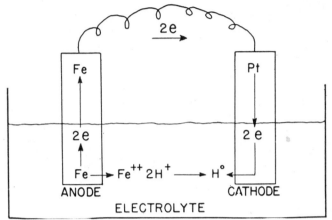

Courtesy Corrosion Magazine

Figure 4.3.   Corrosion of dissimilar metals in a uniform electrolyte (galvanic couple cell).

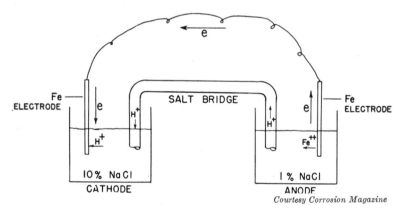

Courtesy Corrosion Magazine

Figure 4.4.   Illustration of corrosion due to variation in concentration of electrolyte.

If dissimilar metals are connected by a salt bridge or a metallic conductor and immersed in an electrolyte, corrosion begins immediately. Figure 4.3 illustrates what happens when iron and platinum are coupled.

Corrosion can also take place or will be accelerated when iron, for example, is immersed in an electrolyte of variable concentration. The electrons flow to the iron electrode in the cell of higher concentration. Figure 4.4 illustrates such a cell.

The question arises, "Where do these two examples fit in practice?" Figure 4.5 represents a layer of mill scale on steel. Under certain conditions a concentration cell is formed as the result of variation in the concentration of oxygen in the moisture. The combination of oxide and a metal is an example of dissimilar metals connected by a metallic conductor.

Mears and Brown compiled a list of eighteen causes of potential difference in metals. A few of the items include difference in grain size, presence of grain boundaries, differential thermal treatment, differential strain, presence of local scratches, differential illumination, differential heating, etc.

Another concept of the mechanism of corrosion is indicated by a study of free energy. Dodge[15] states the following rule for determining quickly, but only approximately, whether any given reaction is promising at a given temperature:

If ΔF is less than zero, the reaction is promising; if greater than zero, but less than 10 kg-cal/mol, the reaction is doubtful, but warrants inves-

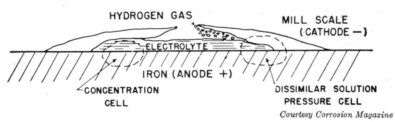

Courtesy Corrosion Magazine

Figure 4.5. Corrosion caused by variation in concentration of oxygen and metal-metallic oxide combination.

tigation; if greater than 10 kg-cal/mol, it is very unfavorable. Some values for ΔF at 25°C and atmospheric pressure are as follows:[16]

$$4Ag^\circ + O_2 \longrightarrow 2Ag_2O$$
$$\Delta F \text{ is } -2.59 \text{ kg-cal/mol}$$

$$2Fe^\circ + O_2 + 2H_2O \longrightarrow 2Fe(OH)_2$$
$$\Delta F \text{ is } -115.7 \text{ kg-cal/mol}$$

$$4Au^\circ + 3O_2 \longrightarrow 2Au_2O_3$$
$$\Delta F \text{ is } 18.7 \text{ kg-cal/mol}$$

$$2Na^\circ + O_2 \longrightarrow Na_2O_2$$
$$\Delta F \text{ is } -105 \text{ kg-cal/mol}$$

On the basis of the above, gold is a very inert material; on the other hand sodium and iron readily corrode.

Mechanism of Corrosion Inhibition

There are three main classes of inhibitors:[17]

(1) Anodic inhibitors, e.g., red lead, zinc yellow, and Pigment E (barium potassium chromate).

(2) Cathodic inhibitors, e.g., zinc oxide and calcium bicarbonate.

(3) Adsorption inhibitors, e.g., various colloids such as albumin, gelatine, etc., and nitrogenous inhibitors used in acid-pickling of steel. These may be adsorbed over the whole surface or act selectively at cathodic or anodic areas.

The following is a possible explanation for the inhibitive action of certain partially soluble chromate pigments such as zinc yellow and Pigment E. These chromates form thin films on the ferrous surface by reacting with the soluble ferrous salt to precipitate a mixture of ferric and chromic oxides. A different view of the inhibiting action of chromates is expressed in the electron configuration theory[18] which claims that chromate ions form an adsorbed layer on iron. According to Uhlig,[18] "the chromate film shares electrons from surface iron atoms and satisfies secondary valence forces, but does not disrupt the metal lattice; wherefore the metal surface is less reactive and is more noble in the galvanic series."

The inhibitive mechanism of red lead is somewhat similar to that of chromates but more complex. In addition to its oxidizing properties, red lead forms soaps in the dry film. These soaps undoubtedly enhance the mechanical properties of the film and under certain conditions of moisture, hydrolyze to release organic acids and soluble lead compounds. Mayne[19] has shown that soluble hydrolysis products of certain lead soaps can inhibit the corrosion of steel. On the basis of this work and of work done by Hawke and Shaw[20] at the National Lead Company Research Laboratories, it appears that inhibition or passivation of steel under a red lead paint film can occur by three mechanisms, either singly or in combination so that one supplements the other. The three mechanisms are:

(1) Anodic adsorption of organic acid molecules. It has been observed that a water extract of linseed oil fatty acids (no lead compound present) has a definite inhibitive effect.

(2) Anodic adsorption of soluble lead compounds. Under certain conditions, soluble lead compounds will inhibit corrosion.

(3) Anodic precipitation by oxidation. In the presence of red lead, ferrous compounds are oxidized to ferric compounds and precipitated on the metal.

Hypotheses to explain the protective mechanism of these corrosion-inhibitive pigments are many and varied, but none of them fully explains all the observations. A classic and provocative survey of the action of metal-protective paints has been prepared by Elm.[21] There is still much work to be done.

MANUFACTURE OF ANTICORROSIVE PIGMENTS

Zinc Yellow. A crude form[22] of this pigment was prepared in the early part of the nineteenth century. In 1829 Lampadius[23] suggested its use as a paint pigment. Because of its poor tinting strength it found little use for this purpose. The modern zinc yellow pigment is made by precipitation and produces various shades of yellow. In commercial practice the pigment is made by dissolving potassium dichromate in water and adding zinc oxide and sulfuric acid. It is highly probable that zinc yellow is not a true chemical compound. On the basis of chemical analyses the generally accepted chemical formula[24] for commercial zinc yellow is $K_2O \cdot 4ZnO \cdot 4CrO_3 \cdot 3H_2O$. Generally speaking, zinc yellow comprises 40 to 60 per cent of the pigment portion of a paint.

Two types of zinc yellow are currently manufactured in the United States. The principal differences in the types are reflected in Federal Specification TT-Z-415, October 28, 1944. Type I is a low chloride-sulfate product, and Type II is the regular product. A review of a number of United States Government specifications indicates that the regular or high salt content zinc yellow is often permitted.

According to Specification TT-Z-415, the maximum allowable sulfate, as SO_3, is 3.0 per cent, or the maximum allowable chloride, as Cl, is 0.8 per cent. If both are present, the sum of the percentages of each divided by its maximum permissible percentage (3.0 for SO_3 and 0.8 for Cl) shall not exceed 1.0. For example, if a sample contains 1.8 per cent SO_3 (0.6 of the maximum for sulfates) and 0.3 per cent chlorides (0.4 per cent of the maximum for chlorides), the sample just meets the maximum requirements of the specification in this respect.

Barium Potassium Chromate.[25] This is a relatively new type of chromate pigment for use in anticorrosive paints. As a chemical compound it was first reported by Gröger[26] in 1907. It is a pale yellow salt which forms a precipitate when aqueous solutions of potassium chromate and barium chloride are mixed. This procedure results in poor yields, variable compositions, and contamination with chlorides. Further investigation proved that barium potassium chromate or "Pigment E," as it is more popularly known, could be made in a rotary kiln. The process is based on the fact that potassium dichromate dissociates rapidly at 500°C into normal potassium chromate and chromic acid. If barium carbonate is present during this dissociation, the formation of barium potassium chromate takes place. The chemical reactions are as follows:

$$K_2Cr_2O_7 \xrightarrow{\;\;\;\;\;\Delta\;\;\;\;\;} K_2CrO_4 + CrO_3$$

$$CrO_3 + BaCO_3 \xrightarrow{\;\;\;\;\;\Delta\;\;\;\;\;} BaCrO_4 + CO_2$$

$$BaCrO_4 + K_2CrO_4 \xrightarrow{\;\;\;\;\;\Delta\;\;\;\;\;} BaK_2(CrO_4)_2$$

The product from the furnace forms a brittle sintered mass. After cooling it is ground to pigment particle size. X-ray diffraction patterns show no lines indicative of the presence of uncombined potassium chromate or barium chromate.

One of the unusual characteristics of Pigment E is its low sulfate and chloride content. When compared with the low chloride-sulfate type zinc yellow, Pigment E has approximately only half as much sulfates, as SO_3, and about one-sixth as much total chlorides. When compared with the regular zinc yellow, Pigment E contains about one twenty-fifth the amount of sulfates, as SO_3, and about one-fiftieth the allowable amount of total chlorides, as the regular zinc yellow. Practically all authorities agree that low chloride and low sulfate content in anticorrosive pigments is highly desirable.

In most instances the Pigment E content of the paint pigment is 30 to 50 per cent. Properly formulated paints are suitable for protecting iron, steel, and the light metal alloys. One very unique property of Pigment E is that it does not promote embrittlement of baked films. In fact,

TABLE 4.1. PHYSICAL PROPERTIES OF PIGMENT E*

Color	Pale yellow
Specific gravity	3.65
Bulking value (gallons per pound)	0..0329
Weight of 1 solid gallon (pounds)	30.4
Oil absorption (grams per 100 grams)	11.6
Refractive index	1.9
Stability in paint vehicles	Excellent

*This pigment is easy to grind and has excellent compatibility with a wide variety of vehicles.

TABLE 4.2. CHEMICAL COMPOSITION OF PIGMENT E

Barium oxide (calculated as BaO)	34.2%
Alkali oxides (calculated as K_2O)	21.0%
Chromium oxide (calculated as CrO_3)	44.6%
Combined water	None
Total chlorides as Cl	0.015%
Total sulfates as SO_3	0.11%
Water-soluble sulfates as SO_3	0.04%
Organic colors and lakes	None

Pigment E films have greater tensile strength and elongation than any other chromate pigment now commercially available.

Red Lead is a pigment of ancient origin. Vitruvius[27] describes how it was discovered. It seems that some jars with white lead—then used as a cosmetic—were heated during the burning of a house. For centuries after, red lead was made by roasting white lead.

Pure red lead is an oxide of lead, with the chemical formula Pb_3O_4, and is the lead salt of orthoplumbic acid (plumbous ortho-plumbate). In the United States, the practice has been to make litharge first, then convert the litharge to red lead. Expressed in equation form we have:

$$2Pb + O_2 \xrightarrow{\Delta} 2PbO$$
$$6PbO + O_2 \xrightarrow{\Delta} 2Pb_3O_4$$

By this method the character of the red lead is controlled by the character of the litharge from which it is made.

While the chemical reactions remain the same, there are two distinct processes generally employed in the manufacture of red lead which differ only in the method used to convert elemental lead to litharge. In the more widely used method, the metallic lead is heated in a furnace until it is converted to litharge. In the other process, molten metallic lead is "atomized" by forcing it into the center of a gas flame with compressed air. This immediately converts most of it into litharge as a fume which is collected in filter bags. When these two litharges are subsequently converted to red lead they are called furnace and fume red leads, respectively. The final conversion of both types of litharge to red lead is achieved by means of further furnacing.

Basically, the difference between the two types of red lead (fume and furnace) lies in their particle size, since the chemical composition and specific gravity are the same for both. Fume red lead is the finer of the two with regard to particle size. Furnace red lead, of intermediate particle size, is slightly coarser than fume red lead. Some indication of the com-

TABLE 4.3. COMPARATIVE PIGMENT SIZE OF THE TWO TYPES OF RED LEAD

	No. Particles/cc	Specific Surface, sq m/cc
Furnace red lead	723×10^9	2.0
Fume red lead	$3,572 \times 10^9$	5.4

parative pigment particle size of the two types may be noted in Table 4.3. The difference in particle size of these two types of red lead affects the consistency of the paints made from them when equal weights of each type are used. The finer particle size pigment results in paints of heavier, more puffy consistency, while the coarser particle size gives lower paint consistency and subsequently more leveling and flowing in applied films.

Properties data of the two types of red lead are shown in Table 4.4.

TABLE 4.4. PROPERTIES DATA OF THE TWO TYPES OF RED LEAD

	Type of Red Lead						
	85% Furnace	95% Furnace	95% Fume	97% Furnace	97% Fume	98% Furnace	98% Fume
% True red lead (Pb_3O_4)	85–87	95–96	95–96	97–98	97–98	98–98.7	98–98.7
Specific gravity	9.00	8.9	8.9	8.9	8.9	8.8	8.8
Pounds per solid gallon (av.)	75.0	74.1	74.1	74.1	74.1	73.3	73.3
Gallons per pound	0.0133	0.0135	0.0135	0.0135	0.0135	0.0136	0.0136
Oil absorption (g/100 g)	5.0–7.0	5.0–7.0	7.0–9.0	5.0–7.0	7.0–9.0	5.0–7.0	7.0–9.0
Apparent density (g/cu in)	17–21	17–21	12–16	17–21	12–16	17–21	12–16
Fineness (325 mesh)	0.03%	0.02%	0.02%	0.02%	0.02%	0.02%	0.02%
Average part. size (microns)	3.0–3.5	3.0–3.5	1.5–2.0	3.0–3.5	1.5–2.0	2.8–3.3	1.5–2.0

A chemical analysis of red lead shows it consists chiefly of red lead (Pb_3O_4) and litharge (PbO). For certain purposes the lesser amounts of the other metals may be important. Table 4.5 shows the analysis of two samples of furnace grade red lead. These two samples were not made from the same metallic lead, which probably accounts for the wide variation in the metal impurities.

TABLE 4.5. ANALYSIS OF TWO SAMPLES OF FURNACE GRADE RED LEAD

Analysis, %	85% Grade Red Lead	97% Grade Red Lead
Red lead (Pb_3O_4)	88.3	97.8
Litharge (PbO)	approx. 11.6	approx. 2.1
Copper	0.0056	<0.0008
Silver	0.0025	0.0011
Bismuth	0.015	0.0059
Tin	0.00066	<0.001
Arsenic	<0.0008	<0.0008
Antimony	0.0046	0.0017
Iron	0.03	0.014
Cadmium	<0.0008	<0.0008
Zinc	0.0012	<0.0005
Aluminum	0.0065	0.0044
Manganese	0.00022	0.000096

APPLICATION AND SERVICE TESTING OF ANTICORROSIVE COATINGS

Importance of the Condition of the Metal Surface. Theory is yet too incomplete to allow for accurate predictions as to what anticorrosive pigments to use with particular vehicles in order to achieve corrosion inhibition under given conditions of service. Practical testing of coatings in the laboratory and in service is necessary to provide such data. As soon as practical test results are considered, a critical variable enters into the picture which is at least as important as, and sometimes more important than, the differences between the several paint formulas that are being compared. This important variable is the condition of the surface to which the paint is applied.

A clean steel surface is one of the prime prerequisites for its adequate and long-lasting protection by present-day paint coatings. The degree of surface preparation should be governed by the wetting characteristics of the vehicle, the exposure environment (atmospheric or underwater), and the number of years of protection desired. When these requirements are evaluated some decision can be reached as to the extent of surface preparation, based on its relation to other paint costs. Evans[32] shows how a 200 per cent increase in the cost of paint and other materials (not including labor) can be justified if the period of time until repainting can be increased from 3 to 4 years.

Before describing the various methods of preparing metal surfaces for painting, it will be well to consider the mechanisms of adhesion.

Adhesion Mechanisms. There are two principal mechanisms by which adhesion operates. One is *mechanical*. This involves the anchoring of the paint film to the roughened surface (see Figure 4.6). Under a micro-

Courtesy Corrosion Magazine

Figure 4.6. Idealized cross section of a sandblasted surface.

scope a roughened surface appears to have many valleys and pits. Burns and Schuh[28] estimated that sandblasting a surface produces at least a twentyfold increase in the actual surface area per unit of microscopic area. By microscopic measurement the average distance from valley to peak on a sandblasted surface averages 1 mil; the lateral distance from peak to peak varies from 2.5 to 4.9 mils.

The other mechanism by which adhesion operates is called *specific adhesion.* This type depends on the adsorption forces at the interface as well as on the chemical affinity of certain coating components toward the metal itself. For example, when aluminum is anodized, the surface product is a tightly adherent oxide. Many of the more suitable vehicles for anodized aluminum have free carboxyl groups. The attraction or interaction of the aluminum oxide and the carboxyl groups tends to promote adhesion. McLaren and Hofrichter[29] state, "It has been shown that for an electrically conducting surface, the force of attraction of a dipole can be obtained by substituting in place of the surface a mirror image of the dipole in the surface (film) with the poles reversed." The value of this attractive force has been given by Moll.[30]

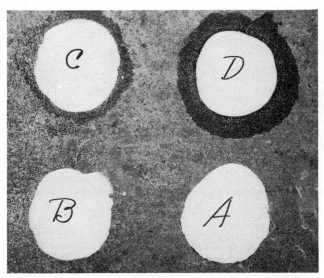

Figure 4.7. Wetting effect of paints containing varying amounts of free linseed oil on a rusted steel panel. Dark concentric circle shows degree of penetration.

Experience long ago found that the wetting of the steel substrate by the paint vehicle was one of the dominant factors in the subsequent protective performance of the paint coating. The presence of mist, mill scale, oil, etc., has varying detrimental effects on the durability of the organic coating. A semiquantitative test to determine the wetting ability of paint vehicles is indicated in Figure 4.7. These paints contained various ratios of linseed oil and synthetic resin:

A — 100% synthetic resin
B — 25% linseed oil, 75% synthetic resin
C — 50% linseed oil, 50% synthetic resin
D — 100% linseed oil

By the use of contact angle measurements, Miller[31] was able to estimate the wetting ability of paints on rusted and nonrusted surfaces (see

Figure 4.8). A practical evaluation of the effect illustrated in Figure 4.7 may be noted in Figure 4.9. All four structural steel angles in the latter figure were allowed to corrode until about 60 to 80 per cent of the mill

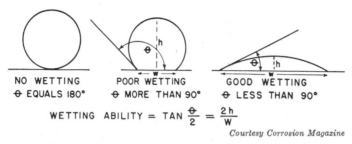

NO WETTING   POOR WETTING   GOOD WETTING
θ EQUALS 180°   θ MORE THAN 90°   θ LESS THAN 90°

$$\text{WETTING ABILITY} = \text{TAN} \frac{\theta}{2} = \frac{2h}{W}$$

Courtesy Corrosion Magazine

Figure 4.8. Wetting ability illustrated by contact angles.

scale was loosened. The surface was wire-brushed prior to painting. The angles were painted as follows:

1C2	100% oil vehicle with pigment
15C3CP	50% oil vehicle, 50% synthetic resin with pigment
5C1NP	100% synthetic resin with pigment
8C1NP	Thin coat of raw linseed oil, then 100% synthetic resin with pigment

Figure 4.9. Corrosion versus vehicle composition.

The excellent wetting properties of raw linseed oil are evident when 5C1NP is compared with 8C1NP. All paints were applied 2 mils dry film thickness. The angles were exposed outdoors 45° south for 9 months in a highly industrial atmosphere. Figure 4.10 shows in graphic form the

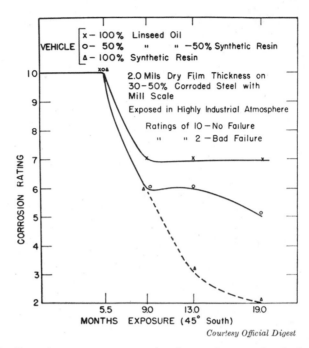

Figure 4.10. Corrosion versus exposure for three paints varying in free linseed oil content of the vehicle. These paints were applied over 30–50% corroded hot rolled structural steel angles. Exposure was in a highly industrial atmosphere.

Figure 4.11. Corrosion versus surface condition. Angle 5A2CP, tightly adherent mill scale; angle 5B4CP, 30–50% rusted; angle 5C1NP, 60–80% rusted; angle 5D2CP, pickled.

corrosion ratings of three paints whose vehicles had varying linseed oil contents, over a number of months' exposure.

In Figure 4.11 the effect of surface condition vs. paint performance is illustrated. All four structural steel angles were wire-brushed and painted with a 100 per cent synthetic vehicle pigmented and applied at 2 mils dry film thickness. The surface condition was as follows:

5A2CP	Tightly adherent mill scale
5B4CP	30 to 50% rusted
5C1NP	60 to 80% rusted
5D2CP	Pickled

These angles also were exposed outdoors 45° south for 9 months in an industrial atmosphere. The marked advantage of applying paint over a properly prepared surface is self-evident.

Methods of Surface Preparation. The user of paint, or the maintenance engineer, has a large variety of cleaning procedures from which to make a choice. Broadly speaking, the cleaning may be either chemical or mechanical or a combination of the two.

Chemical cleaning agents are as follows:

(1) Alkali washing. This involves the use of trisodium phosphate, sodium silicate, soda ash, etc.

(2) Pickling. Requires the use of dilute hydrochloric or sulfuric acids.

(3) Electrochemical, e.g., cathodic cleaning or anodizing.

(4) Phosphatizing. This method uses phosphoric acid in combination with activating agents and metallic phosphates. There also are numerous proprietary materials of this type. Some are designed for application at atmospheric temperature and others at elevated temperatures up to 190°F.

(5) Chromate treatments.

(6) Solvent degreasing with tri- and tetrachlorethylene.

(7) Weathering to remove mill scale.

(8) Flame conditioning. Figures 4.12 and 4.13 illustrate the use of a modified oxyacetylene torch for flame conditioning. Preferably the gas to use is a mixture of oxygen and acetylene. Other gases can be used, but acetylene has an unusually high Btu content along with a flame temperature approximating 5,500°F.

$$2C_2H_2 + 5O_2 \longrightarrow 4CO_2 + 2H_2O + 3,000 \text{ Btu}$$

If hydrogen is used instead of acetylene the equation becomes

$$2H_2 + O_2 \longrightarrow 2H_2O + 800 \text{ Btu}$$

The flame is rapidly passed over the steel surface. The heat tends to loosen the scale and dehydrate the rust. The steel surface is then wire-brushed and painted while warm and dry.

Figure 4.12. Brush type torch for use on large flat surfaces.

Figure 4.13. Jet type torch for angles and crevices.

Mechanical cleaning involves the following methods:
(1) Sandblasting, wet or dry.
(2) Shotblasting.

(3) Scraping and chipping. Chipping hammers are usually of special design in order not to raise sharp points on the steel surface.

(4) Wire brushing, hand or power.

The painting of new galvanized surfaces can cause considerable difficulty—e.g., paint failure by peeling. There is some evidence[33] that heavy rainfall and low temperatures are contributing factors. There are indi-

Courtesy Official Digest

Figure 4.14. The beneficial effect of chemically pretreating galvanized steel can be noted by the comparison of panel on left which had no chemical pretreatment and panel on right which received a chemical pretreatment. Both panels were new galvanized steel and were painted with a proprietary primer with and without a finish coat. The subsequent loss of adhesion on the untreated surface after 23 months' atmospheric exposure is typical. While direct application without chemical pretreatment has been advocated in a few instances, this practice is very precarious and the adhesive life of the coating is unpredictable.

cations[34] that the formation of zinc formate between the paint film and the galvanized surface is detrimental to good adhesion.

Porter and Pollard[35] conducted a rather extensive study to determine the relationship between paint composition and surface treatment of the zinc-coated steel. They used approximately ten different treatments varying from proprietary phosphate-phosphoric acid washes to the popular home-made mixtures of hydrochloric acid, vinegar, copper sulfate, zinc sulfate, etc. On the basis of accelerated tests none of the home-made mixtures is to be recommended.

Figure 4.14 shows the beneficial effect of properly pretreating galvanized iron before painting.

Outdoor Testing. Outdoor paint-testing has progressed from the stage of applying paint in a hit-or-miss fashion to the point of recording temperature; humidity; film thickness; drying time; type of surface (kind of wood or type of metal); surface preparation; direction of exposure (facing north or south); angle of exposure (45° or vertical); date exposed; environment; etc.

The average person regards outdoor weather as something which repeats itself with monotonous regularity—each of the four "seasons" from year to year being identical with the previous one. Few things could

Figure 4.15.   Painted steel angles exposed in an industrial environment.

be further from the truth. Mr. Ralph Wirshing of General Motors Corporation demonstrated quite conclusively at the 1951 annual meeting of the American Society for Testing Materials how different the weather can be from year to year—which may readily explain some of the discrepancies often noted in carefully conducted paint tests.

To record some of the differences in the daily weather, the paint technologist has gone to considerable trouble to obtain a true and reasonable record of atmospheric changes. Automatic recording instruments include (1) an automatic recording rain gauge; (2) a hydrothermograph which makes a dual record of humidity and temperature on the same chart; (3) an anemometer to measure and record the wind velocity and direction; or (4) a pyrheliometer to record radiation in terms of calories per minute per square centimeter of surface.

Figure 4.15 shows the general construction of a rack for exposing painted steel angle irons out of doors.

Lominska's[36] lengthy and interesting discussion, "The Philosophy of Paint Exposure Testing," describes test fence construction, weather recording instruments, panel construction, variations in paint performance due to different species of wood, and a host of other considerations—all important to the true evaluation of protective coatings.

For the development of paints suitable for marine use, a partially enclosed salt water basin simulates the exposure of ships and other marine structures. Figure 4.16 illustrates how test racks can be suspended to

Figure 4.16. Marine exposure racks for tide range and underwater tests.

make exposure 2 feet above high tide, at tide range, and complete immersion. This environment corresponds to the superstructure of a ship, the boottopping area, and the bottom of the hull, respectively. Regardless of how carefully exposure tests are conducted they do not exactly duplicate the conditions on a ship. However, the tests do indicate the more promising protective coatings. The next step after these trial tests is to apply a sizeable test patch on some commercial vessel.

La Que[37] has also presented an excellent detailed discussion on precautions and rack construction for conducting sea-water corrosion tests.

References

1. Uhlig, H., *Corrosion,* **6,** 29 (Jan. 1950).
2. Mitchell, F. K., *Corrosion,* **7,** 269 (Aug. 1951).
3. Bancroft, W. D., *J. Phys. Chem.,* **28,** 822 (Aug. 1924).
4. Dunstan, W. R., Jowett, H. A. D., and Goulding, E., *J. Chem. Soc.,* **87,** 1548 (1905).

5. Traube, M., *Ber.*, **15**, 2434 (1882).
6. Bengough, G. D., and Stuart, J. M., *J. Inst. Metals*, **28**, 31–144 (1922).
7. Gardner, H. A., *Trans. Am. Electrochem. Soc.*, **39**, 223–225 (1921).
8. Walker, W. H., *et al.*, *J. Am. Chem. Soc.*, **29**, 125–1264 (1907).
9. Shaw, W. E., and Hawke, D. L., unpublished data obtained at National Lead Co. Laboratory.
10. Whitney, W. R., *J. Am. Chem. Soc.*, **25**, 395 (1903).
11. Bancroft, W. D., *J. Phys. Chem.*, **28**, 785–871 (Aug. 1924).
12. Hoar, T. P., and Evans, U. R., *Proc. Royal Soc.* (*London*), Series A, **137**, 343 (1932).
13. Thornhill, R. S., and Evans, U. R., *J. Chem. Soc.*, 2109 (1938).
14. Mears, R. B., and Brown, R. H., *Trans. Electrochem. Soc.*, **74**, 495 (1938); **81**, 455 (1942).
15. Dodge, B. F., "Chemical Engineering Thermodynamics," p. 498, McGraw-Hill Book Company, New York, 1944.
16. Latimer, W. M., "Oxidation States of the Elements and Their Potentials in Aqueous Solution," 2nd ed., Prentice-Hall, Inc., New York, 1952.
17. Evans, U. R., "Metallic Corrosion, Passivity and Protection," p. 535, Longmans, Green, & Co., New York, 1945.
18. Uhlig, H., Ed., "Corrosion Handbook," p. 31, John Wiley and Sons, New York, 1948.
19. Mayne, J. E. O., *J. Soc. Chem. Ind.*, **65**, 196–204 (1946).
20. Hawke, D. L., and Shaw, W., unpublished observations.
21. Elm, A. C., *Paint, Oil Chem. Rev.*, 16 (August 19, 1948).
22. Thompson, T., *Phil. Mag.* (*2*), **3**, 81 (1828).
23. Lampadius, A. J., *Tech. Oekon. Chem.*, 4–443 (1829).
24. Brizzolara, R. R., *et al.*, *Ind. Eng. Chem.*, **29**, 656 (June 1937).
25. Kebrich, L., U. S. Pat. 2,382,157 (August 14, 1945).
26. Gröger, W. Z., *Anorg. Chem.*, **54**, 187 (1907).
27. Vitruvius, "De Architectura," **7.12**, ca. 15 B.C.
28. Burns, R. M., and Schuh, A. E., "Protective Coatings for Metal," pp. 313–315, Reinhold Publishing Corporation, New York, 1939.
29. McLaren, A. D., and Hofrichter, C. H., Jr., *Paper Trade J.*, **125**, No. 19, 96 (1947).
30. Moll, W. L. H., "A Study of the Dielectric Constant, Polarization and Dipole, Moment in Collodial Systems," *Kolloid Zeitschrift*, **76**, 200–210 (1936).
31. Miller, N. F., *J. Phys. Chem.*, **50**, No. 4, 300 (July 1946).
32. Evans, U. R., "Metallic Corrosion, Passivity and Protection," pp. 686–687, Longmans, Green, & Co., New York, 1945.
33. Gardner, H. A., Nat. Paint, Varnish & Lacquer Assoc. Circ. 451, p. 38, 1934.
34. Wing, Henry J., *Ind. Eng. Chem.*, **28**, 2, 242–3 (1936).
35. Porter, W. C., and Pollard, R. E., BMS Report No. 44, Nat. Bur. Standards U. S.
36. Lominska, C. A., *Official Digest Federation Paint & Varnish Clubs* (Oct. 1950).
37. La Que, L. F., in "Corrosion Handbook," edited by R. Uhlig, p. 1060, John Wiley & Sons, New York, 1948.

5 : Design for Reflectance Properties

J. R. DeVORE

*The New Jersey Zinc Company (of Pennsylvania)
Palmerton, Pennsylvania*

A paint film has two essential functions to fulfil: (1) to protect the surface on which it is laid and (2) to alter the appearance of the surface; the latter function can satisfy other purposes such as to increase or decrease the reflection of light or other radiation. The pigment phase of the paint film plays a vital role in both functions because it has a marked effect on the physical properties, both mechanical and optical, of the paint film. It is with its effect on the optical properties that this discussion is concerned.

Optical Properties

The important optical properties of a paint film include color, brightness, hiding power, gloss, haze, and sheen in the visible region of the spectrum and reflection or absorption in the infrared or ultraviolet portions of the spectrum. These optical properties are determined primarily by the absorption, refractive index, and particle size of the pigments in the paint, the vehicle usually playing a minor role. Let us consider these three characteristics of a pigment individually and see how they affect the optical properties of the paint film. In doing so we must realize that this is a slightly artificial procedure because the optical properties of the paint film are a result not only of the three properties individually but also of the interaction of these properties.

Absorption

Absorption by a pigment is the process of converting a portion of the radiant energy falling upon the surface of the pigment into energy of another form—usually heat. The absorption can occur over a narrow portion of the spectrum, over a wide portion, or over several portions simultaneously.

The first effect of the absorption by the pigment is control of the color of the pigment and hence of the paint. In this study we are concerned with the portion of the electromagnetic spectrum, ranging from the ultraviolet at the short wavelength end, through the visible spectrum, and into the infrared at the long wavelength end. The visible spectrum starts with violet at the short wavelength end (4,000Å) through blue, green, yellow, and orange into red at the long wavelength end (7,000Å). The color of a light depends on the relative amounts of the various portions of the visible spectrum in the light. Contrary to the practice in physics, black, gray, and white are often considered colors when discussing paints. In this discussion, we shall assume that the paint film is illuminated with white light which contains essentially equal luminosities of all the portions of the visible spectrum. If the paint reflects essentially all the light falling upon it, the paint is white. If the paint absorbs equal portions of all the colors, the paint is gray, and the larger the fraction that is absorbed, the darker is the gray. When all the light falling on the paint is absorbed, the paint is black.

When the absorption of the pigment is selective with respect to the various portions of the visible spectrum, we get colors in the true sense of the word. Here, however, we are dealing with subtractive colors. Thus, a blue pigment is blue because it absorbs the green, yellow, and red end of the visible spectrum and reflects the blue. Conversely, a red pigment absorbs the blue, green, and yellow and reflects the red. A green pigment absorbs red and blue but reflects green. A purple pigment absorbs green but reflects blue and red.

These bands of absorption and reflection of colored pigments are rather broad bands, and this fact explains the effect of mixing paints. Thus, a blue pigment reflects blue predominately, but it also reflects some green. A yellow pigment reflects yellow and red predominately, but it also reflects some green. When blue and yellow are mixed, the color that is reflected predominately by both pigments is green so the color of the mixture is green.

The problem of calculating and predicting the color that will result from a mixture of two or more colors has been studied by a number of workers. J. L. Saunderson[1] and D. R. Duncan[2] each have published descriptions of somewhat simplified systems for calculating color mixtures. These systems also make it possible to determine (1) whether a desired color can be attained by suitable mixtures of available colors and (2) what the suitable mixtures are. Duncan has pointed out that calculations of this type made it possible to change the formulation of camouflage paints so as to obtain the same colors by using smaller amounts of certain colored pigments which were in short supply during World War II. In peacetime such results would still be useful if it would make it possible to reduce the percentage of high cost pigment in a formulation or to substitute lower cost pigments for more expensive ones.

With white pigments, the important factor is to avoid absorption in the visible spectrum. In order to get a clearer picture of this, let us consider just how a pigment functions in a paint film. A white pigment is a powdered transparent material. The whiteness and brightness is a consequence of successive reflections of the incident light at the various particle surfaces. The way the successive reflections build up is inter-

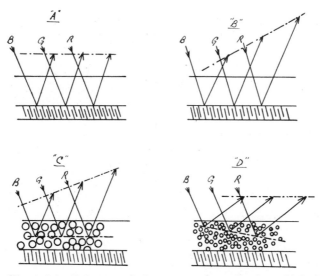

Figure 5.1. Influence of pigment on absorption by vehicle.

esting. A good metallic mirror may give 90 to 95 per cent reflection at the surface, but that is the limit—the remainder is lost by absorption. In contrast, the reflection at a single magnesium oxide-air interface is less than **7** per cent, but the remainder is transmitted through the crystal, and successive reflections within a thick layer of the powder build up an absolute reflectance in excess of **99** per cent for the visible spectrum. When the pigment is dispersed in a liquid vehicle, light absorption by the liquid must be considered. This may vary from hardly anything in some of the water-white resins to practically complete absorption, particularly in the ultraviolet and blue, for even thin layers of many varnishes. Figure 5.1 is a rough schematic sketch of the consequence of the vehicle absorption with a white pigment.

A represents a hypothetical white light consisting of equal luminosities of blue, green, and red light being reflected from a nonselective white plate covered with a film of a colorless liquid. In this case, the reflected

light has the same spectral distribution as the incident light. *B* represents
the conditions when the plate is covered with a film of yellow-colored
vehicle. Because of the selective absorption of blue light by such a vehicle,
red light predominates in the reflected radiation, which, therefore, appears
yellow. In *C,* the conditions are the same as in *B* except that a nonselective pigment has been added to the film. This decreases the penetration
of light into the film, so the vehicle has less opportunity to manifest its
selective absorption in the blue. As a result, the reflected light is greater
in intensity than in *B,* but the reflected radiation is still definitely yellow.

D represents the ideal case. Because the pigment has its maximum
efficiency in the blue region of the spectrum, it can reduce the penetration of blue light into the film and thus turn the blue out of the film
before it can be absorbed by the vehicle. At the same time, the greater
general opacity of the pigment reduces the over-all penetration of incident light more than in *C,* thereby decreasing the opportunity for selective absorption of blue light by the vehicle. As a result of these factors,
the reflected light, although reduced somewhat in intensity by absorption
of the vehicle, will tend to retain the same spectral distribution as the
incident light.

Since the high total reflection of a white pigment is achieved by reflection at a large number of interfaces, it is evident that the light has been
transmitted through a large number of particles in the process. If the
pigment were to have an appreciable amount of absorption, the light
would be distinctly colored by the time it had penetrated a distance
into the paint film and been returned.

In respect to the lack of absorption in the visible spectrum, it might
be pointed out that some of the white pigments just barely qualify as
white. The outstanding example of this is rutile TiO_2. In this material,
the ultraviolet absorption band actually extends into the visible violet
portion of the spectrum. This absorption in the violet gives the pigment
a yellowish undertone that is quite apparent when a paint made with
rutile is compared with a paint made with anatase TiO_2.

It was stated at the beginning of this discussion of absorption and
color that we would assume that the paints are illuminated by white
light. When the illumination is not white, the absorption bands of the
pigment still have an important effect on the appearance of the paint,
but the spectral character of the illumination is equally important. For
example, let us assume that the illumination is spectrally pure red. A
white paint reflects all colors incident on it so under this illumination the
white paint will appear red. A red paint reflects red and absorbs other
colors so it will still appear red. An orange paint and a yellow paint both
reflect appreciable amounts of red so they both will appear red. On the

other hand, green and blue paints absorb red light so under this illumination they will appear black. In similar fashion, illumination by other colors will alter the appearance of colored surfaces. This is the reason that things often look peculiar under mercury arc lights. The light from a mercury arc is particularly deficient in red so, under mercury arcs, red objects appear brown or black. This effect produces the changed appearance of a person's lips under mercury arcs. Under sodium arcs, such as are used for some highway illumination, the alteration of color and appearance is much more marked than in the case of mercury arcs because of the greater spectral purity of the lights.

This relationship between appearance and the spectral characteristics of the illumination and the surface has become important with the advent of fluorescent lights for general use and mercury arcs for special use such as high-intensity lights for factory illumination. In the case of mercury arc illumination, the arcs are usually supplemented by incandescent lights which provide some of the red that is lacking in the mercury light. In the case of fluorescent lighting, the color correction is achieved both by adjustment of the lights and compensation through selection of proper paints. Thus, a white fluorescent light and, to a greater extent, a daylight fluorescent light emit too high a proportion of blue light for objects to have the warm pleasant appearance we have become used to under incandescent lights. When multiple lamp fixtures are used, this red deficiency can be corrected by using one yellow lamp to every two or three white lamps. If the fixtures are single lamp fixtures, this kind of compensation is not as successful because the distribution of the light will not yield a uniform color. However, yellow or cream-colored walls and ceiling would help to correct the color because the selective absorption of blue by the walls and ceiling would reduce the dominance of the blue light.

Absorption in Ultraviolet or Infrared

Thus far in the discussion, we have considered only absorption in the visible portion of the spectrum. The absorption in the ultraviolet and infrared portions of the spectrum is of importance also. Practically all vehicles absorb ultraviolet light, and the energy from the absorbed ultraviolet induces chemical reactions and changes that lead to breakdown and failure of the paint film. This is what happens when a paint chalks. By incorporating into the paint a pigment that absorbs ultraviolet, the paint vehicle is protected from the ultraviolet because the pigment absorbs it before it has a chance to penetrate any appreciable distance into the film. By adjusting the amount of such a pigment in the paint, the manufacturer is able to control the amount of chalking since it is possible to get any condition between extreme chalking when no ultraviolet-absorbing pigment is present to essentially no chalking when the paint contains a large proportion. On the other hand, one will occasionally find conditions where it is desirable to use a paint having a high ultraviolet reflectance. In such cases, the vehicle should be selected to have as low an ultraviolet absorption as possible, and the pigments

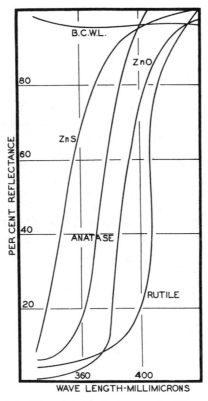

Figure 5.2. Ultraviolet reflectance of white pigments.

should be selected to avoid ultraviolet absorption. The range in ultraviolet absorption among white pigments is shown in Figure 5.2. They range from B.C.W.L. which is transparent through the near ultraviolet, to rutile which is practically opaque through the ultraviolet. The intense absorption of ultraviolet by these pigments is illustrated in Figure 5.3 which shows zinc oxide and carbon black photographed in visible light and in ultraviolet light. In ultraviolet light, the zinc oxide is blacker than this carbon black.

Absorption in the near infrared is of importance in more or less special cases. One such case is camouflage paints. During World War II the army was interested in obtaining paints that could be used for camouflage purposes. This meant that objects painted with such paints should have the same appearance as natural surroundings, particularly when observed from the air. The similarity in appearance must exist for both visual and photographic observation. In photographic reconnaissance, it is not only possible but customary to use infrared photography. Consequently, the camouflage paints had to match natural colors not only through the visible spectrum but also through the near infrared out to the limit of sensitivity of photographic film, that is, out to about 11,000

Figure 5.3. Zinc oxide and lampblack in visible and ultraviolet light. The lampblack is in the center. Left, white light; right, ultraviolet light.

or 12,000 Ångstrom units. This requirement strongly restricted the usable formulations. For example, it is not too difficult to prepare a paint which has the same green color as leaves; there are many pigment combinations that will produce this color. However, very few of these combinations will have the high infrared reflectance of leaves, so most of the formulations are of no use for camouflage work. If a camouflaged area in a forest is painted with an improperly formulated paint and then photographed on infrared sensitive film, the painted area will stand out as if it had been painted with black paint. This is the reason that the infrared absorption of the pigments is so important for this work.

Another case in which the infrared absorption is important is the case of painting gasoline storage tanks to keep them as cool as possible so as to reduce the loss by evaporation. The problem here is to apply a paint that will reflect a maximum amount of the sun's radiation since that is the principal cause of heating of the tanks. At the earth's surface, the sun's spectrum has a maximum in the green, falls off very rapidly in the ultraviolet, and falls off less rapidly in the infrared. In formulating a paint for this purpose, it is necessary to have the highest possible reflectance in the visible spectrum where the sunlight has maximum energy. Since a metallic mirror will only reflect 90 to 95 per cent of the light that falls upon it, a metallic paint such as aluminum paint, which is essentially a lot of little metallic mirrors incorporated in a vehicle, will not reflect more than 90 to 95 per cent of the light falling on it. However, a good white paint will reflect 98 per cent or more of the visible light incident upon it, and consequently is better than a metallic paint. The white pigments do not have absorption bands in the very near infrared, so that does not enter into the picture. However, it sometimes is decided to use a light-colored paint rather than a white one for aesthetic reasons. In such cases care should be taken that the colored pigment does not absorb strongly in the near infrared. The absorption in the longer wavelengths of infrared is of no importance in this problem because the amount of radiant energy in this region is small. In formulating white paint for this job, anatase TiO_2 or zinc sulfide would be the desirable pigments to use because they absorb less in the near ultraviolet than zinc oxide or rutile TiO_2 and they have higher total reflectance in the visible than white lead.

Index of Refraction

Next to absorption, index of refraction is the most important property which determines the optical characteristics of a pigment, particularly a white pigment. It was pointed out previously that a white pigment is a powder form of a transparent material and that it is white because it reflects practically all the light incident upon it by successive reflections at pigment-vehicle interfaces. The extent to which absorption by the vehicle can influence the color of a pigment is dependent upon the depth to which the light penetrates into the film before being completely reflected. The depth of penetration is dependent upon the fraction reflected at a single surface, and this, in turn, is dependent upon the refractive indices of the pigment and the vehicle. The basis for this effect of refractive index is given by the Fresnel equation giving the fraction of light reflected at the interface between a medium of refractive index of n_1 and a medium of refractive index n_0:

$$R = \frac{(n_1 - n_0)^2}{(n_1 + n_0)^2}$$

Figure 5.4 is a plot of the reflection coefficient for pigments of different indices immersed in an oil medium of refractive index 1.5. It is obvious from this that the higher the refractive index of the pigment, the smaller is the number of interfaces that will be required to obtain complete hiding. It is on the basis of refractive index that white pigments are classified into the two groups, hiding pigments and inert or extender pigments. The hiding pigments, which comprise those from lead sulfate on up, provide the opacity in the paint film. The extender pigments, which are those below lead sulfate, have practically no opacity in the paint film but are used to provide the mechanical properties.

The commercial development of the high-index pigments zinc sulfide, anatase TiO_2, and rutile TiO_2 was a major boost for the paint industry. It made it possible to obtain the hiding power with a smaller volume of hiding pigment, thereby allowing the use of a larger amount of extender pigment. This enables the paint formulator to exercise greater control over other paint properties such as flow and leveling, can settling, etc.

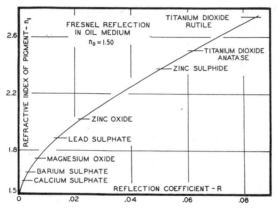

Figure 5.4. Reflection coefficient vs. index of refraction of some white pigments.

The effect of change of refractive index of the medium on the reflection occurring at a single interface is utilized in the manufacture of flat wall paints which have excellent dry hiding power. These paints are formulated in such a way that the vehicle does not wet the pigment well, so that when the volatile thinner evaporates there are many pigment-air interfaces within the film instead of the usual pigment-vehicle interfaces. Looking at the Fresnel reflection equation again, we see that when n_0 is changed from 1.5 to 1.0 the reflection increases appreciably. Consequently, when these paints dry and the pigment-air interfaces develop, the hiding power increases markedly.

Particle Size

Particle size is a less important factor in determining optical properties of a pigment than either absorption or refractive index. However, the pigment manufacturer and, to a lesser extent, the paint manufacturer are more concerned with particle size than with either of the other properties because it is the one factor that can be varied. The only variation in absorption results from variation in impurity content, and the refractive index cannot be varied—that is a characteristic of the material. Since we can control the particle size, let us consider just what the effect of particle size is. In this discussion, we shall, for the present, consider only white pigments.

We have already seen that the high brightness of a white paint is achieved by having a multiplicity of pigment surfaces or oil-pigment interfaces, each of which returns a relatively small proportion of the incident light toward the surface of the paint. Now as a primary consideration, it is necessary to have the particles small in order that the required number of surfaces will be attained in a reasonable thickness of paint. This is best illustrated by considering a pile of glass plates in air that will reflect 98 per cent of the incident light. If each plate is 1 mm thick (about the thickness of a microscope slide), the pile will be about 2 inches thick. However, if the individual plates were 1 micron thick, the pile would be only 0.002 inch thick. Such a pile of plates would not look white because the incident light would all be reflected in one direction just as if a mirror were used. In order to produce the effect of a white surface, the individual plates must be randomly oriented so that the light will be reflected in various directions. This condition exists in a pile of snow where the individual snow crystals act like the individual glass plates just considered. In order to achieve this random orientation, it is necessary to have the lateral dimensions of the individual plates small so they will not tend to "leaf" or pile with their flat surfaces in one direction.

From the preceding consideration, it would appear that the finer the individual particles of pigment can be made, the more desirable pigment it will be. However, this is not the case because the optical behavior of a pigment particle changes as the size of the particle decreases. In discussing particle size, it is convenient to talk in terms of the diameter of a spherical particle although it must be understood that the discussion applies in a general way to particles of other shape. Furthermore, in discussing the size of a particle (insofar as its optical behavior is concerned), we always use the wavelength of light as the comparison standard. Thus, a particle is large or small depending upon whether the diameter is large or small compared to the wavelength of the light in which it is being used.

Now let us assume we have a large, spherical particle—say $d = 100\lambda$—and consider its optical behavior as the diameter is reduced. Let us define a function K as the ratio of the scattering cross section to the geometric cross section of the particle. Then an increase in the value of K means an increase in the light-scattering efficiency of the particle, that is an improvement in its ability to turn the incident light back out of the film. We find that for this large particle, K has the value 2. The light is specularly reflected from the surface, and consequently there is not the uniform distribution of reflected light that is desired in a good white paint. The reflection is nonselective, and so it does not offer the color correction which we saw, in Figure 5.1, is desirable. The pigment particles would

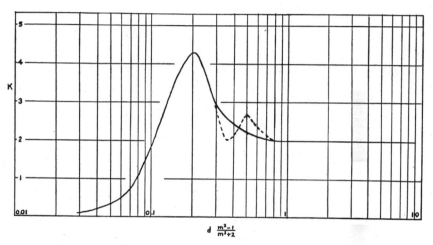

Figure 5.5. Universal scattering curve.

appear similar to glass beads. As the diameter is decreased, the value of K remains 2 and the nature of the reflected light remains the same until d/λ reaches a value of about 10. (See curve in Figure 5.5. In this graph the values of the abscissa are different, but the curve is the same as the one being described. The value of d/λ would increase to the right on this graph.) As the diameter decreases from $d/\lambda = 10$ to $d/\lambda = 0.1$, the optical behavior of the particle passes through a transition range, the discussion of which will be postponed for a moment. When $d/\lambda < 0.1$, the particle does not show specular reflection but scatters in accordance with Rayleigh's law. The value of K drops rapidly to infinitesimal values. The particle shows selective scattering;; that is, the blue end of the spectrum is scattered more strongly than the red end. (This effect can be predicted from the curve because if d is held constant and λ is increased, d/λ is decreased and the curve shows a decrease in K as d/λ decreases. Consequently, the scattering efficiency is lower for the red end of the spectrum than for the blue. This predominance of blue in the scattered light and red in the transmitted light is the effect observed in a Tyndall beam in a colloidal suspension. This selectivity is desirable in a paint pigment, but the opacity is low so that particles in this size range are too fine to be good pigments.

Now let us consider the optical behavior of a particle falling in the transition range. As the diameter decreases from the upper limit of this range, the value of K increases to a maximum of 2.7, decreases to 2, then increases again to a value slightly larger than 4, and decreases smoothly into the Rayleigh region. It will be seen that in this transition region

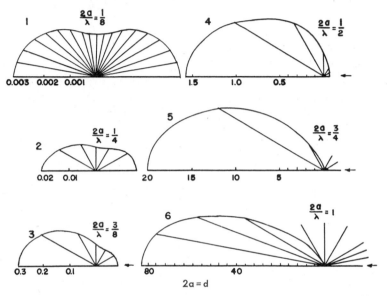

Figure 5.6. Variation of Directional Scattering Power with Particle Size.

the individual particles are much more efficient optically than in either of the other two regions. Furthermore, if the particles are slightly smaller than the size corresponding to the maximum, they will show the desired selective scattering.

Scattering efficiency curves can be calculated from the theoretical equations of Mie[3] and Debye.[4] These theoretical curves are specific for the relative refractive indices of particle and surrounding medium for which they were calculated. However, Bailey[5] found empirically that if the ratio of particle size to wavelength (d/λ) is multiplied by the Lorentz refractive index coefficient, $(m^2 - 1)/(m^2 + 2)$, where m is the relative index of refraction, then the resultant scattering curve is independent of the refractive index of the particle or the medium. Such a universal scattering curve is shown in Figure 5.5.

In addition to the change in the value of K as the particle size changes, there is a radical change in the angular distribution of the scattered light. In Figure 5.6 are a series of diagrams, taken from a paper by Ruedy,[6] showing the intensity of scattered light as a function of angle. In these graphs the length of the radius vector is proportional to the intensity of the light scattered in that direction. The diagram for a particle in the Rayleigh region does not appear on this slide. The envelope of the

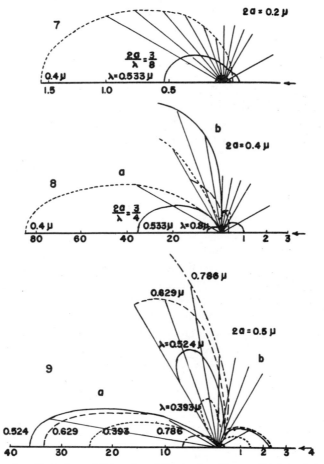

Figure 5.7. Variation of Directional Scattering Power. (Enlarged Scale).

radius vectors for such a particle would be a circle. It is evident from these diagrams that as d increases, the scattering in the forward direction increases. In terms of a paint, this means less light is returned out of the film per particle.

If we examine some of these curves in greater detail, we find the interesting phenomenon that is shown in Figure 5.7. Here the scale for the radius vector varies with direction so as to make the different maxima visible. It is apparent that there are several maxima and that the angle at which the maxima appear changes with the size. Conversely, if the size is held constant, the maxima for different colors will appear at different angles. This means that if a dispersion of very uniform size particles is illuminated by a beam of white light, the color of the scattered light will change with the angle at which the suspension is viewed. This phenomenon gives a beautiful appearance and is strikingly demonstrated by sulfur sols which are formed under conditions that produce a high degree of uniformity of particle size. The preparation of these sulfur sols is described by LaMer and Barnes.[7]

In the discussion so far, we have been considering the scattering by a single particle as the size of the particle changes. What we are really interested in is the scattering of a given mass of particles as the particle size changes. This is related to the scattering of a single particle by the function $1/d^3$, since the number of particles in a given mass is proportional to $1/d^3$. The changes this produces in the scattering curve are in three conditions: (1) the maximum is shifted toward smaller sizes; (2) the relative size of the secondary maximum is greatly reduced; (3) the curve does not level off at large particle sizes but continues to decrease as the size increases.

In a practical white pigment, we never have a perfectly uniform particle size such as was assumed in the hypothetical material we have just discussed. Instead, a white pigment is composed of a range of particle sizes grouped about a size showing the greatest frequency. The size of peak frequency and the range of the sizes will vary from sample to sample. Let us now consider how these various features of scattering are affected by the fact that the sample contains a range of sizes.

If we look at the last figure again, we see that the angles at which the various scattering maxima occur change as the size of the particle changes. Consequently, the scattered light from a practical white pigment will not show these angular maxima because they are blurred out. The envelope of intensities of scattered light will be a smooth curve like the ones in Figure 5.6 even if they are plotted on the scale used in Figure 5.7. This disappearance of the maxima is a desirable feature. If a paint were prepared from a pigment having the high degree of uniformity first postulated, it is evident that a surface painted with such a paint would not be white. If it were illuminated by a beam of white light, the surface would appear more or less strongly colored and the color would depend upon the viewing angle. Consequently, the elimination of the maxima is beneficial.

Now let us consider the scattering curve again. It was stated earlier that the ordinate referred to as size is a function of d/λ. Consequently, if we consider particles of a fixed size and study the scattering in different colors of light, it will be seen that we can get the curve of scattering versus λ from this one. The large values of size correspond to small values of λ and vice versa. Now particles of slightly different size will have the same type of scattering curve, but it will be displaced along the λ axis. When a mixture of particle sizes exists, the scattering curve will be a kind of summation of the curves for the component sizes. The effect of this summation is (1) to wash out the secondary maximum, and (2) to broaden and reduce the intensity of the primary maximum. The more nonuniform a pigment is, the less selective will be its reflectance and the lower will be its opacity. On this basis an ideal white pigment would be just nonuniform enough to eliminate the angular selective scattering and of such size that its scattering maximum would fall, not in the green where you would locate it for maximum opacity, but toward the blue so that the selective scattering will compensate for the absorption of the vehicle so as to yield a white surface.

The effect of particle size on colored pigments is less pronounced but there is an effect and it is important. Colored particles scatter the incident light just as white particles do and this scattered light from colored particles has the same sort of spectral composition as the light scattered from white particles. Consequently, the scattered light acts to dilute the color with white. By way of illustration, consider a coarse, red iron oxide. If this iron oxide is ground finer, there is no change in chemical composition and no change in absorption spectrum of the pigment. However, it will be found that the red color becomes paler in color as the size is reduced. This results from two factors working simultaneously: (1) the increased scattering of the incident white light dilutes the color and (2) the increased scattering reduces the depth of penetration into the film so that the colored pigment has less chance to selectively absorb. Furthermore, when the particles become fine enough to show the selective scattering that was discussed with white pigments, paints made from the red pigment will begin to develop a blue undertone which is a result of the higher proportion of blue in the scattered light. Consequently, this reduction in size is detrimental to the color quality. On the other hand, the decrease in size (up to a certain point) produces an increase in opacity and hiding power. The manufacturer is forced to try to strike a desirable balance between the effect on color and the effect on hiding power. His control of particle size becomes very important when he is trying to duplicate color from one batch to another.

The discussion of the effect of particle size should be completed with a note of caution. Predictions and conclusions involving particle size should be made with care. This warning is best illustrated in Figure 5.8.

Here are shown photomicrographs of two samples of zinc sulfide. These two samples appear as nearly identical as it is possible to get two different samples. Sample A had a tinting strength of 70 per cent and Sample B, 120 per cent of a given standard. When the paints were examined by an infrared transmission method for studying particle size, it was evident

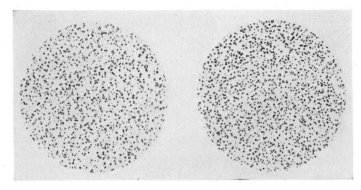

Figure 5.8.   Photomicrographs of zinc sulfide samples. Left, sample A; right, sample B.

that Sample A was badly aggregated. These aggregates had been broken down in preparing the microscopic mounts whereas they were not broken in the tinting strength rubout. This well illustrates the point that, in applying the theory we have discussed, it is necessary to use the particle size as it exists in the paint.

Other Optical Properties

The discussion thus far has been concerned with the optical behavior of pigments that affects color, brightness, hiding power, and tinting strength. Texture in paints is a matter of particle size and wetting. Poor texture is produced by either very coarse particles or, more commonly, lumps of pigment protruding above the general pigment level so that they produce small bumps on the surface of the paint. Poor texture is a result of having very coarse aggregates in the paint or of poor wetting of the pigment by the vehicle so that large flocculates are formed which distort the surface of the film just as the aggregates do. The cure for poor texture is the removal of coarse material from the pigment and adjustment of the vehicle to improve wetting.

The control of gloss, haze, and sheen is more difficult because the factors that influence these properties have not been definitely identified. Results of some experiments will indicate that particle size is a very important factor in these properties, but then experiments designed to confirm this will yield negative results. Again, properties like particle shape or wetting appear to be the controlling factors, but when this is checked the results are inconclusive. The problem in working with these properties is twofold. First, the properties are dependent upon the integrated effect of several factors including particle size, surface properties such as wetting and adhesion, and chemical reactivity of vehicles and pigments. It is extremely difficult to isolate the effect of any one factor. Secondly, gloss, haze, and sheen are visual effects of the paint film that involve a sensory and mental process on the part of the user. The psychological problems involved in these properties have been a constant source of trouble in attempts to measure these properties by means of instruments. A number of instruments have been designed to measure gloss or haze but with any of these instruments, the correlation with visual gradings is not too good. The presence of the psychological factors adds confusion to attempts to correlate these paint properties with physical characteristics of the pigment and vehicle. As a result of the difficulties with these properties, the development has been almost entirely empirical. In that respect, although we have nice theories about hiding power, brightness, etc., we cannot formulate paint on a theoretical basis alone and attain the desired result. For these properties also the results are partially empirical. In fact, the status of the subject has best been stated by an English physicist, A. C. C. Newman,[8] who said, "It has for many years been thought that the particle size characteristics of pigments have a profound influence on the properties of paints, or at least there has been an uneasy feeling that a close correlation ought to exist even though so far the hope of its scientific demonstration has in many ways receded the more it has been pursued."

After this pessimistic view of the situation, it would be well to cite one instance where the theoretical approach to a paint problem really worked. The problem involved almost all the optical factors at one time and the successful solution of it is encouraging to fundamental research on pigment behavior. During World War II, meteorologists encountered a problem with the instruments they were sending up in the air to 30,000 and 40,000 feet to transmit back to ground the weather conditions at these altitudes. The problem was that, because of absorption of radiation, the temperature inside the instrument box rose so much above that of the ambient atmosphere that the recorded data were incorrect. The late Dr. Pfund of the Physics Department at Johns Hopkins University was asked to work out a solution. During a discussion of the problem, the physical characteristics of a suitable coating were listed:

(1) High reflectance in the visible spectrum.
(2) High reflectance in the ultraviolet which is plentiful at these alti-

tudes and extends to shorter wavelengths than at the earth's surface. This means a pigment with an ultraviolet absorption band cannot be used.

(3) High reflectance in the near infrared. This means a relatively coarse pigment, without absorption bands in the near infrared.

(4) It would be desirable to have an absorption band in the region of 8 to 10 microns in the infrared so the pigment would act as an efficient radiator to dissipate the heat that is absorbed.

Dr. Pfund chose a pigment and vehicle that might be expected to fulfil these conditions and prepared a coating which reflected over 95 per cent of the total sun energy at those altitudes and which kept the temperature within the instrument case to less than one degree elevation over the ambient temperature. The paint he found suitable for this application consisted of basic carbonate of white lead in a minimum amount of water-white vehicle. This paint had:

(1) High reflectance in the visible spectrum because the use of only a small amount of vehicle produced many pigment-air interfaces.

(2) High reflectance in the ultraviolet because the pigment does not absorb in the near ultraviolet.

(3) High reflectance in the near infrared because the pigment was coarse.

(4) An absorption band farther out in the infrared so that it would act as a radiator to dissipate the heat that is absorbed.

Such a paint would not be of value for ordinary applications, but it was designed to fulfil these special specifications and it did the job well.

References

1. Saunderson, J. L., *J. Optical Soc. Am.,* **32,** 727 (1942).
2. Duncan, D. R., *J. Oil & Colour Chemists' Assoc.,* **32,** 296 (1949).
3. Mie, G., *Ann. Physik,* **25,** 377 (1908).
4. Debye, P., *Ann. Physik,* **30,** 57 (1909).
5. Bailey, E. D., *Ind. Eng. Chem., Anal. Ed.,* **18,** 365 (1946).
6. Ruedy, R., *Can. J. Research,* **21,** 99 (1943).
7. LaMar, V. K., and Barnes, M. D., *J. Colloid Sci.,* **1,** 71 (1946).
8. Newman, A. C. C., Soc. Chem. Ind., Symposium on Particle Size Analysis, Feb. 4, 1947.

6 : Luminescent Coatings

PART A: INORGANIC PIGMENTS

J. R. DeVORE

The New Jersey Zinc Company (of Pennsylvania)
Palmerton, Pennsylvania

In its broadest sense, luminescence means the emission of radiation as a result of processes other than thermal emission or incandescence. It includes fluorescence, phosphorescence, triboluminescence, chemiluminescence, etc. When speaking of luminescent pigments, however, we are dealing only with fluorescence and phosphorescence. Fluorescence and phosphorescence are the process of absorbing energy in the form of electromagnetic radiation or radioactive emanation (including cathode rays) and emitting at least a portion of that energy as radiation. For pigment work we are interested only in those materials that emit in the visible portion of the spectrum. The process of absorbing energy we shall designate as excitation; the process of radiating energy we shall designate as emission regardless of whether it is fluorescence or phosphorescence.

Several different criteria are used for differentiating between fluorescence and phosphorescence. The one that will be used here, although it is rather an arbitrary one, probably is more commonly used than any other. Fluorescence is the emission that ceases as soon as the excitation ceases while phosphorescence is the emission that continues after the excitation ceases.

In the inorganic field, an amazing number of compounds have been found to be luminescent. However, many of these compounds are unsuitable for pigment use because of their physical and chemical properties. Luminescent pigments, which are often referred to as phosphors, consist of sulfides, oxides, silicates, and tungstates with a few miscellaneous compounds such as titanates and selenides. For reasons which will be discussed later, the silicates and tungstates are largely used in fluorescent lamps and the principal pigments for paint use are sulfides and oxides. The largest volume paint pigments are zinc sulfide, mixed zinc and cadmium sulfides, mixed calcium and strontium sulfides, and zinc oxides.

99

Excitation of Pigments

Excitation by Electromagnetic Radiation. There are two basic laws applying to electromagnetic excitation of phosphors. First, in order for radiation to excite a pigment it must be absorbed by the pigment, so the exciting radiation must fall within an absorption band of the pigment. Second, the emission must obey Stokes' law which states that the emitted radiation cannot have a shorter wavelength than the exciting radiation. In general, luminescent pigments emit at longer wavelengths than the exciting light.

The pigments may be roughly divided into two groups. The first group consists of those which are effectively excited by moderately short wavelength ultraviolet, particularly by the mercury line at 2,536Å. The silicates and the tungstates fall in this group which is the reason they are used in fluorescent lamps. A fluorescent lamp is a low-pressure mercury arc within a glass tube coated with a phosphor. About 70 per cent of the energy in the arc is radiated in the 2,536Å line. The phosphor then converts most of this energy to visible light, thereby producing the relatively high efficiency of these lamps. Phosphors in this group are not used in paints for three reasons. (1) It is very difficult to obtain a high-intensity source of light in this wavelength region. (2) Ultraviolet light in this wavelength region is strongly absorbed by glass and by most paint vehicles. Consequently, the light source would have to be fabricated of fused quartz, thereby making it very expensive. Furthermore, the formulation of the paints would be greatly complicated by this severe limitation on the vehicles. (3) The most important reason is that ultraviolet of this wavelength is harmful to the eyes and even if the source were adequately shielded, the ultraviolet reflected by the paint would be harmful.

The second group consists of those pigments which are effectively excited by longer wavelength ultraviolet—3,000 to 4,000Å. Ultraviolet in this wavelength is popularly called black light. Since black light makes the eyes fluoresce, it is a bit annoying to look directly at the source, but the light does not harm the eyes. Furthermore, the light is readily transmitted by glass. There are two commercially important sources of black light: (1) the high-pressure mercury arc light covered with a filter to remove the visible light and (2) the fluorescent lamp made up with a special phosphor designated 360 BL and covered with a filter to remove the visible light. These two sources enable the users of luminescent pigments to illuminate displays with spotlights or floodlights or large area sources. This second group of pigments includes the zinc and zinc-cadmium sulfides, the zinc oxides, and the calcium-strontium sulfides.

Some of the phosphorescent pigments can be excited by the blue end of the visible spectrum.

Excitation by Radioactive Emanations. Suitable luminescent pigments can be excited by any of the radiation from radioactive materials, i.e., alpha, beta, or gamma rays. Excitation can also be achieved by cathode rays as in a television tube, or by x-rays as in a fluoroscope. The usual method of utilizing radioactive excitation of pigments is to mix a radium or thorium salt with the pigment. This mixture can then be incorporated in a vehicle to form a paint. Such radioactive luminescent paints have the merit of maintaining the brightness without requiring an external source for exciting them. Uses of such paints will be discussed later. The pigments usually employed with radioactive excitation are zinc sulfides and some zinc-cadmium sulfides.

Luminescent paint pigments are no more of a health hazard than ordinary paint pigments. However, radioactive luminescent pigments must be handled with care because of the danger of poisoning by the radioactive salt. Precautions must be taken principally in the preparation and application of the paint. In normal uses, the radioactive radiation from the painted surfaces is low enough that there is no danger of being burned.

Manufacture of Pigments

The essential requirement and principal problem in the manufacture of luminescent pigments is purity of materials. The luminescence of a pigment material is vitally affected by impurities in concentrations of the order of magnitude of a few parts per million. The luminescence is produced by the presence in the base material of traces of selected impurities called activators. The activators must be present in the right amount because if there is too little or too much activator the pigment will not be luminescent. Furthermore, there are impurities called poisons or killers which, if present in the compound, will destroy the luminescence even though the proper amount of activator is present. In addition to the requirements about purity and proper activator addition, the pigment must be properly muffled to develop the crystal structure correctly or again the product will not be luminescent. Let us consider the preparation of a silver-activated zinc sulfide as an example.

The procedure for making white pigment grade zinc sulfide is to dissolve a zinc sulfide ore in sulfuric acid, forming a zinc sulfate solution and liberating hydrogen sulfide. The zinc sulfate and hydrogen sulfide are each carefully purified and then recombined to precipitate zinc sulfide. The purification processes eliminate the impurities that discolor the sulfide so that the precipitated product is white. The procedure for making luminescent grade zinc sulfide is essentially the same except that greater care must be exercised in the purification procedure because the luminescence is affected by even smaller amounts of impurities than will discolor the white zinc sulfide.

After the pure zinc sulfide base has been prepared in this way, the proper amount of a silver salt, e.g., silver nitrate, is thoroughly mixed with the proper amount of sodium chloride and this mixture is thoroughly mixed with the zinc sulfide. This mixture is charged to a silica crucible and muffled at about 900°C for 40 minutes in an inert atmosphere. The crucible is cooled in an inert atmosphere so as to prevent oxidation. When

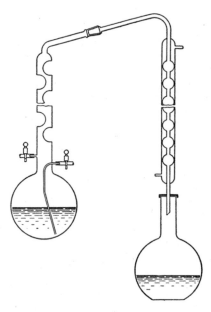

Figure 6.1. Still for preparing purified water.

cooled, the material is discharged from the crucible, broken up with a minimum of grinding, and screened to remove the coarse material.

The silver salt is added for the purpose of providing the silver activator atoms. The sodium chloride is a flux and has the double function of improving the crystallization of the zinc sulfide during muffling and assisting the introduction of the silver ions into the zinc sulfide lattice. In breaking up the muffled pigment, it is necessary to hold the grinding to a minimum because excessive grinding of a luminescent pigment reduces or destroys the luminescence.

The necessity for maintaining high purity applies all the way through the process. An impurity will have the same effect regardless of whether it is present in the base material or is introduced somewhere in the processing. Consequently, in addition to starting out with high purity zinc sulfide, the sodium chloride must be of equal purity. Likewise, the containers in which the materials are mixed and the crucible in which the sample is muffled must be extremely clean. When making phosphors on a laboratory scale the need for cleanliness is especially great. Since air-borne dusts must be avoided, it is necessary either to work in special, dust-free rooms and require a change of clothing when entering the rooms, or to use special apparatus such as are shown in the Figures 6.1 and 6.2.

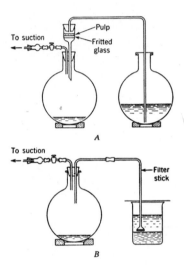

Figure 6.2. Apparatus designed to avoid contamination by air-borne dusts.

It may seem that purity and cleanliness have been overemphasized. However, when color control is important, these items cannot be stressed too much. This point can be illustrated by a story that came out of a laboratory working on phosphors during World War II. A silver-activated zinc sulfide is blue and a copper-activated zinc sulfide is green. If copper and silver activators both are present, the copper activation is dominant so that the resultant phosphor is green or at least has a greenish shading. In this laboratory they were working with silver-activated zinc sulfide, but many of the samples had an undesirable green undertone which appeared in spite of extreme care to eliminate copper during the purification. At last they found that the copper contamination was produced by the sparking of a trolley line in the street outside the window of the laboratory.

Colors of Pigments

Luminescent Colors. It is characteristic of inorganic luminescent pigments that the emission is a broad band. This can be seen in Figure 6.3
which shows the spectral emission of several fluorescent pigments. How-

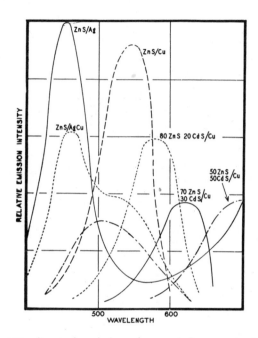

Figure 6.3. Spectral emission of several fluorescent pigments.

ever, in spite of the broad band emission, the colors of luminescent pigments are more saturated, i.e., more strongly colored, than artist's colors.

The fluorescent inorganic pigments cover the entire spectrum. The
colors of the pigments in Figure 6.3 are:

ZnS/Ag	Blue
ZnS/Cu	Green
80 ZnS 20 CdS/Cu	Yellow
70 ZnS 30 CdS/Cu	Orange
50 ZnS 50 CdS/Cu	Red

Magnesium titanate provides a more pronounced red pigment that is
not so bright as the ZnS-CdS red. In addition to the colors, there are
near whites available such as the bluish white ZnS/AgCu in Figure 6.3
and ZnO/Zn which is a greenish white.

The line of phosphorescent pigments does not cover so much of the spectrum as the fluorescent. The colors of the phosphorescent pigments are:

CaS-SrS/BiCu	Blue
ZnS/Cu	Green
ZnS-CdS/Cu	Yellow

There are no satisfactory red phosphorescent pigments. In addition to the color difference, there is a difference in the duration of phosphorescence between CaS-SrS and the ZnS pigments. Initially, the ZnS pigments are considerably brighter than the CaS-SrS, but within an hour the brightness has dropped below the CaS-SrS and the ZnS pigments are not useful for more than two hours after excitation. The useful brightness of CaS-SrS pigments will last for 10 to 12 hours. It is these differences that usually govern the selection of a phosphorescent pigment rather than the color.

Daylight Color. In the fluorescent colors, the ZnS pigments are near white while the ZnS-CdS pigments are progressively more yellow or brown as the CdS content increases. If it is desired to have the daylight color approximate the fluorescent color, it is necessary to add colored pigment or dye to match. Care must be taken in selecting the colored pigments or dyes so that they do not destroy the fluorescence by absorbing the ultraviolet light that excites the phosphors. Some of the additives have been determined and the information is available.

The daylight colors of the phosphorescent pigments are near white. In this case, however, the problem of tinting them is more involved. When phosphorescent pigments are used, the object usually is to maintain useful brightness as long as possible. Consequently, any dye or colored pigment that will reduce the phosphorescent brightness should be avoided. It has been found possible to tint the blue phosphorescent pigments with phthalocyanine blue so that the daylight color matches the phosphorescent color without adversely affecting phosphorescent brightness. The green and yellow phosphorescent pigments can be tinted so that the daylight color matches the phosphorescent color, but this produces a marked reduction in phosphorescent brightness.

Luminescent Paints

Vehicles suitable for luminescent paint must be as transparent as possible to the exciting and emitted radiation and must maintain this transparency upon aging. Furthermore, the vehicle should not react with the pigment. Linseed oil vehicles are undesirable because of the transparency requirement. Many nitrocellulose lacquers react with the pigments and hence are unsuitable. Alkyd resin vehicles are satisfactory. If drier is needed, cobalt driers are recommended. Manganese driers discolor too badly and lead driers tend to degrade the luminescence of the pigments.

In formulating the paints, an inert extender pigment such as whiting or diatomaceous silica may be added to increase the body of the paint when this is found necessary. The high index pigments should be avoided because the hiding power of these pigments will reduce the amount of exciting radiation reaching the luminescent pigment. Since the luminescent pigments, particularly the phosphorescent ones, are coarse pigments, it is common practice to add a suspending agent such as zinc palmitate or aluminum stearate in order to reduce the amount of settling.

The method of preparation of the paints depends on whether the pigment is fluorescent or phosphorescent. Fluorescent pigments may be dispersed in the vehicle by a moderate amount of ballmilling. In other words, the preparation of fluorescent paints is not appreciably different from the preparation of ordinary paints except that it is advisable to avoid excessive grinding which might degrade the luminescence. Phosphorescent paints are prepared by stirring the pigment into the vehicle. Grinding *must* be avoided because it is very harmful to phosphorescence. If the inert pigment must be milled in the vehicle in order to disperse it properly, it should be milled in the vehicle first and the phosphorescent pigment stirred into this mixture.

In applying the paints, the best results are obtained if a white undercoat is used. Lead pigments in the undercoater are undesirable because the lead has a detrimental effect on the luminescence. Zinc sulfide or titanium dioxide are the most satisfactory pigments for the undercoater. The luminescent paints may be applied by brushing or spraying. Particularly in the case of phosphorescent paints, several coats may be required to develop maximum luminescent brightness. With the zinc sulfide and zinc-cadmium sulfide pigments, several coats are sufficient. However, the calcium and strontium sulfide pigments will react with moisture and, since paint films are porous to moisture to some degree, it is advisable to apply a top coat of clear vehicle over paints made with these pigments. Paints protected in this way can be expected to give several months' service under reasonable conditions of outdoor exposure.

Uses and Applications

We can do no more than mention a few of the uses of luminescent pigments. The uses of the paints and the selection of suitable paints depend on the following properties:

(1) Fluorescent pigments require continuous excitation by black light sources. They are relatively bright when the excitation is strong.

(2) Phosphorescent pigments will glow for periods of 1 to 12 hours

after the excitation ceases. They can be excited by daylight or "Mazda" or fluorescent lights as well as by black lights. The phosphorescent brightness is a lower order of magnitude than the fluorescent brightness, and dark adaptation is necessary in order to get the full benefit of the pigment after the brightness has decayed a short time.

(3) Radioactive luminescent pigments require no external excitation. The brightness of these materials depends on the concentration of radioactive material, but at best it is only a little higher than the early period brightness of phosphorescent matherials. They maintain brightness rather than decaying as the phosphorescent pigments. The radioactive pigments are expensive, the cost increasing rapidly as the concentrations of radioactive material and consequently the brightness increases.

The use of fluorescent paints in advertising—particularly on billboards—is increasing. Such displays are attractive and striking because the contrast between the luminescent paint and the black-appearing nonluminescent background is much greater than can be achieved with white lighting. Furthermore, because the paint is the source of light, a properly prepared display can give a third dimensional effect that cannot be achieved in a white-lighted sign. The best effects can be obtained by using white light part of the time and black light part of the time and this is the method that has been adopted by black light advertisers.

A number of automobile manufacturers have adopted fluorescent markings on the instrument panels thereby eliminating the distracting effect of white light from the instrument panel during night driving.

Fluorescent paints have been used extensively for decoration in places where the level of general illumination is low such as theaters and night clubs. They have also been used for decorations in rooms designed for viewing television.

The principal uses of phosphorescent materials fall into two classes: (1) novelties and (2) safety markings. Under novelties, we have objects like phosphorescent Christmas tree ornaments, phosphorescent flowers, scatter pins or other types of jewelry for nighttime use, phosphorescent pictures in children's books, etc. Under safety markings, we have exit signs, passage markings, and fire equipment markings in public buildings. These signs and markings will continue to function in case of power failure. Because phosphorescent brightnesses are low, it is necessary to use relatively large luminous areas and use large letters for any legends in order that they will be legible. We can also include under safety markings items for home use like phosphorescent switch plates and phosphorescent flashlight cases.

Radioactive luminous materials have two principal uses. (1) They are used for marking watches, clocks, and instruments that must be used in the dark without continuous black light excitation. In this use, the higher level of brightness than phosphorescent materials permits the use of smaller symbols while still maintaining legibility. (2) They are used for safety markings in locations where phosphorescent materials would not receive adequate excitation.

The wartime applications of these materials have not been listed because they are too numerous and diverse to discuss here.

Theoretical Aspects of Luminescence

Many investigators have tried to explain just what happens within the crystal during luminescence. Of these various theories, we shall attempt to develop a rough picture of some of the more plausible ones.

The atoms in a crystal are close enough to each other that their fields interact to the extent that the electron orbits (using the picture of the Bohr atom) are shifted and distorted. The outer orbits are distorted so much that an electron in these orbits is not tied to one atom but can move freely from one atom to another. These orbits are also broadened so that they overlap and form a continuous band. This band in which the electrons can move freely through the crystal is designated as the conduction band. A dielectric material in its normal, unexcited state has no electrons in the conduction band. Now let us consider the energy levels of electrons in a crystal. We have the filled bands, perhaps some more or less narrow empty bands above them, and the broad conduction band above these:

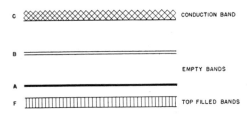

The absorption process results in lifting an electron from the filled band to an empty band or the conduction band. Emission occurs when an electron falls from one of these upper levels into the hole left in the occupied level. The wavelength of the emitted radiation is determined by the energy difference between the levels involved. It is an inverse relationship so that the larger the energy difference, the shorter will be the wavelength. If an electron is raised from F to A and then, without further change, falls back to F, the emitted light will have the same frequency as the exciting light. Such a phenomenon is called resonance radiation and, while it often occurs in gases, it is a rare occurrence in crystals. In order to explain why the emitted radiation is of longer wavelength than the exciting radiation in such a system, Mott and Seitz have proposed the following theory. If we set up a generalized coordinate which defines the positions of all the atoms at once, we can make a graph of the energy of the system against this configurational coordinate and obtain Curve 1 in Figure 6.4. The energy graph for the system when an electron has been raised to an excited position is Curve 2.

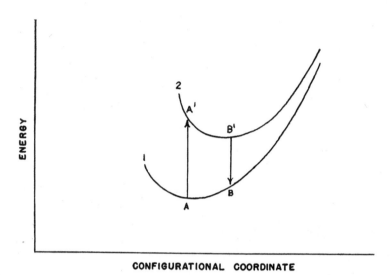

Figure 6.4. Configurational energy graph for crystal in excited and unexcited states. (Mott and Seitz).

The atoms tend to arrange themselves so that the energy of the system is a minimum; so point A represents the normal arrangement of the system. Normal optical transitions occur without changing the atomic configuration; so the process of excitation raises the system from point A to point A'. The configuration at A' is not stable because the energy is not a minimum, so the atoms rearrange themselves to correspond to B'. The energy difference from A' to B' goes into vibration and heat. On emission, the system drops from B' to B and then rearranges itself to A, dissipating as heat the energy from B to A. Since the absorption frequency depends on the energy A to A' and the emission frequency depends upon the energy B' to B it is obvious that the emission will have lower frequency or longer wavelength.

Before continuing this discussion, it should be stated that the absorption spectra of luminescent pigments indicate that at ordinary temperatures almost all phosphors have no unfilled levels below the conduction band so excitation consists, in general, of raising an electron into the conduction band; thus photoconductivity normally accompanies luminescence.

Let us return to our first diagram and consider the effect of introducing an activator. The activator consists of foreign atoms which are scattered through the crystal lattice. These foreign atoms introduce additional energy levels but these additional energy levels are local, i.e., they are effective only in the vicinity of the impurity atoms. The additional energy levels can be of two types: (1) a filled level located a little above the top filled level of the original lattice or (2) an empty level located a little below the conduction band. Let us consider the two cases separately.

(1) A filled level located a little above the top filled level of the original lattice. The energy level diagram now looks like this:

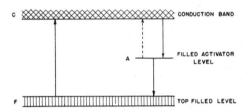

When an electron has been raised from A to C by absorption of radiation, a positive hole is left in A and an electron can fall from C to A, producing the luminescent emission. When an electron is raised from F to C, two things can happen: (a) an electron can drop from C to F, emitting light and filling the hole and (b) the hole can migrate through the lattice. If during this migration, it comes under the level A, an electron can drop from A to F, filling the hole in F but creating a hole in A which will now accept an electron from C, giving rise to the same kind of emission as in the first instance. Which of these two emissions occurs is a matter of probability and depends on several factors including the number of electrons in the conduction band and the mobility of the positive holes.

(2) An empty level located a little below the conduction band. The energy level diagram now looks like this:

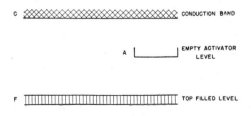

The conditions under which this picture becomes important and significant are in the explanation of phosphorescence. In this case, the level A is assumed to be a metastable state with direct transitions from A to F forbidden. (This metastable state is indicated in the diagram by making A a kind of well.) In this system, an electron which has been raised into the conduction band travels about in this band until it finds a hole in F into which it can fall or until it gets above one of the A levels and falls into it. Once an electron is trapped in this way it remains in this level until it is lifted (usually by thermal motion) again to the conduction band whereupon it can move about until it falls into a hole in the F level or is retrapped. The longer the electrons remain in the traps, the longer the elapsed time between absorption of radiation and emission of radiation and the longer the duration of phosphorescent light. The length of time the electrons remain in the trap is a function of the thermal energy of the electrons and the depth of the trap, i.e., the difference in energy between C and A. The depth of the trap is fixed for a particular sample but the thermal energy of the electrons depends upon the temperature. As the temperature is increased, the thermal energy of the electrons is increased and the traps are emptied faster. This means that the phosphorescent emission occurs at a higher intensity for a shorter period of time. Conversely, by cooling a phosphor, the thermal energy can be decreased until the probability of electrons escaping from the traps is almost zero. The two extreme conditions have often been demonstrated by the following experiments. If a phosphorescent film is cooled with liquid air and excited while cold, it will show essentially no phosphorescent emission. However, if this film is now warmed up without further excitation, there is emission of phosphorescent light during the warming up process. In fact, this technique has been used to measure the depth of the traps and establish the existence of traps of different depths. At the other extreme, if a phosphorescent pigment is heated up enough, the phosphorescence disappears entirely and the light is emitted as fluorescence. Under these conditions, the thermal energy of the electrons is high enough that they escape from the traps as fast as they fall into them.

When more than one activator is present, some additional phenomena occur which can be explained by a theory advanced by H. A. Klasens. Let us take a ZnS/Ag, Cu phosphor as an example and first list the phenomena.

(1) At normal temperatures, the fluorescent emission tends to be blue at high intensities of excitation and green at low intensities of excitation

(2) The phosphorescence is green.

(3) The fluorescent emission tends to be blue at low temperatures and green at high temperatures

(4) Killers attack the phophorescence preferentially; nickel, iron, cobalt, and manganese are some of these killer elements.

(5) The quenching temperature for fluorescence is high at high intensities and low at low intensities. Killers shift the quenching action toward lower temperature.

On the basis of Klasens' theory, the energy diagram looks like this:

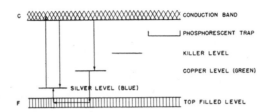

A hole can be made in the silver level either by raising an electron to C or by filling a hole in F. This hole can be filled from C with the emission of blue radiation. If there is sufficient thermal energy, the hole can also be filled by an electron jumping from F up to the silver level. When the latter has happened, the hole left in F can migrate and be filled from another silver center or from a copper center. If it is filled from a copper center, the hole in the copper level can be filled from C with the emission of green radiation. Since the copper level is higher than the silver level, the probability of transfer of the holes from the blue centers to the green centers is much higher than in the reverse direction. The probability of transfer of the hole from the blue to the green center depends on the mobility of the holes which is a function of temperature and the elapsed time between creation of the hole and the filling of it from the conduction band. The latter is a function of the concentration of electrons in the conduction band.

The killer atoms introduce additional levels which are high enough that the transition of an electron from C to the killer level does not produce visible emission. The holes can be transferred from either the blue or the green levels to the killer levels by the mechanism postulated above. This transfer would result in a decrease of visible luminescence.

Let us now see how this theory explains the facts we have listed.

(1) At high excitation intensities, the concentration of electrons in the C band is high, so the time between the formation of a hole and the filling of it from C is short. Consequently, there is little opportunity for the holes to transfer from the blue centers to the green centers and the emission tends toward the blue. Conversely, when the excitation intensity

is low the concentration of electrons in the *C* band is low. This means a larger elapsed time between the formation of a hole and the filling of it from the conduction band, and consequently more opportunity for the holes to transfer from blue levels to green levels. This would make the emission tend toward green at low intensities.

(2) Phosphorescence automatically means a long time elapsed between the formation of a hole (excitation) and the filling of it from the conduction band (emission). This means great opportunity for the holes to migrate to the green centers, so the phosphorescence is green.

(3) At low temperatures, the mobility of the holes will be low, so they will tend to remain in the blue centers, making the low temperature fluorescence blue. At high temperatures, the mobility is high and the holes move readily to the green centers, making the high temperature emission green.

(4) If killers are present, the migration of the holes to the killer centers is governed by the same rules that governed the migration to the green centers. Consequently, the process of phosphorescence which allowed the highest transfer to the green centers will allow the highest transfer to the green centers will allow the highest transfer to the killer centers. As a result, phosphorescence is more affected by killers than fluorescence.

(5) Quenching probably involves lattice defects that function in a manner similar to killer centers. The quenching temperature is the temperature to which the phosphor must be raised so that nearly all the holes migrate to the quencher centers before they have a chance to be filled from the conduction band. As was pointed out in the first point, increasing the excitation intensity reduces the time between the formation and the filling of a hole so the holes must have higher mobility in order to reach quencher centers before being filled. This means a higher temperature to achieve quenching. When killers are present, they increase the number of quenching centers so that the holes do not have to be as mobile in order to reach the quenching centers before being filled. This means a lower quenching temperature when killers are present.

Thus we see that this theory explains all these observed phenomena.

Special Phosphors

In concluding this discussion, we might consider two special kinds of phosphors principally because they are interesting and quite different from the ordinary luminescent pigments.

The first group comprises the infrared sensitive phosphors. These materials were studied and developed extensively during World War II. They have the property that they can be excited by ultraviolet or radioactive emission and store part of that energy so that it will be released when the phosphor is irradiated with infrared light. This energy remains stored long after the normal phosphorescence ceases. In fact, some samples which have been excited and stored for as long as six months have, without additional excitation, produced emission at useful brightness upon being irradiated with infrared. One possible theory is that the materials contain electron traps so deep that ordinary thermal motion will not release the electrons, and that they require the extra boost of the infrared in order to get out of the traps. One point that should be emphasized is that emission of these phosphors under infrared radiation does not represent a failure of Stokes law. The energy for the emission is supplied by the ultraviolet during excitation. The infrared merely acts as a trigger to release it.

Phosphors of the other class to be mentioned have been developed largely in the Eastman Kodak Laboratories and have been designated by them as superlinear phosphors or thermographic phosphors. In the graph of fluorescent intensity versus temperature, there is a portion of the curve that shows an appreciable decrease in fluorescent brightness as the temperature increases. The superlinear phosphors have been developed to emphasize that variation so that a small change in temperature produces a relatively large change in fluorescent brightness.

This property of high-temperature sensitivity has suggested some interesting uses. Thus, a piece of equipment which operates at something other than ambient temperature, e.g., a condenser, can be painted with a superlinear phosphor and enable the designer to see at a glance the temperature distribution over the whole apparatus. This can be of great help in trying to improve the design or operation of the equipment.

Another application which would not be immediately obvious is in the design of airplane wings. A model of a wing can be painted with a superlinear phosphor and then placed in a wind tunnel. Any turbulence or uneven air flow over the wing model will produce localized heating or cooling and this can easily be seen by the change in brightness of the superlinear phosphor. These are just two of the applications of these phosphors. Their interesting properties will probably lead to many odd applications.

Bibliography

1. Demont, V., and Petzold, O., "Fluorescent and Phosphorescent Pigments," *Paint Manuf.*, **10** (1940).
2. Garlick, G. F., Jr., "Luminescent Materials," New York, Oxford University Press, 1949.

3. Leverenz, H. W., "An Introduction to Luminescence of Solids," New York, John Wiley and Sons, Inc., 1950.
4. Kröger, F. A., "Some Aspects of the Luminescence of Solids," New York, Elsevier Publishing Co., 1948.
5. Symposium, Held at Cornell University, Oct. 24–26, 1946, "Preparation and Characteristics of Solid Luminescent Materials," New York, John Wiley and Sons, Inc., 1948.

PART B: ORGANIC COLORS

EDWARD G. BOBALEK

Case Institute of Technology

Many organic dyes, both natural and synthetic, exhibit the property of luminescence.[1] A number of theories have been proposed regarding the nature of this phenomenon for organic materials. Reviews of such theoretical material have been published.[2]

Organic compounds will luminesce effectively only in dilute solution. As the dye concentration is increased from very low to higher values, luminescence increases, passes through a maximum, and finally decreases sharply. Solvents vary in their capacity for sensitizing the luminescence, and show different positions of the maxima and different colors. Where luminescence occurs at all, the intensity maxima may be located at concentrations as low as a fraction of a per cent and seldom at concentrations exceeding five per cent. Sometimes luminescence is enhanced if the dye is adsorbed on a colloid, such as soap micelles, hydrous oxides of aluminum, textile fibers, silica gel, or gel particles of high polymers. Here the surface of the colloid may provide an even greater sensitizing effect than that of the solvent from which the dye is adsorbed. Sometimes, impurities in the solution, such as some metal ions, have the effect of quenching the fluorescence of the dye even in a suitable medium.

In general, it can be said that fluorescence of organic dyes depends on:
(1) Molecular structure of the dye.
(2) Use of an effective sensitizing solvent or carrier.
(3) Optimum concentration.
(4) Absence of quenching impurities.
(5) Sufficient intensity of exciting radiation.

Dyes for Organic Luminescent Pigments

A limited number of synthetic organic colors have been used to prepare organic pigments of the luminescent type. These have in recent years found considerable usage in advertising display. When properly

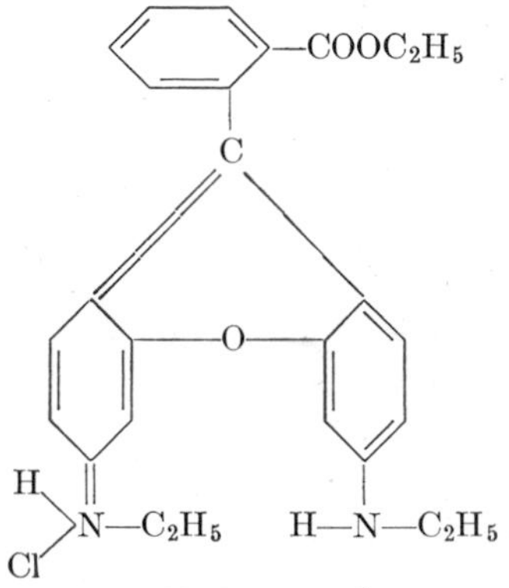

Rhodamine 6G

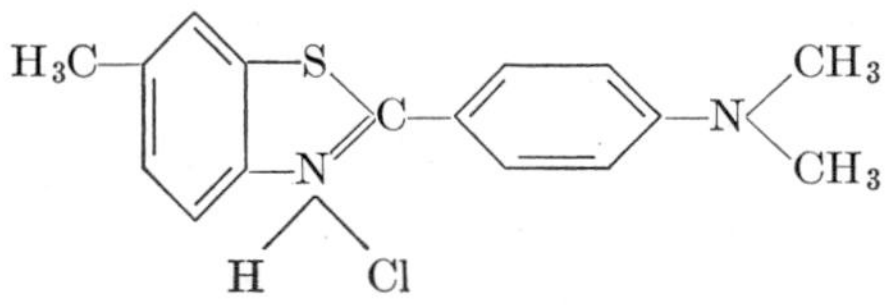

Thioflavin-T

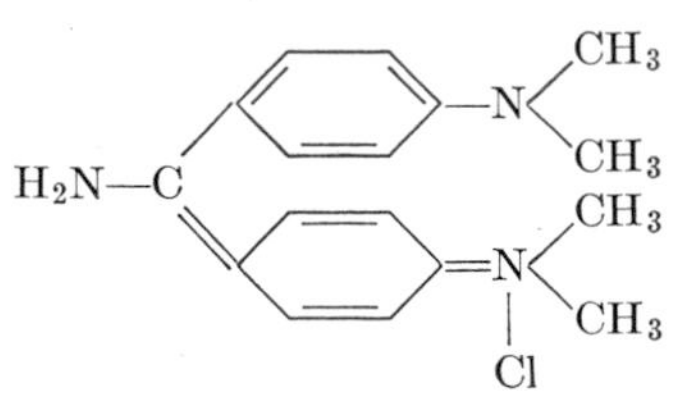

Auramine-O

Figure 6.5.   Some representative dye colors used in luminescent pigments.

compounded by adsorption or reaction with a suitable *carrier* material, a powdered pigment can be prepared which can be mixed with paint vehicles. At least in the earlier stages of the development of these pigments, the types of coloring materials employed most commonly were dyes of the rhodamine, flavin, or auramine types. Figure 6.5 illustrates some structures that are characteristic of these types of dyes.[3] These materials can be excited by ultraviolet light, and, to a considerable extent, even by radiation in the visible range of wavelengths.

The rhodamine colors are bright orange to red, whereas the auramine or flavin types are yellow to greenish-yellow. Combinations of these dye-stuffs allow for formulation of a series of luminescent colors that cover adequately the spectral range of yellow through orange to bright red. Blue dyes of comparable brightness and durability are rare, and it has been customary to formulate the green, blue, purple range of colors by mixing the fluorescent rhodamine or flavin types with other nonluminescent pigment dyes. Care must be taken, of course, that these modifying colors do not absorb strongly at the wavelengths of the emitted radiation of the luminescent pigments or at the wavelengths of the exciting radiation.

Composition of the Pigments

Commonly, the fluorescent dyes are dissolved in a solution of alcohol or water-soluble urea-formaldehyde resin. The dyed resin solution is subsequently heated to condense the resin to an insoluble state. Each particular dye is used in the limited concentration range which experiment has shown to be most effective for each particular resinous carrier.[4]

Amino resins are particularly suitable carriers, for the following reasons:

(1) The resinous compound is insoluble. It can be precipitated from solution as a fine powder as the thermosetting resin cures, or the dyed resin, free of the original solvents, can be pulverized into a fine powder. An average particle size range of 10 to 30 microns is about optimum for the pigment powder.

(2) The cured resin-dye complex is more durable to exterior exposure than are dye-complexes on less water-resistant carriers.

(3) The resin serves as an effective sensitizing medium for the dye. The brightness maximum occurs at a sufficiently high dye concentration to allow for a great strength of color. This is important. If the maximum should occur at too low concentrations, there would be less color saturation because the quantity of dye would be insufficient, even if the small amount present was functioning at its peak brightness. Because the brightness curve drops off rapidly with increasing concentration beyond the maximum, there is little opportunity to build up brightness by increasing concentration, unless the maximum covers a broad concentration range, or unless it occurs at dye concentrations sufficiently high to give adequate color strength.

(4) The thermosetting resin has low absorption and reflection for

either the exciting or the luminescent radiation. The pulverized and dyed resin acts as a flatting extender of very low index of refraction which results in a pleasant texture for coatings in which these colors are used.

Luminescent Paints

The same restrictions on the vehicle and other pigments already described on page 105 apply also to paints containing organic luminescent colors. Greater care must be taken to avoid solvents which attack the resinous carrier or which might cause the dye to bleed. Grinding of the pigment so as to reduce particle size too greatly is detrimental to color strength.

The organic colors are not particularly light fast, and degrade in a few weeks, or at most in a few months of exterior exposure. This, however, is sufficient durability for such purposes as advertising posters. Since the principal weakness of these dyes is their tendency to fade on exposure to light, it is unlikely that much can be done in extending their durability by using better resinous carriers. Further progress would require building better light-fastness into the dyes.

As compared to the inorganic types the organic colors are much more intense, and the fact that less energy is required to excite luminescence is a very important practical advantage. If further developments can improve the durability without sacrificing other advantages, these types of pigments might have considerable influence on the future design of paint colors.

References

1. DeMent, J., "Fluorochemistry," New York, Chemical Publishing Company, 1945.
2. Ellis, C., Wells, A. A., and Heyroth, F. F., "The Chemical Action of Ultraviolet Rays," New York, Reinhold Publishing Corporation, 1941.
3. Pratt, L. S., "The Chemistry and Physics of Organic Pigments," New York, John Wiley and Sons, Inc., 1947.
4. Switzer, J. L., and Switzer, R. C., U. S. Patent 2,498,592 (March 2, 1950); Switzer, J. L., U. S. Patent 2,475,529 (August 5, 1949).

7 : Reflectance Spectrophotometry of Pigmented Materials: Color Matching Calculations

J. L. SAUNDERSON*

The Dow Chemical Company
Midland, Michigan

Calculations based on appropriate spectrophotometric data can predict the colors of many pigment mixtures used in paints and plastics. The most complete theoretical treatment of such procedures of calculation has been proposed by Duntley.[1] This theory, however, was developed for the most general case of turbid media and is so complicated as to be inconvenient for routine use. If the general theory is restricted to apply only to the special case of opaque samples, such as are most paint films, then greatly simplified procedures are possible for both color measurements and color calculations. The experience with the more simplified procedures is the subject of this chapter.

All methods of color calculation require for their working data a catalog of constants describing the light absorption and light reflection properties of individual pigments. Whereas the more complete treatment of Duntley requires six constants, the method here employed contains only two. From the data for the individual pigments, it is possible to predict with useful accuracy the spectrophotometric curve for light reflected from samples containing various compositions of mixed pigments. Exceptionally good accuracy is usually obtained when calculating changes to be expected from small variations in pigment concentrations. Thus the method is particularly applicable in making color corrections on production batches to bring the color closer to a standard.

Color calculations are most successful where all the pigments involved are of the type that achieve a reproducible and uniform condition of random dispersion in paint vehicles in their whole useful range of pigment-volume concentrations. Unusual flocculation or orientation effects that depend on concentration, or which are induced by the influence of one pigment on another, can complicate the problem. The exceptions to

---

* Present address: Baird Associates, Inc., Cambridge, Mass.

ideal behavior are sufficiently numerous to be disturbing. Some experience with the method enables one to recognize and qualify these exceptional cases. However, even though such exceptions are recognized, it has been established that the method is workable in a sufficient number of circumstances to allow for its extensive practical use.

The method has numerous applications in color matching and quality control work. It is useful, for example, in predicting whether a particular color match is possible with an alternate choice of less expensive pigments. Sometimes it can be established that a particular line of colors can be formulated even though certain pigments are eliminated from standard stocks. This is not always apparent by the trial and error method of color matching. Not infrequently the situation arises where the number of pigments that can be used is limited; for example, for reasons of durability, reactivity with the vehicle, etc. In such instances considerable experimental effort might be saved by calculating the range of colors possible with this limited number of pigments. Such information of frequently great commercial importance may not be obvious to even an experienced color formulator if he is not already familiar with operating under such particular restrictions in choice of materials. In production work where minor adjustments must be made on standard formulas, color calculations have found numerous applications.

It is improbable that there will ever come a time when calculations based on spectrophotometric data alone will effect a complete systematization of the art of color formulation. However, these types of physical measurements can eliminate at least part of the confusion and some of the wasteful effort that exists unnecessarily in the art.

The principles of color calculation described here are illustrated by practical examples derived from the author's work on pigmented polystyrene. In pigmented plastics, pigment concentrations are smaller and sample thicknesses greater than is customary for most paint films. However, these general principles can be accommodated to measurements of paint films, provided that the sample is opaque and the nature of the individual pigments is such that their optical effects are additive in proportion to their concentrations over all composition ranges that are studied. Even when the above conditions are not fulflled, much help can be obtained when making small variations in pigment concentrations. Some practical examples of successful color calculations on paint films are reviewed by Duncan.[2]

The mathematical theory involved in color calculations is not difficult, but the quantity of calculation can be considerable, involving frequently the solution of systems of simultaneous equations for three or more unknowns. In many cases, however, well-known short cuts and methods of approximation can be applied. Where a considerable quantity of calculations are involved for similar types of systems, a large part of the calculations can be made in advance and summarized in tables, graphs, nomographs, or other devices so as to minimize the quantity of work involved in routine practice. An especially convenient method for solution of simultaneous equations, based upon the use of calculating machines of the Monroe or Friden type, is described by Crout.[3]

General Theory

The most general type of light-diffusing system is one containing colored particles dispersed in a colored vehicle, and bounded by reflecting surfaces. For this case, Duntley[1] has described the properties in terms of six constants—two absorption coefficients and four scattering coefficients. A rather involved experimental procedure was developed to evaluate these coefficients in order to avoid the complications of the surface reflections. This theory is particularly appropriate for translucent samples. If, however, one restricts all measurements to opaque samples, this general theory can be approximated by the greatly simplified two-constant theory of Kubelka and Munk,[4] which has been adapted to this particular system of color calculations.[5]

Here it is assumed that the optical properties of a pigmented system can be described by the constants μ and ρ, which will be called the absorption and scattering coefficients. For each pigment, μ and ρ will assume specific values which vary with the wavelength λ, but which are generally assumed to be independent of the pigment concentration. Although the latter is probably never strictly true, this assumption is a great convenience and in many cases is sufficiently valid to permit calculations of acceptable accuracy. When additional accuracy is required, the values of μ and ρ must be calculated at the approximate concentration of interest.

The constants μ and ρ are defined such that the decrease of intensity $-dI$ of light due to absorption in passing through a thickness of sample dt is $I\mu dt$, and that due to scattering in the same thickness is $I\rho dt$. In the paper of Kubelka and Munk[2] regarding the opacity of translucent materials, these assumptions lead directly to two differential equations which have the following solutions:

$$T' = \frac{2ae^{-at}}{\mu + \rho + a - (\mu + \rho - a)e^{-2at}} \tag{1}$$

$$R' = \frac{\rho(1 - e^{-2at})}{\mu + \rho + a - (\mu + \rho - a)e^{-2at}} \tag{2}$$

where T' = transmittance; R' = reflectance; t = the sample thickness; and $a = (\mu^2 + 2\mu\rho)^{1/2}$.

If the coloring material has only an absorption coefficient, as in the case of dyes, then $\rho = 0$, and equation (1) reduces to Beer's law, $T' = e^{-\mu t}$, and $R' = 0$.

For the special case where the medium is thick enough to be opaque $(t = \infty)$, the equations become

$$T' = 0$$

$$R' = \frac{\rho}{\mu + \rho + a} = \frac{1}{\frac{\mu}{\rho} + 1 + \left(\frac{\mu^2}{\rho^2} + 2\frac{\mu}{\rho}\right)^{\frac{1}{2}}} \equiv \frac{\mu}{\rho} + 1 - \left(\frac{\mu^2}{\rho^2} + 2\frac{\mu}{\rho}\right)^{\frac{1}{2}} \qquad (3)$$

Equation (3) can be obtained also from the more complicated theory of Duntley with certain simplifying assumptions for the special case of an opaque sample. This is the fundamental equation used in the calculation of the spectrophotometric curves for light reflected from opaque samples. It should be noted that R' is a function of the ratio μ/ρ, and hence only this ratio and not the absolute values of μ and ρ may be determined from reflection measurements alone. However, since calculation of reflectance curves is the main objective, only relative values of μ and ρ are necessary, and these can be obtained subject to certain assumptions that will be discussed later.

The critical assumption upon which color calculations of a pigment mixture are based is that the total absorption coefficient, $\bar{\mu}$, and the total scattering coefficient, $\bar{\rho}$, can be obtained by summing the μ's and ρ's of the individual pigments in proportion to the respective pigment concentrations; that is,

$$\bar{\mu} = C_1\mu_1 + C_2\mu_2 + C_3\mu_3 + \cdots = \Sigma C_i\mu_i \qquad (4)$$

$$\bar{\rho} = C_1\rho_1 + C_2\rho_2 + C_3\rho_3 + \cdots = \Sigma C_i\rho_i \qquad (5)$$

where the subscripts indicate the several different pigments. As mentioned above, when the μ's and ρ's are not independent of pigment concentrations, or when the above summation is not valid because of the effects of one pigment on another, computation of color corrections can be based upon values of the constants which have been specifically calculated for the situation of interest.

The general procedure of color calculation involves two problems:
1. From reflection data on properly selected pigment mixtures, deduce relative values of μ and ρ for the individual pigments.
2. Reverse the procedure, and use these known values of μ and ρ to calculate the reflectance curves for any composition of mixed pigments.

The Surface Correction

The R' of equation (3) represents the reflectance a sample would have in the absence of any reflection of light at the surface. For some samples, for example cloth or matte paper, the reflectance of light at the surface is negligible and R' would be essentially the same as the measured reflectance. For such materials, equation (3) can be used without change, as has been done by many workers (see references 6 and 7). Some types of samples, however, such as paint films, plastics, and ceramics, can be classed as dielectric materials with a characteristic refractive index. When light passes through the surface of such a material, either on its way into the sample or on its way out, the abrupt change in refractive index causes some of the light to be reflected. For samples classed as dielectric materials, therefore, surface reflectance corrections must be applied to equation (3) before use.

It is evident that if samples could be viewed and measured immersed in a medium having the same refractive index as the sample, then no surface reflection corrections would be necessary. Duntley has proposed measurement of samples immersed in an oil bath, thus simplifying the theory but complicating the reflectance-measuring apparatus. The alternative is to work the surface reflectance corrections into equation (3) so that the absorption and scattering coefficients are given as a function of the observed or measured reflectance R rather than the idealized reflectance R'.

It can be deduced mathematically that the relation between the measured reflectance R and the idealized reflectance R' has the following form

$$R = k_0 + (1 - k_1)(1 - k_2)\frac{R'}{1 - k_2 R'} \tag{6}$$

in which the k's are constants depending upon the conditions of measurement and the refractive index of the sample. The constant k_1 is the fraction of the incident light that is reflected from the front surface of the sample. It can be calculated from Fresnel's law of reflection. For light incident normally upon the front surface of the sample,

$$k_1 = \left(\frac{n - 1}{n + 1}\right)^2$$

where n is the refractive index of the sample. When n is near the usual value of 1.5, k_1 is about 0.04, meaning that about 4 per cent of the incident light is reflected at the first surface. Because of this surface reflectance, the fraction $(1 - k_1)$, or about 96 per cent, of the incident light enters the sample where it is reflected by the pigment particles immersed in the vehicle. The light then emerges from the sample after passing through the surface where again some reflection losses occur. The fraction of light reflected at the surface for light passing from within the sample to the air outside, designated by k_2, is far greater than that corresponding to k_1. Values for k_2 as large as 0.58 have been used,[2] and $k_2 = 0.4$ has been used extensively for plastic samples.[5] It may seem surprising that 40 per cent or more of the light incident on the surface from within the sample is back-reflected. However, it should be remembered that the light reflected from within the sample is quite diffuse. Light incident on the surface from within the sample at an angle exceeding the critical angle (about $42°$ for $n = 1.4$) is totally reflected, and light incident at slightly less than the critical angle is highly reflected. Equation (6) takes into account the multiple reflections which occur within the sample. If $k_2 = 0.4$, only 60 per cent of the light internally reflected the first time escapes from the sample, while 40 per cent is

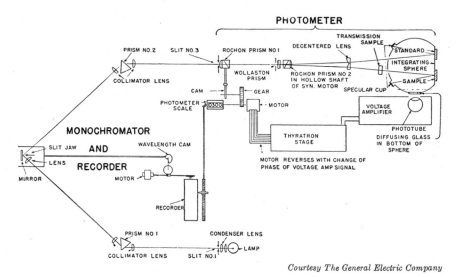

Courtesy The General Electric Company

Figure 7.1. Schematic diagram showing operation of the General Electric Spectrophotometer. (See also Figure 1.3, page 16.)

returned to be again internally reflected by the factor R', and so on indefinitely. When these reflections are summed properly, equation (6) results.

The constant k_0 has to do with the specularly reflected light and is a function of instrument design. For instruments designed to exclude the specular reflectance from the measurement, k_0 is zero. The General Electric recording spectrophotometer (Figure 7.1) having black cups on the integrating sphere to absorb the specularly reflected light is an instrument of this kind. Another is the Beckman spectrophotometer used with the reflectance attachment, having normal illumination and $45°$ viewing.

When white cups are used on the integrating sphere of the General Electric recording spectrophotometer the specular reflectance is included in the measurement and so for this case $k_0 = k_1$. Since in this case the direction of the incident light is nearly normal to the surface, the equation above relating k_1 and n can also be used to calculate k_0. An inter-

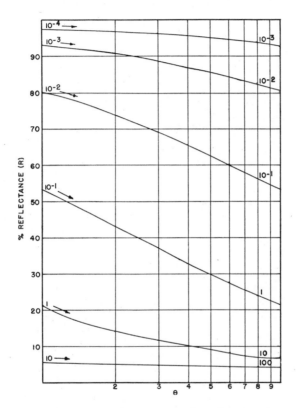

Figure 7.2. Semilogarithmic plot (6-cycle) of the θ-function (equation 9) where
$$\theta = \frac{0.45(1 - R)^2}{(R + 1.4)(R - 0.04)}, \quad \text{and} \quad 0 < R < 1.$$

mediate situation is that of the older type integrating sphere supplied with the earlier recording spectrophotometers made by General Electric. In these instruments the light is incident normally upon the surface of the sample but because of the divergence of the light beam only about half of the specularly reflected light escapes from the integrating sphere through the entrance port. Hence about half of the specular beam is measured, so that for this case $k_0 = k_1/2$.

Taking for the k's the values $k_0 = k_1 = 0.04$ and $k_2 = 0.4$, equation

(6) becomes, after solving for R',

$$R' = \frac{R - 0.04}{0.4R + 0.53} \tag{7}$$

and this equation can be combined with equation (3) to eliminate R'. Since equation (3) is a function of the ratio of the total absorption coefficient to the total scattering coefficient, it is convenient to designate this ratio by θ, that is,

$$\theta \equiv \frac{\bar{\mu}}{\bar{\rho}} = \frac{\Sigma C_i \mu_i}{\Sigma C_i \rho_i} \tag{8}$$

When R' is eliminated by combining equations (7) and (3), one obtains

$$\theta = \frac{0.45\,(1 - R)^2}{(R + 1.4)(R - 0.04)} \tag{9}$$

which is the equation relating the measured reflectance R to the quantity defined above as θ, equation (8). Equation (9) is of such importance, relating the measured reflectance R to the concentrations of the pigments in the sample, that a graph of this equation has been constructed for determining conveniently values of θ for a given R and vice versa (Figure 7.2).

According to equation (8), the value of θ (and hence the value of the observed reflectance R) is dependent only upon the ratio of $\bar{\mu}$ to $\bar{\rho}$ providing the sample is opaque. If the vehicle of the sample or the medium in which the pigment particles are suspended has neither an absorption or a scattering coefficient, then it is evident that a change in the total concentration of pigment in a sample (for example, doubling each constituent) does not affect the value of θ nor the reflectance R. Thus the reflectance R could be changed only by varying the pigment ratios in the mixture. Also the absolute values of the absorption and scattering coefficients of equation (8) are of no importance since only their relative values affect the value of θ. Hence only relative values of these constants can be determined by reflectance measurements alone.

CALCULATION OF PIGMENT CONSTANTS

Constants for White Pigments

Equation (8) and the graph of equation (9) are used for the calculation of pigment constants, the absorption and scattering coefficients. It is convenient to calculate the constants for a white pigment first. Consider a medium having absorption coefficient μ_0 and scattering coefficient ρ_0 containing a concentration of white pigment C_w. Pigment concentrations are conveniently expressed in units of per cent. Equation (8) becomes

$$\theta = \frac{\mu_0 + C_w\mu_w}{\rho_0 + C_w\rho_w} \tag{10}$$

assuming that C_w is sufficiently small that the base material is not appreciably diluted, so that a concentration factor is not required with μ_0 and ρ_0. In this general case, it is necessary to assign an arbitrary value to one of the constants, and to calculate the remaining three from the values of θ for three different concentrations of white pigment. Some simplification, however, is almost always desirable. Commonly $\rho_0 = 0$ and sometimes also either $\mu_0 = 0$ or $\mu_w = 0$ so that the calculation of the constants for the white pigment is often considerably simplified. Three special cases are discussed below.

1. Calculation of μ_w for $\mu_0 = \rho_0 = 0$

If $\mu_0 = \rho_0 = 0$, equation (10) becomes

$$\theta = \frac{C_w\mu_w}{C_w\rho_w} = \frac{\mu_w}{\rho_w} \tag{11}$$

showing that ideally θ and hence R should be independent of the pigment concentration C_w. This conclusion also holds for any mixture of pigments as long as $\mu_0 = \rho_0 = 0$, that is, the color is not changed by changes in the total concentration of pigment. This statement is only approximately verified by experience, but is a good approximation for really opaque samples, especially where the spectrophotometric curve is not too high. Deviations from the ideal case, that is, dependence of reflectance upon total concentration, are discussed later.

As mentioned previously, only one of the two constants in equation (11) is independent, and it is convenient to set $\rho_w = 1$ at all wavelengths. It will be seen that the constants for all pigments will be relative to this value for ρ_w. If $\rho_w = 1$, equation (11) is simply

$$\theta = \mu_w \tag{12}$$

and the absorption coefficients μ_w are found at all wavelengths desired by this relationship.

Example: The reflectance of a sample containing 0.8 per cent white is 76 per cent at 500 mμ. From the θ graph (Figure 7.2), θ is 0.0166. Hence $\mu_w = 0.0166$ at 500 mμ.

2. Calculation of μ_w and μ_0 for $\rho_0 = 0$

If $\rho_0 = 0$ and $\rho_w = 1$ as before, equation (10) becomes

$$\theta = \frac{\mu_0 + C_w \mu_w}{C_w} \tag{13}$$

and two concentrations of white are required to calculate μ_w and μ_0. Suppose a second concentration of white C_w' gives θ', or

$$\theta' = \frac{\mu_0 + C_w' \mu_w}{C_w'} \tag{14}$$

then simultaneous solution of equations (13) and (14) gives the following

$$\mu_w = \frac{C_w \theta - C_w' \theta'}{C_w - C_w'} \tag{15}$$

$$\mu_0 = C_w(\theta - \mu_w) = \frac{C_w C_w'(\theta' - \theta)}{C_w - C_w'} \tag{16}$$

Example: Given $R = 80$ per cent for $C_w = 1$ per cent and $R = 75$ per cent for $C_w' = 0.5$ per cent. Then $\theta = 0.0105$ and $\theta' = 0.0184$. Hence, $\mu_w = 0.0026$ and $\mu_0 = 0.0079$.

3. Calculation of μ_0 assuming $\mu_w = \rho_0 = 0$

Inspection of equation (15) shows that when $C_w \theta < C'_w \theta'$, that is, when on decreasing the concentration of white, θ increases by a greater factor than C_w decreases, then μ_w becomes negative. This is of course a breakdown of the theory, and is largely due to the lack of opacity of the sample. When this happens it is probable that a better approximation than the case discussed above in paragraph 1 is obtained by assuming $\mu_w = 0$ (as well as ρ_0), and letting μ_0 take care of the variation of reflectance with white concentration. This is a mathematical fiction, but one which nevertheless helps to extend the use of the theory to cover samples of incomplete opacity. Actually variations in reflectance with total concentration of pigment are to be expected for several reasons.

Under these assumptions, with $\rho_w = 1$,

$$\theta = \mu_0/C_w \tag{17}$$

and if μ_0 is to remain constant it follows that θ must be inversely proportional to C_w. The following table shows how well this is followed in the case of a white pigment in polystyrene.

$C_w(\%)$	R	θ	μ_0	θ calc. for $\mu_0 = 0.0075$	R calc. for $\mu_0 = 0.0075$
1.0	83.4	0.007	0.0070	0.0075	82.8
0.5	77.1	0.015	0.0075	0.015	77.1
0.2	65.7	0.041	0.0082	0.0375	66.9
0.1	54.0	0.097	0.0097	0.075	57.7

It is evident from the table that equation (17) will compensate for all but about 10 per cent of the change in reflectance with change in concentration of the white pigment, despite the fact that the samples having the smaller white pigment concentrations were far from being completely opaque.

Constants for Colored Pigments

1. Calculation of μ_p for $\rho_p = 0$; $\mu_0 = 0$

This is the case of a soluble pigment, here called a dye. If the scattering coefficient ρ_p of a pigment or dye is negligible, the reflectance curve of a sample containing only the pigment or dye should be zero (or should equal the first surface reflectance) at all wavelengths. Sometimes a dye is so transparent at some wavelengths that reflectance from the rear surface of the sample becomes appreciable, giving rise to a ficticious reflectance maximum which should not be taken as evidence for a value of ρ_p differing from zero. Only one constant, the absorption coefficient μ_p, need be calculated. Given a mixture of C_w white and C_p pigment, equation (8) giving θ_m for the mixture becomes

$$\theta_m = \frac{C_w\mu_w + C_p\mu_p}{C_w}$$

from which follows

$$\mu_p = \frac{C_w}{C_p}(\theta_m - \mu_w) \tag{18}$$

Example: Given $R = 15$ per cent for a mixture of one per cent white and 0.1 per cent black, and $\mu_w = 0.01$. Then $\theta_m = 1.90$, and $\mu_p = 18.9$.

2. Calculation of both μ_p and ρ_p; $\mu_0 = 0$

In order to evaluate two constants, two reflectance measurements must be made. The simplest method is to consider a sample containing only the pigment, for which

$$\theta_p = \frac{C_p\mu_p}{C_p\rho_p} = \frac{\mu_p}{\rho_p} \tag{19}$$

and a second sample containing a mixture of the pigment with white, for which

$$\theta_m = \frac{C_w \mu_w + C_p \mu_p}{C_w + C_p \rho_p} \qquad (20)$$

Simultaneous solution of equations (19) and (20) gives

$$\rho_p = \left(\frac{C_w}{C_p}\right)\left(\frac{\theta_m - \mu_w}{\theta_p - \theta_m}\right) \qquad (21)$$

$$\mu_p = \theta_p \rho_p = \theta_p \left(\frac{C_w}{C_p}\right)\left(\frac{\theta_m - \mu_w}{\theta_p - \theta_m}\right) \qquad (22)$$

Example: Given $R = 20$ per cent for a sample containing only the pigment, and $R = 50$ per cent for a sample containing equal amounts of the pigment and white, and $\mu_w = 0.05$. Then $\theta_p = 1.12$ and $\theta_m = .127$, so that $\rho_p = 0.0775$ and $\mu_p = 0.0868$.

3. Indeterminate Cases

When the reflectance of a sample containing a pigment is very low, approaching the surface reflectance, it can be shown in spite of the fact that the scattering coefficient may be large; it is nevertheless negligible compared to the absorption coefficient. If R_p is not much greater than the surface reflectance, θ_p is very large and cannot be determined accurately. This causes a corresponding uncertainty in the value of ρ_p as determined from equation (21). The absorption coefficient μ_p can still be determined accurately, however, and this turns out to be the important property of the pigment. If θ_p is very large, equation (22) becomes

$$\mu_p = \frac{C_w}{C_p}(\theta_m - \mu_w) \qquad (23)$$

which is identical with equation (18) given for the case for $\rho_p = 0$. The following example shows the extent of validity of this approximation.

Example: Given $\theta_m = 1.0$ for a mixture of 0.4 per cent white and 0.1 per cent pigment, and $\mu_w = 0.01$. If the reflectance R_p of a sample containing only the pigment is less than 5 per cent (for $n = 1.5$), θ_p becomes difficult to evaluate because 0.1 per cent uncertainty in R_p causes a large uncertainty in θ_p. Assuming values of θ_p of 40 and 60 the following values of ρ_p and μ_p result from the use of equations (21) and (22):

θ_p	$\rho_p = 4\dfrac{\theta_m - \mu_w}{\theta_p - \theta_m}$	$\mu_p = \theta_p \rho_p$	%R for 0.1%W + 0.4%P	%R for 0.4%W + 0.01%P
40	40.99/39 = .1015	0.1015 × 40 = 4.06	6.3	52.1
60	40.99/59 = 0.672	0.0672 × 60 = 4.032	6.1	52.2
∞	Assumed 0	4(1.0 − .01) = 3.96*	5.7	52.3

* From equation (23).

Calculation of reflectances for the two pigment and white mixtures are given in the last two columns to show that the actual value of ρ_p is relatively unimportant.

A second case of indeterminacy occurs when the reflectance of the sample containing the pigment and of the sample containing the white are nearly equal. Thus if $\theta_p = \theta_m = \theta_w$, equations (21) and (22) become indeterminate. Both μ_p and ρ_p can, however, be determined by adding a pigment different from white, such as a black whose constants have been first determined by the previously described methods. Thus if θ_m is the result of mixing C_p of pigment with C_b of black, one has the following equations:

$$\theta_m' = \frac{C_p\mu_p + C_b\mu_b}{C_p\rho_p + C_b\rho_b} \tag{24}$$

$$\theta = \frac{\mu_p}{\rho_p} \tag{25}$$

Simultaneous solution of these equations gives

$$\rho_p = \left(\frac{C_b}{C_p}\right)\left(\frac{\mu_b - \theta_m'\rho_b}{\theta_m' - \theta_p}\right) \tag{26}$$

$$\mu_p = \rho_p\theta_p = \theta_p\left(\frac{C_b}{C_p}\right)\left(\frac{\mu_b - \theta_m'\rho_b}{\theta_m' - \theta_p}\right) \tag{27}$$

Usually ρ_b is negligible so that equations (26) and (27) are further simplified.

Example: Given $\theta_m = 0.6$ for a mixture of 0.4 per cent pigment and 0.01 per cent black having an absorption coefficient $\mu_b = 40$. If the reflectance of the pigment alone is 53.5 per cent, $\theta_p = 0.1$. If $\rho_b = 0$, then $\rho_p = 2.0$ and $\mu_p = 0.2$.

4. Calculation of μ_p and ρ_p; $\mu_0 = 0$

If μ_0 is not negligible, the equations become somewhat more cumbersome but the same principles as discussed in the preceding three cases apply. To treat the general case, the equation for a sample containing a concentration C_p' of the colored pigment is

$$\theta_p = \frac{\mu_0 + C_p'\mu_p}{C_p'\rho_p} \tag{28}$$

and that for a mixture of C_w white and C_p pigment is

$$\theta_m = \frac{\mu_0 + C_w\mu_w + C_p\mu_p}{C_w\rho_w + C_p\rho_p} \tag{29}$$

Again taking $\rho_w = 1$ and solving the above equations simultaneously,

$$\rho_p = \left(\frac{C_w}{C_p}\right)\left(\frac{\theta_m - \mu_w}{\theta_p - \theta_m}\right) - \mu_0\left(\frac{C_p' - C_p}{C_p'C_p(\theta_p - \theta_m)}\right) \tag{30}$$

and

$$\mu_p = \theta_p\rho_p - \frac{\mu_0}{C_p'} \tag{31}$$

These equations reduce to equations (21) and (22) for $\mu_0 = 0$. It is also interesting to notice that equation (30) assumes the simpler form of equation (21) for the special case $C_p' = C_p$, which can be easily arranged for the sake of simplifying the calculations. If ρ_p is negligible,

$$\theta_m = \frac{\mu_0 + C_w\mu_w + C_p\mu_p}{C_w} \tag{32}$$

from which

$$\mu_p = \frac{C_w}{C_p}(\theta_m - \mu_w) - \frac{\mu_0}{C_p} \tag{33}$$

which reduces to equation (18) for $\mu_0 = 0$.

As suggested by equation (17), changes of reflectance with changing opacity are effectively handled by method of taking $\mu_w = 0$ and $\mu_0 \neq 0$. In place of equation (30) one has

$$\rho_p = \frac{C_w}{C_p} \cdot \frac{\theta_m}{\theta_p - \theta_m} - \frac{\mu_0(C_p' - C_p)}{C_p'C_p(\theta_p - \theta_m)} \tag{34}$$

and the equation for μ_p is the same as before (Equation 31). By taking $C_p' = C_p$, equation (34) becomes simply

$$\rho_p = \frac{C_w}{C_p}\frac{\theta_m}{\theta_p - \theta_m} \tag{35}$$

in which case the calculation of both ρ_p and μ_p becomes relatively simple. For the case where ρ_p is negligible, one has

$$\theta_m = \frac{\mu_0 + C_p\mu_p}{C_w} \tag{36}$$

from which follows that

$$\mu_p = \frac{C_w}{C_p}\theta_m - \frac{\mu_0}{C_p} \tag{37}$$

Equations (35) and (31), or equation (36) where applicable, are probably the most satisfactory in the general case. Obviously, little difference exists between the values found for μ_p and ρ_p from these equations and the values found by equations (21) and (22). However, equations (35) and (31) (or equation 36) have the advantage of being able to compensate quite well for changes in opacity.

The cases of indeterminacy still exist when considering $\mu_w = 0$ and $\mu_0 \neq 0$. As before, the first type of indeterminacy is handled by use of equation (36) (assuming $\rho_p = 0$). The second type can be handled as before with a mixture with black, in which case

$$\theta_m' = \frac{\mu_0 + C_p'\mu_p + C_b\mu_b}{C_p'\rho_p} \tag{38}$$

and

$$\theta_p = \frac{\mu_0 + C_p\mu_p}{C_p\rho_p} \tag{39}$$

assuming that the scattering coefficient $\rho_b = 0$. By taking $C_p' = C_p$, these equations have the simple solutions

$$\rho_p = \frac{C_b\mu_b}{C_p(\theta_m' - \theta_p)} \tag{40}$$

and

$$\mu_p = \theta_p\rho_p - \frac{\mu_0}{C_p} \tag{41}$$

CALCULATION OF COLOR MATCHES

The calculation of a color match is accomplished by reversing the procedures discussed above for the calculation of pigment constants; that is, the absorption and scattering coefficients are assumed to be known and equations are solved for the concentrations of the pigments. One first looks at the spectrophotometric curve of the sample to be matched and decides what pigments will be required to duplicate the reflectance curve. Experience and good judgment are required for this decision. Frequently, because of a limited number of pigments available, it is necessary to make planned departures from the spectrophotometric curve of the sample in order to arrive at the best visual color match. Good judgment and experience are required at this point also. Generally speaking, when necessary to make planned departures from the curve, the curve of the trial sample should be made to cross the curve of the standard as many times as practical, and deviations in the middle of the visible spectrum (say from 500 to 600 millimicrons) should be kept as small as possible. That is, greater weight should be given to the visual importance of deviations in the middle of the visible spectrum where the normal observer has the greater sensitivity than to the two extremes near 400 mμ and 700 mμ. Color matches made in this manner are called "metameric" color matches; the acceptance of the match is often rather sensitive to the type of illumination used for viewing.

When the pigments have been chosen, the next step is to decide upon the wavelengths to be used for the calculation of the pigment concentrations, and the reflectance values the curve is to have at these wavelengths. Ordinarily one chooses wavelengths close to the positions of maximum absorption of the pigments in order to obtain the optimum accuracy. Black, however, is an exception, having a nearly constant absorption at all wavelengths in the visible spectrum, so that for this pigment a wavelength is chosen where the other pigments in the mixture have the least effect (smallest absorption coefficients). Also, when two pigments having similarly shaped curves are used in a mixture it is often better to take wavelengths somewhat different from the wavelengths of maximum absorption of the individual pigments in an effort to get better "leverage" for solving the simultaneous equations. Occasionally two pigments are so nearly alike that they should be lumped together for the calculation of concentrations, and the ratio of the concentrations established by visual inspection for hue. These details will be discussed more fully below.

Base Material Constants Negligible ($\mu_0 = \rho_0 = 0$)

For this case the θ equation as given by equation (8) does not contain either μ_0 or ρ_0 so that θ is a function only of the pigment concentration ratios and not their absolute values or the total concentration of pigment. The total concentration of pigment or the concentration of one pigment must be chosen arbitrarily. This choice can be based upon the opacity desired, or on the knowledge that under some circumstances the reflectance does depend upon the total pigment concentration, but this cannot be calculated from the θ equation. However this choice is made, one is inherently using either the equation (for a four-constituent mixture)

$$C_A + C_B + C_C + C_D = C_T \text{ (total concentration),} \tag{42}$$

or an equation saying that the concentration of one of the pigments has a certain value, such as

$$C_A = \text{constant.} \tag{43}$$

In either case, once the values of pigment concentration ratios, C_B/C_A, C_C/C_A, and C_D/C_A, have been determined, use of either of the two above equations gives the absolute concentrations of all four pigments. As far as the equation is concerned, the pigment ratios are the unknowns, and it is to be noted that there are one fewer unknowns than the number of pigments in the mixture. The unknowns (concentration ratios) can be determined from simultaneous equations of which there will be the same number as the number of pigment concentration ratios to be determined. This means that the spectrophotometric curve can in general be made to have arbitrary reflectances at the same number of wavelengths as the number of concentration ratios. For a four-constituent mixture, then, the calculated curve can be made to match the desired curve at only three wavelengths. Coincidence at additional wavelengths is accidental as far as the reflectance theory is concerned, but, of course, good curve-matching over extended wavelength regions is possible if the pigments used in the two cases are very similar.

For a four-constituent mixture, three equations of the type are set up

$$\theta = \frac{C_1\mu_1 + C_2\mu_2 + C_3\mu_3 + C_4\mu_4}{C_1\rho_1 + C_2\rho_2 + C_3\rho_3 + C_4\rho_4} \tag{44}$$

using the values of θ desired at three wavelengths and μ and ρ values for the pigments at these same wavelengths. Using unprimed symbols at the first wavelength λ, single primes at the second wavelength λ', and double primes at the third wavelength λ'', these equations become

$$(\mu_2 - \theta\rho_2)\frac{C_2}{C_1} + (\mu_3 - \theta\rho_3)\frac{C_3}{C_1} + (\mu_4 - \theta\rho_4)\frac{C_4}{C_1} = \theta\rho_1 - \mu_1 \tag{45}$$

$$(\mu_2' - \theta'\rho_2')\frac{C_2}{C_1} + (\mu_3' - \theta'\rho_3')\frac{C_3}{C_1} + (\mu_4' - \theta'\rho_4')\frac{C_4}{C_1} = \theta'\rho_1' - \mu_1' \tag{46}$$

$$(\mu_2'' - \theta''\rho_2'')\frac{C_2}{C_1} + (\mu_3'' - \theta''\rho_3'')\frac{C_3}{C_1} + (\mu_4'' - \theta''\rho_4'')\frac{C_4}{C_1} = \theta''\rho_1'' - \mu_1'' \tag{47}$$

if the concentration ratios are based upon the concentration of pigment 1.

Almost always considerable simplification of the above three equations is possible. Consider for example a mixture in which the largest constituent is white (pigment 1), and the other three pigments are black (2), red (3), and yellow (4). The shape of the spectrophotometric curve might be as shown in Figure 7.3. It is generally a good approximation in such a case to assume that the scattering coefficients for all the pigments except the white are zero, so that the equations become (with $\rho_w = 1$),

$$\frac{C_b}{C_w}\mu_b + \frac{C_r}{C_w}\mu_r + \frac{C_y}{C_w}\mu_y = \theta - \mu_w \tag{48}$$

$$\frac{C_b}{C_w}\mu_b' + \frac{C_r}{C_w}\mu_r' + \frac{C_y}{C_w}\mu_y' = \theta' - \mu_w' \tag{49}$$

$$\frac{C_b}{C_w}\mu_b'' + \frac{C_r}{C_w}\mu_r'' + \frac{C_y}{C_w}\mu_y'' = \theta'' - \mu_w'' \tag{50}$$

Another simplifying approximation is possible in this example by a proper choice of wavelengths for the three above equations. Thus, at wavelengths in the red region of the spectrum it will be found that μ_b is considerably larger than either μ_r or μ_y, so that equation (48) becomes approximately (at, say, $\lambda = 660$ mμ)

$$\frac{C_b}{C_w} = \frac{\theta - \mu_w}{\mu_b} \tag{51}$$

Likewise, at a wavelength where μ_r' is much larger than ρ_y' (perhaps $\lambda' = 560$ mμ), equation (49) is approximately

$$\frac{C_r}{C_w} = \frac{\theta' - \mu_w'}{\mu_r'} - \frac{C_b}{C_w}\frac{\mu_b'}{\mu_r'} \tag{52}$$

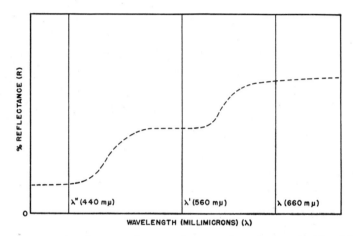

Figure 7.3.   Example of spectrophotometric curve for mixture of white, black, red, and yellow pigments (with reference to equations 44 to 56).

Finally equation (50) is solved directly for C_y/C_w at some wavelength where μ_y'' is large (say $\lambda'' = 440$ mμ),

$$\frac{C_y}{C_w} = \frac{\theta'' - \mu_w''}{\mu_y''} - \frac{C_b}{C_y}\frac{\mu_b''}{\mu_y''} - \frac{C_r}{C_y}\frac{\mu_r''}{\mu_y''} \tag{53}$$

In the above example the equations (48), (49), and (50) have been solved simultaneously, but the solution was considerably simplified by neglecting the smaller terms. Actually the approximation is good only if in the final mixture,

$$C_b\mu_b \gg C_r\mu_r + C_y\mu_y \tag{54}$$

and

$$C_r\mu_r' \gg C_y\mu_y' \tag{55}$$

Also the approximation is dependent upon the assumption that

$$C_w\rho_w \gg C_b\rho_b + C_r\rho_r + C_y\rho_y \tag{56}$$

that is, that in the final mixture the white pigment accounts for most of the total scattering at the wavelength λ. The inequality similar to (56) at λ' is less important, and that at λ'' still less important since it has been shown earlier that at wavelengths where $\mu_p \gg \rho_p$ the approximation that $\rho_p = 0$ is very good.

Equations When $\mu_0 \neq 0$

In the previous section it was shown that when θ is expressed omitting μ_0 and ρ_0 as in equation (44) the number of "degrees of freedom" of the spectrophotometric curve is one less than the number of pigments in the mixture. One additional degree of freedom is available, the total pigment concentration, and this can be used to adjust the opacity but not the spectrophotometric curve at another wavelength.

If the absorption coefficient μ_0 of the base material is not taken as zero, the θ equation becomes (see equation 10)

$$\theta = \frac{\mu_0 + \Sigma C_i \mu_i}{\Sigma C_i \rho_i} \tag{57}$$

and by use of this equation the number of degrees of freedom of the spectrophotometric curve (number of wavelengths which can be made to have an arbitrary reflectance) is in principle equal to the number of pigments in the mixture. When used in this manner it will be evident from the discussion below that one has lost the degree of freedom of the choice of opacity. An example will illustrate the difference in the use of equations (44) and (57).

Let it be required to calculate the pigment concentrations necessary to give the curve shown in Figure 7.4. Suppose this curve is to be made with a mixture of red and white pigments. Writing the θ equation as in equation (44) but with only two pigments, the mixture required to give the reflectance R at λ can be found from the equation

$$\theta = \frac{C_w \mu_w + C_r \mu_r}{C_w + C_r \rho_r} \tag{58}$$

which has the solution,

$$\frac{C_r}{C_w} = \frac{\theta - \mu_w}{\mu_r - \theta \rho_r} \tag{59}$$

There is now no degree of freedom remaining with which to fix the reflectance at λ'. In spite of the fact that in practice the reflectance R' at λ' will vary somewhat with total pigment concentration, the equation relating θ' to the pigment constants at λ' will be similar to equation (58), namely,

$$\theta' = \frac{C_w \mu_w' + C_r \mu_r'}{C_w + C_r \rho_r'} = \frac{\mu_w' + \dfrac{C_r}{C_w} \mu_r'}{1 + \dfrac{C_r}{C_w} \rho_r'} \tag{60}$$

Hence θ' is determined by the ratio C_r/C_w, and in fact the reflectance at all wavelengths has been fixed by this ratio. In practice, if a series of specimens of different white concentrations is available, a plot of R' vs. C_w can be used to deduce approximately the white pigment concentration to be used to obtain a given R' at λ'. Then, since the reflectance R at λ is not very much affected by changes in opacity, the ratio C_r/C_w can be obtained from equation (59).

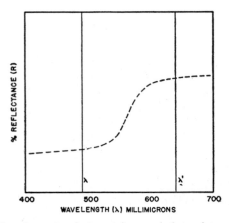

Figure 7.4. Example of spectrophotometric curve for mixture of red and white pigments (with reference to equations 58 to 70).

Again, suppose the same curve is to be made with a mixture of three pigments, red, black, and white, again assuming that μ_0 and ρ_0 are zero. This case now has two degrees of freedom as far as pigment concentrations are concerned. The concentration of white pigment will be chosen arbitrarily, and C_b/C_w and C_r/C_w will be found by simultaneous solution of the two equations

$$\theta = \frac{C_w\mu_w + C_b\mu_b + C_r\mu_r}{C_w + C_b\rho_b + C_r\rho_r} \tag{61}$$

$$\theta' = \frac{C_w\mu_w' + C_b\mu_b' + C_r\mu_r'}{C_w + C_b\rho_b' + C_r\rho_r'} \tag{62}$$

which generally can be simplified considerably as explained previously by assuming some constants to be zero. Thus if $\rho_b = \rho_b' = 0$, $\rho_r = \rho_r' = 0$, $\mu_r' = 0$, the solutions are

$$\frac{C_b}{C_w} = \frac{\theta' - \mu_w'}{\mu_b'} \tag{63}$$

$$\frac{C_r}{C_w} = \frac{\theta - \mu_w}{\mu_r} - \frac{C_b}{C_w}\frac{\mu_b}{\mu_r} \tag{64}$$

With C_b/C_w and C_r/C_w determined, the choice of total concentration remains, which can be used to obtain the desired opacity. In practice, it is obvious that the above approach is feasible only when a value of C_w is chosen which will give a reflectance higher than R'. The most accurate results will obviously be obtained when C_w is the same as for the mixtures used for calculating μ_r and μ_b.

On the other hand, equation (57) can be used to obtain both C_w and C_r when matching the curve with just red and white, when μ_0 is not taken as zero. The equations are

$$\theta = \frac{\mu_0 + C_w\mu_w + C_r\mu_r}{C_w + C_r\rho_r} \tag{65}$$

$$\theta' = \frac{\mu_0' + C_w\mu_w' + C_r\mu_r'}{C_w + C_r\rho_r'} \tag{66}$$

which rearrange as follows

$$C_w(\theta - \mu_w) + C_r(\theta\rho_r - \mu_r) = \mu_0 \tag{67}$$

$$C_w(\theta' - \mu_w') + C_r(\theta'\rho_r' - \mu_r') = \mu_0' \tag{68}$$

If the same simplifying assumptions are made, the above equations have the simple solutions

$$C_w = \frac{\mu_0'}{\theta'} \tag{69}$$

$$C_r = \frac{\theta}{\theta'}\frac{\mu_0'}{\mu_r} - \frac{\mu_0}{\mu_r} \tag{70}$$

The opacity is now fixed by the value of C_w and cannot be set arbitrarily. Thus this two-pigment mixture has two degrees of freedom, that is, R can be fixed at two wavelengths.

One additional example is required. Suppose that equation (57) is used and the curve is to be matched with white, red, and black pigments. In spite of the fact that in principle three degrees of freedom are available for fixing the spectrophotometric curve, it is nevertheless usually impractical to try to calculate the three-pigment concentrations in this case from three equations, that is, to try to fix the reflectance at three wavelengths. Whereas the equations (67) and (68) have a unique solution, with three pigments the two equivalent equations

$$C_w(\theta - \mu_w) + C_r(\theta\rho_r - \mu_r) + C_b(\theta\rho_b - \mu_b) = \mu_0 \tag{71}$$

$$C_w(\theta' - \mu_w') + C_r(\theta'\rho_r' - \mu_r') + C_b(\theta'\rho_b' - \mu_b') = \mu_0' \tag{72}$$

have an infinite number of solutions which means that an infinite number of combinations of C_w, C_r, and C_b will give the two desired reflectances R and R'. The differences between the various possible combinations of

C_w, C_r, and C_b giving reflectances R and R' will be evidenced by small variations in the shape of the curve at other wavelengths, and the magnitude of these variations will depend upon how large μ_0 is and upon the condition that μ_0 and μ_b vary with wavelength in a different manner. Only if μ_0 and μ_b change differently, such as for example a rather yellow base material and a bluish-black pigment, can three independent equations be written for this case. Thus, in this case, the third degree of freedom should be used to set the opacity by assigning a value to C_w, whereupon equations (71) and (72) have unique solutions. With the simplifying assumptions $\mu_w = \mu_w' = 0$, $\rho_r = \rho_r' = 0$, $\rho_b = \rho_b' = 0$, and $\mu_r' = 0$, the equations (71) and (72) have the solutions

$$C_b = \frac{C_w\theta' - \mu_0'}{\mu_b'} \tag{73}$$

$$C_r = \frac{C_w\theta - \mu_0}{\mu_r} - \frac{C_b\mu_b}{\mu_r} \tag{74}$$

These equations are somewhat similar to equations (63) and (64), but they have added accuracy by being able to compensate quite well for differences in opacity.

The above examples have illustrated the following principles:

1. When using the equation,

$$\theta = \frac{\Sigma C_i\mu_i}{\Sigma C_i\rho_i}$$

the reflectance can be arbitrarily set at one fewer number of wavelengths than the number of pigments in the mixture.

2. When using the equation,

$$\theta = \frac{\mu_0 + \Sigma C_i\mu_i}{\Sigma C_i\rho_i}$$

the reflectance can be arbitrarily set at the same number of wavelengths as the number of pigments, except that in some circumstances (principally when using black) it is practical to set the reflectance at only one fewer wavelengths than the number of pigments. Even in this case, however, use of this equation is generally to be preferred for the sake of accuracy.

Choice of Wavelengths

In many cases of pigment mixtures the choice of wavelengths for calculation of the simultaneous equations is easily made and is not critical. The general rule is to select a wavelength for each pigment at which the pigment has a large effect upon the reflectance. If the wavelength chosen for a pigment happens to be a wavelength at which the other pigments have a small or negligible effect, so much the better. In the examples discussed in the above section, a wavelength in the red region was selected for the calculation of the black concentration because it was possible to neglect the effect of small amounts of red and yellow pigments in this region. Next, the calculation of the concentration of red pigment was possible, having already determined the black concentration (which affects all wavelengths), by selecting a wavelength in the green region where the red pigment absorbs strongly but where the effect of the yellow

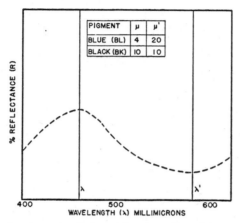

Figure 7.5. Example of spectrophotometric curve for mixture of white, black, and blue pigments (with reference to equations 75 to 77).

pigment could be neglected. Finally, with the concentration of the red and black pigments determined, the concentration of yellow pigment was calculated in the blue region where yellow absorbs strongly by taking into account the effects of the black and red pigments, both of which have strong absorption in the blue.

As another example, suppose that a color is to be made with white, black, and blue, and is to have a curve as shown in Figure 7.5. If the absorption coefficients at λ and λ' are as given in the table, the equations to be solved would be (based upon equation 57)

$$C_{bk}\mu_{bk} + C_{bl}\mu_{bl} = C_w\theta - \mu_0 \tag{75}$$

$$C_{bk}\mu_{bk}' + C_{bl}\mu_{bl}' = C_w\theta' - \mu_0' \tag{76}$$

The "leverage" of a set of equations of this type depends upon the ratios of products of certain elements in the determinant containing the coefficients,

$$\begin{vmatrix} \mu_{bk} & \mu_{bl} \\ \mu_{bk}' & \mu_{bl}' \end{vmatrix},$$

which for this example is

$$\begin{vmatrix} 10 & 4 \\ 10 & 20 \end{vmatrix}.$$

The best leverage is obtained when the inequality

$$\mu_{bk}\mu_{bl}' > \mu_{bk}'\mu_{bl}$$

is at a maximum. This inequality can also be written

$$\frac{\mu_{bk}}{\mu_{bl}} = \frac{\mu_{bk}'}{\mu_{bl}'}, \tag{77}$$

In this example, the latter inequality is

$$\frac{10}{4} > \frac{10}{20}$$

or

$$2.5 > 0.5, \quad \text{or} \quad 5 > 1,$$

that is, the left-hand side is five times larger than the right-hand side. In this example, since the absorption coefficient for black was assumed to be the same at the two wavelengths, it is obvious that the inequality (77) has its maximum value at wavelengths where μ_{bl} is smallest and where μ_{bl}' is largest. In other words, the wavelengths chosen should be the reflectance maximum at λ and the reflectance minimum at λ'.

In the case of two pigments more nearly alike than in the above example, the choice of the best wavelengths may not be so obvious. One should then find the wavelengths for which the inequality (77) is greatest. Suppose that two blue pigments, differing somewhat in hue, are to be mixed with white. The two pigments (here called a and b) mixed individually with white might have curves and absorption coefficients as shown in Figure 7.6. By choosing the wavelengths of maximum absorption of both pigments, λ and λ', the leverage would be determined by the inequality

$$\frac{15}{20} > \frac{12}{22}, \quad \text{or} \quad 1.375 > 1.$$

By choosing another wavelength λ'' to replace λ' where the ratio of absorption coefficients is more favorable, the inequality would be

$$\frac{15}{20} > \frac{2}{15}, \quad \text{or} \quad 5.62 > 1,$$

and much better accuracy would be obtained.

The leverage of three or more simultaneous equations is more difficult to evaluate, but this problem rarely need be met. Almost always it is possible to consider pigments in pairs and thereby arrive at the best wavelengths. Thus, if the example just discussed were to have been black, in addition to the two blues and white, the wavelengths for the two blues would be decided just as was done above, and another wavelength λ''' would be chosen for the black for the same reasons as discussed earlier (example containing equations 75 and 76).

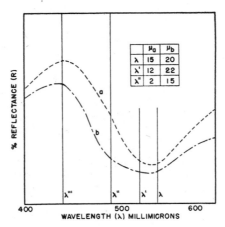

Figure 7.6. Example of spectrophotometric curve of mixture of two blue pigments *a* and *b* with white (with reference to equations 75 to 77).

When two pigments are so similar that poor leverage results at all wavelengths, they should be lumped together for calculation. The ratio of the two pigments could be set at some arbitrary value by inspection of the curve or by the visual hue, and the sum of the two concentrations calculated. In the last example, suppose the ratio of the two blues is to be 3 parts of *a* and 2 parts of *b*. At λ the absorption coefficient for the mixture would be

$$\left(\frac{3}{5}\right)15 + \left(\frac{2}{5}\right)20 = 17.$$

Using this value for the absorption coefficient, the total blue concentration would be calculated, 3/5 of which would be *a*, and 2/5 would be *b*.

The application of the inequality rule which has been discussed above must not be carried to extremes. One must remember that accuracy is also dependent upon the size of the absorption coefficients, and wavelengths should not be chosen where the absorption coefficients are only a small fraction of their value at wavelengths of maximum absorption.

Properties of Two-component Mixtures

Some of the properties of pigment mixtures can be stated in general terms and are useful to remember. Consider the case of a mixture of a green and a red pigment, shown in Figure 7.7.

The equation for any mixture of the two pigments (with $\mu_0 = \rho_0 = 0$, for simplicity) is

$$\theta_m = \frac{C_g \mu_g + C_r \mu_r}{C_g \rho_g + C_r \rho_r}$$

Since $\theta_r = \mu_r/\rho_r$ and $\theta_g = \mu_g/\rho_g$, the equation becomes

$$\theta_m = \frac{C_g \rho_g \theta_g + C_r \rho_r \theta_r}{C_g \rho_g + C_r \rho_r}$$

which can be written as

$$\theta_m = \frac{C_g \rho_g}{C_g \rho_g + C_r \rho_r} \cdot \theta_g + \frac{C_r \rho_r}{C_g \rho_g + C_r \rho_r} \cdot \theta_r \qquad (78)$$

Since

$$\frac{C_g \rho_g}{C_g \rho_g + C_r \rho_r} + \frac{C_r \rho_r}{C_g \rho_g + C_r \rho_r} = 1,$$

it is evident that θ_m always lies between θ_g and θ_r. Hence the reflectance curve of the mixture always lies between the reflectance curves of the

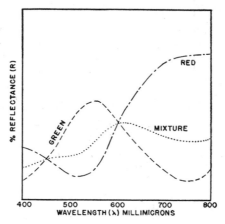

Figure 7.7. Example of spectrophotometric curve for a green and red pigment and for one of their mixtures (with reference to equation 78).

two constituents. At wavelengths where the two reflectance curves cross, $\theta_r = \theta_g$, and it follows immediately that

$$\theta_m = \theta_r = \theta_g$$

Hence the reflectance curves of all mixtures pass through the same point at these wavelengths. At all other wavelengths the reflectance will depend upon the relative proportions of the two constituents. It will be noticed that equation (78) states that the θ of a mixture is a weighted average of the θ's of the two constituents, and that the weighting factors are in the proportion that each constituent contributes to the total scattering coefficient.

In the case of a dye, θ is infinite, ρ is zero, and the above expressions become indeterminate. In order to know anything about the dye in reflectance, it must be mixed with white. Suppose such a mixture is

$$\theta_d = \frac{C_w\mu_w + C_d\mu_d}{C_w}$$

and this in turn is mixed with a pigment. The θ equation for this mixture is

$$\theta_m = \frac{C_w\mu_w + C_d\mu_d + C_p\mu_p}{C_w + C_p\rho_p}$$

which becomes

$$\theta_m = \frac{C_w}{C_w + C_p\rho_p} \cdot \theta_d + \frac{C_p\rho_p}{C_w + C_p\rho_p} \cdot \theta_p$$

Hence, considering the dye and white as one constituent and remembering that $\rho_w = 1$, the same weighting rule is found to apply.

CALCULATION OF COLOR CORRECTIONS

In general two methods may be used for calculating the small changes in pigment concentrations required to make small changes in the spectrophotometric curve. The first of these is the direct application of the equations discussed above for the calculation of color matches, and the second involves use of derivative forms of these equations.

Use of Ordinary Equations

Whenever the reflectance of a trial specimen differs from that for which it was calculated a discrepancy exists which may of course be due to a number of causes. If the discrepancy is large enough so that another trial is desirable, the next calculation should be based upon the previous trial. This can be done in several ways all of which fall into one of two classes. Either the previous trial is used to obtain new values for the pigment constants which are then used in the next calculation, or new values of reflectance or of θ based upon the observed discrepancies are put into the next calculation. Observed changes in pigment constants may be due to

(a) Errors in pigment concentrations in making up the sample.
(b) A new batch of pigment having a different strength may have been used.
(c) The initial values of the constants may be inaccurate, perhaps due to an unfavorable mixture not conducive to good accuracy.

(d) The pigment constants may not be really constant under all circumstances. A few pigments, for example phthalocyanine blue, are especially troublesome. Their absorption coefficients may vary with concentration and with different treatments given the sample.

These methods will be illustrated by a simple example.

1. Calculation of New Constants

Let it be required to calculate the mixture of black ($\mu_b = 36$) with one per cent white to get 42 per cent reflectance ($\theta = 0.220$), with μ_0 taken as 0.015. Equation (57) becomes

$$\theta = \frac{\mu_0 + C_b\mu_b}{C_w} \tag{79}$$

and

$$C_b = \frac{C_w\theta - \mu_0}{\mu_b} = \frac{0.220 - 0.015}{36} = 0.00569 \text{ per cent.}$$

Suppose when this sample is made up it has a reflectance $R' = 38$ per cent ($\theta' = 0.289$). Using θ' in equation (79) along with the value of C_b used, a new value μ_b' can be calculated,

$$\mu_b' = \frac{\theta'C_w - \mu_0}{C_b} = \frac{0.289 - 0.015}{0.00569} = 48.2.$$

The μ_b' can be used again in equation (79) with the desired value of θ to get a new value C_b',

$$C_b' = \frac{C_w\theta - \mu_0}{\mu_b'} = \frac{0.220 - 0.015}{48.2} = 0.00425 \text{ per cent.} \tag{80}$$

It is also possible to make the correction on the white, and the choice between the two possibilities (or a combination of both) should be based upon the size of the change needed and whether or not it is desirable to change the opacity. If the white is to be changed, equation (79) gives

$$C_w' = \frac{\mu_0 + C_b\mu_b'}{\theta} = \frac{\mu_0 + \theta'C_w - \mu_0}{\theta} = \frac{\theta'}{\theta}C_w = \frac{0.289}{0.220}C_w = 1.314C_w \tag{81}$$

Hence the white should be changed according to the ratio of the observed θ to the desired θ, in this case $C_w' = 1.314$ per cent. If it is decided by visual estimate of opacity that the concentration C_w'' of white should be about 1.15 per cent, the concentration of black C_b'' is found from the equation

$$C_b'' = \frac{C_w''\theta - \mu_0}{\mu_b'} = \frac{1.15 \times 0.220 - 0.015}{48.2} = 0.00494 \text{ per cent.} \tag{82}$$

For more complicated mixtures it is of course impossible from the curve of only one mixture to calculate new values for the constants of several pigments each of which affects the reflectance at any given wavelength. In such a case a new constant could be calculated for the pigment having the greatest influence on the reflectance at any wavelength, and this new value could be used along with the old constants for the remaining pigments in any new calculation. This procedure would be a good approximation in many cases.

2. Calculating for New R or θ Values

Although the method discussed above should be followed in cases of serious disagreement between calculated and observed results in order to obtain better constants, thus preventing the same error being made in the future, it is often easier to correct a color by using the original values for the constants and calculating to obtain different values of R or θ.

Thus, in the example discussed above, since the observed reflectance was 4 per cent lower than the calculated value, a new calculation can be made for a reflectance 4 per cent too high. This calculation will be made using the old value of the absorption coefficient. Thus for a reflectance R'' of $42 + 4 = 46$ per cent, θ'' is 0.1675, and the new concentration C_b' of black is

$$C_b' = \frac{C_w \theta'' - \mu_0}{\mu_b} = \frac{0.1675 - 0.015}{36} = 0.00424 \text{ per cent} \qquad (83)$$

which is in good agreement with the result of equation (80). Also the white, or both black and white, can be changed with results similar to equations (81) and (82) by using θ'' in place of θ and μ_b in place of μ_b'.

The new calculation can also be based upon a new value of θ, providing a proportional and not additive correction of θ is made. Thus, in the example being discussed, if the desired θ is 0.220 and the observed θ is $\theta' = 0.289$, a new θ (again called θ'') can be found

$$\theta'' = \frac{\theta}{\theta'} \times \theta = \frac{0.220}{0.289} \times 0.220 = 0.1675$$

which yields the same value for the new θ as was used in equation (83) and hence gives identical results. The use of θ-differences (additive correction) is not recommended for large corrections. That is, the discrepancy between θ and θ', which is $0.289 - 0.220 = 0.069$, if in turn subtracted from θ gives $\theta'' = 0.220 - 0.069 = 0.151$. Use of this new value overcorrects in this instance, but will undercorrect when the observed reflectance is higher than the calculated one. The error involved in the use of θ-differences can be very great in cases of rather large changes, whereas both the R-method and proportional θ-method give almost as good results even for large corrections as does the use of new constants.

3. Example

As another example of color correction the case of matching a curve like that shown in Figure 7.4 will be discussed, using white, black, and red. The equations for this case were (71) and (72). If the white concentration is assigned in advance, the equations can be rearranged as follows:

$$C_r(\mu_r - \theta\rho_r) + C_b(\mu_b - \theta\rho_b) = C_w(\theta - \mu_w) - \mu_0 \tag{84}$$

$$C_r(\mu_r' - \theta'\rho_r') + C_b(\mu_b' - \theta'\rho_b') = C_w(\theta' - \mu_w') - \mu_0' \tag{85}$$

For this example, let the following constants be assumed:

	λ		λ'	
	μ	ρ	μ'	ρ'
White	0	1	0	1
Red	4	0.4	0.1	0.5
Black	5	0	6	0
Base (μ_0)	0.007	0	0.005	0

With these constants in the two above equations, taking $C_w = 0.5$ per cent, the equations become,

$$(4 - 0.4\,\theta)C_r + 5C_b = 0.5\,\theta - 0.007 \tag{86}$$

$$(0.1 - 0.5\,\theta')C_r + 6C_b = 0.5\,\theta' - 0.005 \tag{87}$$

Assume that the reflectances desired are $R = 20.9$ per cent at λ and $R' = 38.5$ per cent at λ', so that $\theta = 0.033$ and $\theta' = 0.278$. The equations simplify to the **form**

$$2.587\,C_r + 5C_b = 0.510$$

$$-0.039\,C_r + 6C_b = 0.134$$

which have the solutions,

$$C_r = 0.110 \text{ per cent} \tag{88}$$

$$C_b = 0.0230 \text{ per cent} \tag{89}$$

The initial sample would be made with these concentrations.

Suppose when this sample is made that it has $R = 21.6$ per cent and $R' = 40.0$ per cent, or reflectance discrepancies $\Delta R = 0.7$ per cent and $\Delta R' = 1.5$ per cent. The new calculation can be made for reflectances

20.9 — 0.7 = 20.2 per cent and 38.5 — 1.5 = 37.0 per cent, for which the new θ's are $\theta = 1.105$ and $\theta = 0.308$. If these θ's are put into equations (86) and (87), the equations become,

$$3.560 \, C_r + 5C_b = 0.546$$
$$-0.054 \, C_r + 6C_b = 0.149$$

which have the solutions

$$C_r = 0.1171 \text{ per cent} \tag{90}$$
$$C_b = 0.0259 \text{ per cent} \tag{91}$$

for the color correction. Using this method, it is almost as much work to make the color correction as it is to make the initial calculation.

Some simplification results if the correction is calculated by using the original θ's on the left side of equations (86) and (87), and the new θ's on the right side. This is almost always an excellent approximation if the changes in θ are not exceedingly large. Using this procedure, some of the work done on the initial calculation can be used in the correction. The correction can be calculated from the equations

$$3.587 \, C_r + 5C_b = 0.5 \times 1.105 - 0.007 = 0.546$$
$$-0.039 \, C_r + 6C_b = 0.5 \times 0.308 - 0.005 = 0.149$$

having the solutions,

$$C_r = 0.1165 \text{ per cent} \tag{92}$$
$$C_b = 0.0258 \text{ per cent} \tag{93}$$

Even greater simplification can be obtained by solving the equations (86) and (87) initially in terms of the unevaluated right hand sides of the equations. The equations to be solved are written as

$$3.587 \, C_r + 5C_b = 0.5 \, \theta - 0.007$$
$$-0.039 \, C_r + 6C_b = 0.5 \, \theta' - 0.005$$

and have the solutions,

$$C_r = 0.276 \, (0.5 \, \theta - 0.007) - 0.230 \, (0.5 \, \theta' - 0.005) \tag{94}$$
$$C_b = 0.00180 \, (0.5 \, \theta - 0.007) + 0.165 \, (0.5 \, \theta' - 0.005) \tag{95}$$

The initial concentrations to be used in the first trial sample can now be found by putting the initial θ's into equations (94) and (95), and corrections can be made in the same way by putting in the new θ's. This of course results in answers identical to equations (88) and (89) for the initial θ's, and to equations (92) and (93) for the new θ's.

Derivative Equations

1. Derivation of General Case

The general θ equation (equation 57) is

$$\theta = \frac{\mu_0 + \Sigma C_i \mu_i}{\Sigma C_i \rho_i}$$

or

$$\theta \Sigma C_i \rho_i = \mu_0 + \Sigma C_i \mu_i$$

and the derivative of this equation is

$$\Delta\theta \Sigma C_i \rho_i + \theta \Sigma \Delta C_i \rho_i = \Sigma \Delta C_i \mu_i$$

or

$$\Sigma \Delta C_i (\mu_i - \theta \rho_i) = \Delta\theta \Sigma C_i \rho_i \qquad (96)$$

If a proportional change in concentrations is made, that is, all pigments are increased or decreased by the same ratio,

$$\Delta C_i / C_i = m$$

and equation (96) becomes

$$\Sigma m C_i \left[\mu_i - \rho_i \left(\frac{\mu_0 + \Sigma C_i \mu_i}{\Sigma C_i \rho_i} \right) \right] = \Delta\theta \Sigma C_i \rho_i$$

Rearrangement gives the equation

$$\frac{m \Sigma C_i \mu_i \Sigma C_i \rho_i - m \Sigma C_i \rho_i \Sigma C_i \mu_i - \mu_0 m \Sigma C_i \rho_i}{\Sigma C_i \rho_i} = \Delta\theta \Sigma C_i \rho_i$$

which easily reduces to

$$-\mu_0 m = \Delta\theta \Sigma C_i \rho_i$$

If $\mu_0 = 0$, as in equation (44), then a proportional change gives $\Delta\theta = 0$, so that no change in reflectance results.

The effect of changing individual pigments is easily calculated from equation (96). If the nth pigment only is to be changed, the equation reads

$$\Delta C_n (\mu_n - \theta \rho_n) = \Delta\theta \Sigma C_i \rho_i \qquad (97)$$

from which the ΔC_n required to give $\Delta\theta$ at one wavelength can be determined. Also from equation (97) the $\Delta\theta$ at any wavelength resulting from the change ΔC_n can be calculated. It will be noticed from equation (97) that when one pigment is changed, the only effect the other pigments have upon the change in reflectance is in proportion to the extent that the other pigments contribute to the total scattering coefficient. For a situation in which only the white contributes to the total scattering coefficient, equation (97) reduces to the simple form

$$\Delta C_n = \frac{C_w \Delta\theta}{\mu_n} \tag{98}$$

Equation (96) is similarly simplified under the same situation, that is, when $\Sigma C_i \rho_i = C_w$,

$$\Sigma \mu_i \Delta C_i - \theta \Delta C_w = C_w \Delta\theta \tag{99}$$

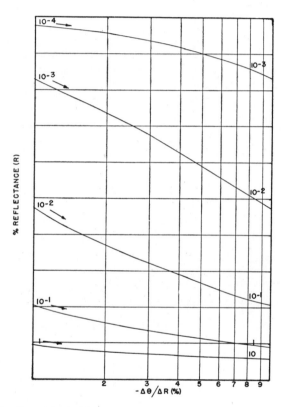

Figure 7.8. Semilogarithmic plot (5-cycle) of the derivative form of the θ-function (equation 100) where $-\dfrac{\Delta\theta}{\Delta R} = \dfrac{-1.512R^2 + 0.9504R + 0.5616}{(R + 1.4)^2(R - 0.04)^2}$ and $0 < R < 1$.

Sometimes it is convenient to substitute ΔR for $\Delta\theta$ which can be done for any θ (or R) from the derivative form of equation (9), which is

$$-\Delta\theta/\Delta R = \frac{-1.512\,R^2 + 0.9504\,R + 0.5616}{(R + 1.4)^2\,(R - 0.04)^2} \tag{100}$$

and is plotted in Figure 7.8.

If

$$-\frac{\Delta\theta}{\Delta R} = k,$$

where k is the function of R given by equation (100), the above equations can be written in terms of ΔR's. For example, equation (96) becomes

$$\Sigma\Delta C_i(\mu_i - \theta\rho_i) = -k\Delta R\Sigma C_i\rho_i \tag{101}$$

and equation (99) becomes

$$\Sigma\mu_i\Delta C_i - \theta\Delta C_w = -kC_w\Delta R \tag{102}$$

In connection with the use of equations (96), (99), (101), and (102), the same relations hold between the number of pigments and the number of equations used as discussed in the section "Equations When $\mu_0 \neq 0$" (page 137). Thus in some cases ΔC_w can be calculated along with changes in the other pigments, and in other cases one of the ΔC_i's (usually ΔC_w) must be chosen and the remaining ΔC_i's calculated from as many equations as there are unknown ΔC_i's.

2. Example

Now let equation (96) be applied to the case discussed in the section "Use of Ordinary Equations" (page 148). The equations to be solved are

$$\Delta C_r(\mu_r - \theta\rho_r) + \Delta C_b(\mu_b - \theta\rho_b) + \Delta C_w(\mu_w - \theta\rho_w) = \Delta\theta(C_r\rho_r + C_b\rho_b + C_w\rho_w)$$

$$\Delta C_r(\mu_r' - \theta'\rho_r') + \Delta C_b(\mu_b' - \theta'\rho_b') + \Delta C_w(\mu_w' - \theta'\rho_w') = \Delta\theta'(C_r\rho_r' + C_b\rho_b' + C_w\rho_w')$$

After substitution of the same constants as before the equations become

$$6.595\ \Delta C_r + 9.191\ \Delta C_b - 1.899\ \Delta C_w = \Delta\theta \tag{103}$$

$$-0.0699\ \Delta C_r + 10.810\ \Delta C_b - 0.496\ \Delta C_w = \Delta\theta' \tag{104}$$

A change for one of the pigments must be decided upon, whereupon the changes for the remaining two pigments can be calculated. If the white is to be left the same ($\Delta C_w = 0$), the solutions to the above equations are

$$\Delta C_r = 0.150\ \Delta\theta - 0.128\ \Delta\theta' \tag{105}$$

$$\Delta C_b = 0.00972\ \Delta\theta + 0.0918\ \Delta\theta' \tag{106}$$

Concentration corrections can be obtained by substituting $\Delta\theta$'s in equations (105) and (106). Thus to make a change in θ of $\Delta\theta = 1.105 - 1.033 = 0.072$ and in θ' of $\Delta'\theta' = 0.308 - 0.278 = 0.030$, the above equations give

$$\Delta C_r = 0.150 \times 0.072 - 0.128 \times 0.030 = 0.0070 \text{ per cent} \tag{107}$$

$$\Delta C_b = 0.00972 \times 0.072 + 0.0918 \times 0.030 = 0.0035 \text{ per cent} \tag{108}$$

so that the new concentrations would be

$$C_r = 0.1170 \text{ per cent}$$

$$C_b = 0.0265 \text{ per cent}$$

with results comparable to the results of equations (90) and (91) and equations (92) and (93). If the correction is to be in the direction to reduce θ, the corresponding $\Delta\theta$ would be negative.

As explained by the transition from equation (96) to (101), in which ΔR's were used in place of $\Delta\theta$'s, equations (105) and (106) can also be expressed in terms of ΔR and $\Delta R'$. For $\theta = 1.033$ or $R = 20.9$ per cent,

$$-\frac{\Delta\theta}{\Delta R} = 0.093$$

from equation (100) or the graph of this equation (Figure 7.8). Also, $\theta' = 0.278$ or $R' = 38.5$ per cent, so that from Figure 7.8,

$$-\frac{\Delta\theta'}{\Delta R'} = 0.0186$$

Thus equations (105) and (106) become

$$\Delta C_r = -0.150 \times 0.093 \, \Delta R + 0.128 \times 0.0186 \, \Delta R' = -0.0140 \, \Delta R + 0.00238 \, \Delta R' \quad (109)$$

$$\Delta C_b = -0.00972 \times 0.093 \, \Delta R - 0.0918 \times 0.0186 \, \Delta R' = -0.000904 \, \Delta R - 0.00171 \, \Delta R' \quad (110)$$

If reflectances change $\Delta R = -0.7$ per cent and $\Delta R' = -1.5$ per cent are required, equations (109) and (110) give the results

$$\Delta C_r = -0.0140 \, (-0.7) + 0.00238 \, (-1.5) \quad = 0.0062 \text{ per cent}$$

$$\Delta C_b = -0.000904 \, (-0.7) - 0.00171 \, (-1.5) = 0.0032 \text{ per cent}$$

which can be compared with the results of equations (107) and (108). Of course the change from $\Delta\theta$'s to ΔR's can be made at any point, as for example in equations (103) and (104).

The use of equations transposed to ΔR's and presolved as in equations (109) and (110) above permits color corrections to be calculated without reference to any data other than reflectance differences.

It is interesting to note the liberties which can be taken with the exact equations and still obtain fairly good results in making color corrections. In the example being discussed, the correction can be calculated by neglecting the scattering coefficient of the red pigment, in which case equation (96) gives the two equations

$$4 \, \Delta C_r + 5 \, \Delta C_b = 0.5 \, \Delta\theta$$

$$0.1 \, \Delta C_r + 6 \, \Delta C_b = 0.5 \, \Delta\theta'$$

which for $\Delta\theta = 0.072$ and $\Delta\theta' = 0.030$ have the solutions,

$$\Delta C_r = 0.0061, C_r = 0.110 + 0.0061 = 0.1161 \text{ per cent}$$

$$\Delta C_b = 0.0024, C_b = 0.023 + 0.0024 = 0.0254 \text{ per cent}$$

These results are in rather good agreement with the results of equations (92) and (93).

References

1. Duntley, S. Q., *J. Optical Soc. Am.*, **32**, 61 (1942).
2. Duncan, D. R., *J. Oil & Colour Chemists' Assoc.*, **32**, 296 (1949).
3. Crout, P. D., *Trans. Am. Inst. Elec. Engrs.*, **60**, 1235 (1941).
4. Kubelka, P., and Munk, F., *Zeits. f. Physik*, **12**, 593 (1931).
5. Saunderson, J. L., *J. Optical Soc. Am.*, **32**, 727 (1942).
6. Stearns, E. I., *Am. Dyestuff Reptr.*, **33**, 1 (1944); *Official Digest*, **336**, 45 (Jan. 1953).
7. Davison, H. R., *J. Optical Soc. Am.*, **42**, 331 (1952).

8 : New Pigments in Modern Color Design

EDMOND C. BOTTI

Pigments Department
E. I. du Pont de Nemours & Co., Inc.
Newark, N. Y.

Color has come to play such an important role in our everyday lives that as a result of its very familiarity we are prone to forget the advances which have been made in recent years. Public response to color psychology and color harmony has led to the widespread adoption of color in many new fields. For instance, railroads now decorate their trains with distinctive colors, shiplines are adopting attractive color schemes, and industrial plants are using various color schemes to improve production and increase employee efficiency.

The story of the establishment and growth of the dye industry in England and Germany in the latter part of the nineteenth century and in this country after World War I is well known. Advances in the somewhat closely related field of colored pigments, especially synthetic products, although less spectacular, have been equally important. Basically, the difference between dyes and pigments lies in their field of use. The chief application of dyes is in the textile industries; pigments are used for paint, printing ink, floor coverings, and other applications demanding the use of insoluble colored materials with physical properties to give finished products which will meet specific requirements.

While certain products, still in use, originated in the days of the alchemist, the majority are recent developments. Pigment research, particularly during the past twenty-five years, has resulted in substantial advances not only in the development of new pigments but in the improvement of existing ones to meet the demand both by the public and the color stylist for brighter, more attractive, and more durable colors.

From a technical viewpoint, the field is one of considerable complexity. The paint technologist has at hand today a large number of pigments, both inorganic and organic, covering the entire spectral range and differing widely in physical properties. It is the purpose of this chapter to review briefly the products which are now available, with emphasis on the current developments. For our discussion, the simplified classification given below is helpful.

CLASSIFICATION OF SYNTHETIC PIGMENT COLORS

Inorganic Types
  Chromates
    Chrome Yellow
    Chrome Orange
    Molybdate Orange
    Zinc Yellow
  Ferrocyanides
    Iron Blue
    Copper Ferrocyanide Maroon
  Mixed Chromate and Ferrocyanide
    Chrome Green
Organic Types
  Azo Types
    Pigment Dyes
      Toluidine Red
      Para Reds, Chlorinated Para Reds
      Arylide Reds and Maroons
      Hansa Yellow
    Precipitated Pigments
      Lithol Reds
      BON Reds and Maroons
    Metallo-Azo Compound
      Nickel-Azo Yellow
  Non-azo Types
    Basic Dye Lakes—Phosphotungstic and Phosphomolybdic Acid Types
    Indanthrones—Blue and Violet
    Phthalocyanines—Blue and Green

INORGANIC PIGMENTS

Chromates

The chromate group includes some of the most important synthetic inorganic pigments. The preparation of the first three, the lead chromate pigments, is based on the following reactions:

(1) $Pb^{++} + CrO_4^= \longrightarrow PbCrO_4$

(2) $Pb^{++} + SO_4^= \longrightarrow PbSO_4$

(3) $2Pb^{++} + 2OH^- + CrO_4^= \longrightarrow PbO \cdot PbCrO_4 + H_2O$

(4) $Pb^{++} + MoO_4^= \longrightarrow PbMoO_4$

Reaction (1) results in *medium chrome yellow,* a normal lead chromate, existing in the monoclinic crystal form; it is the reddest, strongest, and most widely used of the chrome yellows.

Reactions (1) and (2) result in solid solutions of lead chromate and lead sulfate, also in the monoclinic form, and are known as *light yellows;* they are lighter, weaker, and greener than the medium yellows. Precipitation of the lead chromate–lead sulfate mixtures in the rhombic form rather than the monoclinic form yields the so-called *primrose* and *lemon* yellows; they are even greener than the light yellows and generally are poorer in light-fastness.

The chrome yellows are widely used because of their brightness, high strength, opacity, wide range of hues, and low cost. They darken, however, on exposure to light; this disadvantage for certain applications has long been recognized by both the pigment manufacturer and consumer. Considerable research has been devoted to the fundamental mechanisms involved in the darkening of lead chromate, and much progress has been made in the past ten years to improve the light-fastness of these pigments. Precipitation of hydrated metallic oxides on the lead chromate crystal has resulted in pigments more stable to light.[1,2,3] These improvements enable the paint manufacturer to use chrome yellows in certain formulas today where they were excluded some years ago.

Reaction (3), or (3) in combination with (1), yields *chrome oranges* which differ chemically from chrome yellow in that they contain substantial amounts of basic lead chromate. The depth of a chrome orange depends on (a) the basicity of the final product and (b) particle size. High basicity and large particle size favor the formation of redder and weaker products. The reddest products are somewhat sensitive to grinding conditions; overgrinding may produce yellowness and increased strength. All chrome oranges are precipitated in the tetragonal crystal configuration.

Chrome oranges possess excellent exterior durability and good light-fastness, and are equal to chrome yellow in this property. They are useful for formulating economical paints and enamels where only a moderate degree of brightness is required. They are also used in certain metal protective primers, and for this purpose the most basic (the reddest) types are usually used.

Reactions (1), (2) and (4) occurring simultaneously give rise to *molybdate orange,* a tetragonal form of lead chromate. The molybdate oranges are much more brilliant than the chrome oranges and possess greater tinting strength and opacity; their light-fastness is similar to that of chrome yellow. The low cost, high tinting strength, opacity, and outstanding color intensity of molybdate orange render it ideal for use as a single pigment or in combination with other red pigments.

Zinc yellow is a complex basic potassium zinc chromate which has found wide acceptance as a metal protective pigment. It can be prepared according to the following equation:

$$4ZnO + 2K_2Cr_2O_7 + 2HCl + 2H_2O \rightarrow 4ZnO \cdot 4CrO_3 \cdot K_2O \cdot 3H_2O + 2KCl$$

Zinc yellow possesses two distinctive properties which contribute to its success as a metal protective pigment:
(1) Its basic character, which enables it to neutralize acid products developed during corrosion processes.
(2) Its ability to release soluble chromate ions which retard corrosion by passivating metal surfaces.

It is outstandingly effective as a pigment in corrosion-resistant primers for nonferrous metals as well as for iron and steel. Its reputation has been greatly enhanced by experience in World War II, and its use is steadily expanding.

Zinc yellow can also be blended with phthalocyanine pigments to prepare green trim paints of the shades popularly known as "Jade Green," "Apple Green," etc. These blends are brighter and considerably more resistant to darkening than the ordinary chrome greens or similar blends with lead chromate pigments. They are, of course, more expensive than chrome greens but they are being used in high-grade finishes because of their light-fastness and superior performance.

Ferrocyanides

The *iron blues,* variously known as prussian, chinese, and milori blues, are complex ferric ferrocyanides containing an alkali metal or ammonia in the crystal lattice. The formation is normally carried out in two stages, represented by the following fundamental chemical reactions:

$$FeSO_4 + Na_4Fe(CN)_6 + (NH_4)_2SO_4 \longrightarrow \underset{\text{\textit{White Precipitate}}}{Fe(NH_4)_2Fe(CN)_6} + 2Na_2SO_4$$

$$6Fe(NH_4)_2Fe(CN)_6 + NaClO_3 + 3H_2SO_4 \longrightarrow$$
$$\underset{\text{\textit{Iron Blue}}}{6Fe(NH_4)Fe(CN)_6} + NaCl + 3(NH_4)_2SO_4 + 3H_2O.$$

The oxidation reaction occurs rather readily and is reversible to some extent. This tendency to be reduced explains the occasional fading or loss of color of iron blues observed in certain paint systems.

Chinese blue is characterized by its clean or jet masstone and green tint. The milori blues are redder in masstone than the other types and are most widely favored as general purpose blues because of their inherently softer texture. Prussian blue is red in tint and finds its greatest use in the toning of black enamels.

Iron blues are very sensitive to alkali, and usually cannot be used in applications where alkali resistance is a factor. They have excellent durability in full shade but show a tendency to develop bronze on outdoor exposure; this is greatest for the milori and chinese blues and least for prussian blue. Color retention is excellent in dark or medium shades but decreases markedly in light tints. Iron blues are used extensively in paints and printing inks because of their low cost, permanence in dark shades, high strength, and resistance to water, acid, and organic media.

A newly developed inorganic maroon, a copper ferrocyanide pigment, has proven of interest to the paint industry. For many years, there has been a demand for an inexpensive pigment which could be used with the relatively expensive high quality organic reds and maroons to decrease enamel costs without sacrificing color and durability significantly. Commercial iron oxides have not been acceptable for this purpose because they impair gloss and color intensity. The new pigment, on the other hand, retains desirable color, light-fastness, and chalking-resistance properties. As a result, it is finding wide application in quality finishes.

Chrome Greens

Chrome greens are simply intimate mixtures of chrome yellow and iron blue. Families or "lines" of chrome greens are made by varying the proportions of blue to yellow and by changing the type of yellow used. The normal shades of chrome greens are made from chrome yellows stabilized in the rhombic form by means of special chemical agents known as restrainers which inhibit the change to the monoclinic form. The monoclinic type yellows produce "olive" chrome greens.

The general improvement in the light-fastness of chrome yellows and the development of new and controlled processes in the manufacture of chrome greens is reflected in the chrome greens of improved light-fastness and working properties on the market today.

Chrome greens are widely used because of their brightness, opacity, good light-fastness, excellent gloss retention, and relatively low cost. They are not permanent, however, in light tints and, for this reason, light-fast pigments such as copper phthalocyanine blue or green in combination with zinc yellow and chalk-resistant titanium dioxide are usually used instead.

Organic Pigments

For purposes of simplification, the large diverse group of organic pigments has been subdivided into two classes, namely, the azo and the non-azo pigments.

Azo Pigments

The azo pigments contain the characteristic chromophore group —N=N— and cover a wide range of color shades. These pigments are conveniently subdivided into two main classes, namely (1) pigment dyes and (2) precipitated pigments; each will be discussed separately.

Pigment Dyes. The azo pigment dyes include those products which are insoluble in the reaction medium (water) directly upon formation. As a class, they are somewhat soluble in organic solvents and vehicles, and therefore will bleed in some systems. Included in this group are red, orange, yellow, and maroon pigments, of which several will be considered.

Toluidine Red. Toluidine red is the azo coupling of diazotized *m*-nitro-*p*-toluidine with β-naphthol.

The physical nature of this one chemical structure can be varied to produce several toluidine reds varying from light masstone with yellow undertone to dark masstone with blue undertone. Rate of coupling, pH, concentrations, and use of accessory agents are important variables in their preparation. The toluidine reds are characterized by their brilliance, high strength, resistance to acids and alkalis, and ease of dispersion. They produce enamels of excellent film durability and light-fastness, and are frequently used as standards by which other red pigments are measured.

Para Red. The para reds are darker and bluer than the toluidine reds, and less permanent to light. Chemically, they are couplings of diazotized *p*-nitraniline with β-naphthol.

Two types are well recognized, Para Y, the lighter and yellower type, and Para B, the darker and bluer one. The latter is usually obtained by substitution of an accessory agent for part of the β-naphthol. Since the para reds are lower in cost than toluidine reds, they are widely used in the red range where the extra toluidine durability is not required, for example, in farm implement finishes. Their use is limited because of their bad bleeding characteristics.

Chlorinated Para Red. Chlorinated para red is a light red pigment the value of which perhaps is not fully appreciated in the paint trade. There are two types: the *o*-chlor-*p*-nitraniline coupled with β-naphthol, and the *p*-chlor-*o*-nitraniline coupling sometimes referred to as Parachlor Red (formula below).

The *p*-chlor-*o*-nitraniline product is superior to the *o*-chlor-*p*-nitraniline product in masstone and extension light-fastness; in fact, it is even more light-fast than toluidine red. It is an outstanding versatile pigment; when blended with medium chrome yellow, oranges of good light-fastness are obtained.

Arylide Reds and Maroons. This class of pigments covers a wide range of colors from light reds to dark maroons. *Toluidine maroon* will serve as an illustration. It is formed by coupling the diazo of *m*-nitro-*p*-toluidine with the meta-nitroanilide of β-hydroxynaphthoic acid and has the structure:

Toluidine maroon is primarily used for automotive pyroxalin lacquer finishes; it has the curious and as yet unexplained effect of causing early failure in alkyd systems. Other members of this family of pigments show very good performance in both lacquer and enamel systems.

Of particular interest in this class of pigments is a relatively new product which is marketed under the name Arylide Maroon Med. RT-566-D.* It possesses an intense blue undertone, excellent light-fastness, and satisfactory working properties for lacquer and enamels. This pigment, when used alone or in combination with other pigments, produces durable finishes which meet exacting automotive requirements. It is widely used for automotive production line and refinish metallic enamels because of the highly desirable "two-tone" or "flash" effects obtained.

Hansa Yellows. Chemically, the hansa yellows are azo couplings with the arylides of aceto acetic ester. They can be prepared in a series of shades with increasing greenness: Hansa Yellow G, 3G, 5G, and 10G. The structure of Hansa Yellow G is:

There is a growing field for hansa yellows in the formulation of toy enamels in which a demand for lead-free pigments is frequently encountered. They possess greater strength than chrome yellows but the hiding power is lower; the Hansa yellow G is particularly light-fast in masstone.

Precipitated Pigments. The precipitated pigments include those azo products containing salt forming groups, principally sulfonic acid, which require precipitation of the pigment with metallic salts. The salts most commonly used include those of sodium, barium, calcium, strontium, and manganese. In general, this class of pigments is sensitive to the action of alkalies; however, they are nonbleeding, which makes them highly desirable for applications where bleeding must be avoided.

Lithol Reds. One of the more important members of the precipitated pigment dye group is lithol red. The lithol reds comprise a family of pigments prepared by coupling the diazo of β-naphthylamine α-sulfonic acid (Tobias acid) with β-naphthol.

* E. I. DuPont de Nemours and Co. (Inc.), Pigment Department.

They require precipitation with metallic salts to render them completely insoluble; barium produces light reds, calcium darker and bluer shades.

Lithol reds are the most economical organic reds available, and are widely used where brilliancy, hiding, and low cost are of primary importance, as in toy enamels, dipping enamels, and general industrial applications where good durability is not required. They are used only for interior work since they check and fade badly on exterior exposure.

BON Reds and Maroons. A very important group of pigments is that known as the BON Reds and Maroons. This name is derived from the fact that β-hydroxynaphthoic acid serves as the coupling component for an entire family of pigments varying in shade from a toluidine red to a dark maroon. A typical example follows:

$$\left[\underset{SO_3^-}{\text{naphthalene}} - N = N - \underset{OH\ COO^-}{\text{naphthalene}} \right] Ca^{++}$$

These pigments are well recognized for their bleed resistance in most commercial organic vehicles and for their light-fastness. They can be interblended with one another to give intermediate shades; usually, the most satisfactory shades are obtained if adjacent members of the "family" are used as components of the blend.

A relatively new addition to the BON pigments is the product marketed under the name BON Red Dark RT-525-D.* This pigment alone, or in combination with chalk-resistant rutile titanium dioxide or medium chrome yellow, has demonstrated very good light-fastness. The desirable properties of the BON pigments, plus their moderate cost, have enabled them to attain great popularity for quality decorative finishes.

Another example of a BON type pigment is lithol rubine. It is the calcium salt of diazotized p-toluidine-m-sulfonic acid coupled to β-hydroxynaphthoic acid.

$$\left[CH_3 - \underset{SO_3^-}{\text{benzene}} - N = N - \underset{OH\ COO^-}{\text{naphthalene}} \right] Ca^{++}$$

It is a dark red with a blue undertone and is usually resinated to enhance the depth and brilliance of the color. Lithol rubine has the unusual property of blending with light reds without obtaining the dull shades usually associated with such blends. In combination with para-

* E. I. DuPont de Nemours and Co. (Inc.), Pigment Dept.

chlor red or molybdate orange it produces a wide range of bright shades
of good durability. It can also be used as a self-color for decorative
enamels not requiring the highest degree of exterior durability.

Metallo-Azo Complexes. One of the most outstanding pigment developments in recent years is the product marketed under the name Green-
Gold. This pigment is a nickel azo yellow wherein the nickel, instead
of forming a salt, is believed to form a coordinate bond with the azo
linkage and other polar groups present in the molecule. Its masstone is
green and its tint is yellow. It has excellent light, heat, bleed, and chemical resistance.

This new development in the field of yellow pigments compares in
importance with the advent of the phthalocyanine pigments; it is far
superior in permanency to any other yellow pigment available. Unlike
other organic yellows, it is light-fast in masstone, tint, and metallics. The
unique color effects obtained with this pigment have resulted in its wide
acceptance by the automotive finishes industry.

Non-Azo Pigments

The non-azo pigments cover a wide variety of chemical species, and
we shall limit ourselves to a discussion of the types of most interest to
a paint technologist.

Basic Dye Lakes. Basic dyes are basic in character because of the
presence of free or substituted amino groups in the molecule. A series of
tungstated and molybdated pigments can be prepared by precipitating
basic dyestuffs with such acids as phosphotungstic, phosphomolybdic, or
other heteropoly complex acids, either separately or in combination. A
typical structure may be represented as follows:

$$
\left[\,C \begin{array}{c} -\langle\ \rangle -N(CH_3)_2 \\ -\langle\ \rangle -N(CH_3)_2 \\ -\langle\ \rangle -N(CH_3)_2 \\ | \\ + \end{array}\,\right]_6 \quad O_3 \cdot P_2O_5 \cdot 24WO_3
$$

In general, the *phosphotungstic acid pigments* (PTA's) are superior
in light-fastness to the corresponding *phosphomolybdic acid pigments*
(PMA's), although the latter possess greater strength. They are brilliant
high strength colors with good light resistance, but are not considered
sufficiently light-fast to permit their use under severe exterior exposure
conditions.

Indanthrones. *Indanthrone blue*, a vat dye type product, consists of
two anthraquinone nuclei linked through NH groups, e.g.

It possesses excellent durability in both lacquer and enamel systems; the light-fastness is outstanding even when highly extended with prime white pigments. Although less brilliant in color than copper phthalocyanine blue, it bronzes to a lesser degree. It finds application in automotive finishes, sign enamels, and other quality finishes.

A recent development in the field of indanthrone pigments is a dibenzanthrone violet which is marketed under the name Platinum-Violet.* Its light-fastness and durability characteristics are somewhat comparable to those of the copper phthalocyanine pigments. It is especially useful for toning high quality blue and gray enamels, and for developing durable colored finishes of unusual hue and brilliance for the automotive finishes industry.

Phthalocyanine Pigments. The phthalocyanine pigments are distinguished by their excellent fastness to light, exceptionally high tinting strength, extreme stability to heat, and by their resistance to the action of various chemical agents. The structure of the copper phthalocyanine molecule is represented by:

* E. I. DuPont de Nemours and Co. (Inc.), Pigment Dept.

Difficulties have been experienced in the past with flocculation and crystallization which occurred in certain *copper phthalocyanine blue* dispersions, but great progress has been made in overcoming these deficiencies. Pigments considerably improved in flocculation resistance have been developed in recent years, and lakes prepared with aluminum benzoate are now available which are almost completely free from flocculation tendencies in most enamel systems. Another outstanding development has been the preparation of crystal stable types which do not lose strength or color on storage of enamels.

Copper phthalocyanine green is derived from the blue by chlorination, i.e., replacement of fourteen or fifteen of the hydrogen atoms in the molecule with chlorine. The phthalocyanine pigments, both blue and green, are gaining wide use in decorative enamels, automotive finishes, trim paints, and other applications where excellent light-fastness and chemical inertness are required.

References

1. Horning, S. C., U.S. Pat. 2,212,917, Aug. 27, 1940.
2. Botti, E. C., U.S. Pat. 2,365,171, Dec. 19, 1944.
3. Huckle, W. G., and Polzer, C. G., U.S. Pat. 2,316,244, April 13, 1943.
4. Kovalnes, D. E., and Woodward, H. E., U.S. Pat. 2,396,327, March 12, 1946.

9 : Vinyl Resins for Organic Protective Coatings

PART A: GENERAL THEORY OF FORMULATION

R. W. QUARLES

Mellon Institute
Pittsburgh, Pennsylvania

Vinyl Resins

In the broadest sense one can classify as a vinyl polymer any resin made by polymerizing compounds containing the vinyl group $H_2C{=}CHX$. Into this classification fall almost a third of the synthetic resins made in this country in 1950 for use in plastics, coatings, and adhesives. This broad classification would include polymers and copolymers of styrene, ethylene, and acrylic esters as well as those of vinyl chloride and vinyl esters. Industry treats the first three as individual classes of resins because they each have properties which distinguish them from the vinyl chloride copolymers, which were the first of the vinyls to achieve industrial significance. It is these vinyl chloride copolymers that make up the bulk of the resins used in vinyl surface coatings.

The first mention in the literature of vinyl compounds was a description of vinyl chloride by Regnault in 1835. Three years later he disclosed the polymerization of vinylidene chloride to a resin, but it was not until 1872 that the polymerization of vinyl chloride was reported by Baumann. The work of Ostromysslenskii in 1912 marks the modern development of the vinyl chloride resins. Industrial exploitation of the vinyls began with the work of Carbide and Carbon Chemicals Corporation in 1927; pilot production dates from 1933 and large-scale commercial production facilities were placed in service in 1936 for the manufacture of a vinyl chloride-vinyl acetate copolymer.

There was a period of slow development necessitated by the radically new techniques required with the vinyl resins. Ten years ago they entered a period of rapid growth. Although new production facilities were built every year, the supply has scarcely kept pace with the demand. Research has continued and new polymers and copolymers continue to be developed, widening the fields in which the vinyls are used.

One of the earliest large uses for the vinyl resins was in the coatings industry as a lining for beer cans. Other coatings applications have followed, so that the use of vinyls in coatings has kept pace with their use in the plastics field. The actual extent to which these resins are used would astonish most paint men because very often these coating applications have channelled through specialty coatings manufacturers rather than through the conventional paint plants. Just as the vinyls brought new practices and products to the plastics industry, such as calendering of flexible film and elastomeric molded objects, they are now bringing new techniques to the coatings field. Wash primers, organosols, plastisols, and hydrosols are examples of new tools which the coatings formulator is using to widen the fields into which his products go.

Chemistry of the Vinyl Resins

From the many studies of the preparation and the structure of vinyl polymers, evidence indicates that the vinyl monomers form a chain of carbon atoms along which the substituents are spaced in a regular order. Predominantly the polymers consist of a single chain of atoms, although certain anomalies have been interpreted as evidence of some branching of the chain. In any individual type of polymer the toughness, tensile strength, and viscosity in solution increases with increasing chain length. The intrinsic viscosity which is a measure of the chain length is now widely used in characterizing resins.

Other properties of vinyl resins depend on the substituents along the chain. If the substituents are small so that the chains can pack closely, the resins are difficult to dissolve in solvents at room temperature. For example, polyethylene which has only hydrogen atoms on the chain is so readily packed into a lattice that the films are partially crystalline. Although the attractive forces between individual methylene groups in adjoining chains are small, the multiplicity of these van der Waals forces, evenly spaced, produces a strong over-all cohesion. Since the methylene groups have but little attraction for solvents, the resin chains are not readily solvated and separated by solvents at room temperature, and polyethylene is a relatively insoluble resin.

On the other hand, the multiplicity of different groups on the chain introduces randomness so that the chains cannot pack together readily. In this way the attack of solvents is facilitated and more soluble resins result. As an example, polyvinyl chloride is essentially insoluble in methyl ketones. The same is true for polyvinylidene chloride, but a copolymer of the two with equivalent chain length may be quite soluble. Substituent groups such as chlorine or hydroxyl introduce extensive hydrogen bonding between chains with the result that the chains are held together by powerful cohesive forces. Even highly plasticized films retain considerable tensile strength. These cohesive forces make the resin relatively insoluble and incompatible with other classes of resins. When two chlorine atoms are on the same carbon atom as in vinylidene chloride, the cohesion and the symmetry of the molecules increase to such an extent that films and filaments tend to crystallize when the molecules are oriented by stretching. This close packing decreases both the solubility and the vapor transmission to such an extent that the vinylidene chloride resins are outstanding among the organic films in their resistance to moisture vapor transmission.

Chlorine on the chain renders it nonflammable, but it increases the tendency for chloride to be split out from the resin chain by ultraviolet light and by heat. This tends to form a conjugated system of double bonds along the chain, which results in color development and eventually breakdown by oxidation. In practice the effect of ultraviolet light is eliminated by pigmentation. Thermal decomposition is prevented by the use of heat stabilizers such as the basic pigments, amino resins, or organic stabilizers containing glycidyl groups.

When the polymer is made up of vinyl esters such as vinyl acetate, the resin is quite soluble in almost all classes of organic solvents. Films become sticky, soft, and adherent with small percentages of plasticizer. If the esters are hydrolyzed so that hydroxyl groups are on the chain, the resin can be made water-soluble and insoluble in all classes of organic solvents. Small proportions of hydroxyl groups improve the compatibility of the resin with other classes of resins, improve the adhesion to many surfaces such as cellulosic materials, raise the softening point, and increase the tensile strength and shock resistance.

Carboxyl groups on the chain in very small proportions improve the adhesion to metallic surfaces.[12] They contribute a degree of chemical reactivity which permits reaction with resins and basic pigments. Larger proportions of carboxyl groups render the resin soluble in aqueous alkalis. If the carboxyl group is esterified, the solubility in organic solvents increases with the size of the alkyl group.

Copolymerization of two or more monomers introduces intermediate properties into the resin as well as rendering it more soluble. The first of the commercial copolymers was the vinyl chloride and vinyl acetate resin. The judicious balance of properties makes it one of our most versatile resins and sparked the growth of the vinyl resin industry. Most of the polymeric resins used by the coatings industry are copolymers or even tripolymers so as to obtain the balance in properties demanded in a surface coating.

Properties of the Vinyl Resins

Vinyl resins present a unique combination of properties which make them of value in the coatings field. The resins are free from taste or odor and are of a low order of toxicity which makes them useful in the field of sanitary coatings. Since they are thermoplastic, they can be utilized for heat-sealable coatings. They are resistant to aging and weathering. Once the film is freed from solvents, there is no embrittlement or shrinkage because the resins are nonoxidizing. Properly pigmented films exhibit excellent durability on exterior exposure because the chains are not readily degraded. The toughness, flexibility, and excellent adhesion permit coated articles to be crimped, spun, or otherwise fabricated without disturbing the coating. The resins are water-white in color, permitting a wide range of stable colors to be prepared from them. The vinyl resins in which vinyl chloride is the predominant constituent exhibit extreme chemical inertness. Films are not attacked at room temperature by inorganic acids or alkalis. They are insoluble in oils, greases, aliphatic hydrocarbons, and alcohols. They are resistant to water and aqueous salt solutions.

Classification of Solution Coatings Resins

For simplicity it is well to classify the vinyl resins that are used in solution coatings into groups according to their properties and usage. One such classification is:

> Group I: Chlorine-containing resins without reactive groups
>> a. Vinyl chloride-acetate copolymers
>>> "Vinylite" Resin VYLF — low viscosity type
>>> "Vinylite" Resin VYHH — medium viscosity type
>>> "Vinylite" Resin VYNS — high viscosity type
>> b. Vinyl chloride-vinylidene chloride copolymers
>>> "Geon" Resin 200 $\times$ 20 — low viscosity type
>> c. Acrylonitrile-vinylidene chloride copolymers
>>> "Saran" F-120 resin — 40 cp grade
>>> "Saran" F-120 resin — 200 cp grade
>>> "Saran" F-120 resin — 1,000 cp grade
>>> "Saran" F-120 resin — 8,000 cp grade
>
> Group II: Vinyl chloride resins with reactive groups
>> a. Vinyl chloride-acetate-maleic acid resin
>>> "Vinylite" Resin VMCH — medium viscosity type
>> b. Vinyl chloride-acetate-alcohol resin
>>> "Vinylite" Resin VAGH — medium viscosity type

Group III: Vinyl acetal resins
  a. Vinyl formal resin
     "Formvar" Resin
  b. Vinyl butyral resin
     "Vinylite" Resin XYHL
     "Butvar" Resin
     "Butacite" Resin

Group IV: Miscellaneous vinyl resins
  a. Vinyl acetate polymers
     "Vinylite," "Gelva," and "Elvacet" resins of various grades
  b. Vinyl chloride-acetate resins of 60–62% vinyl chloride
     "Vinylite" Resin VYCC — low viscosity type
  c. Acrylic ester resins
     "Acryloid" A10, B7, B72, B75, C10 and F10

In addition to the resins noted in Groups Ia and Ib, there are other copolymers of the "Vinylite" V series and "Geon" 200 series of resins which are designed primarily for hot-processing resins but which have on occasion been used in coatings to achieve special properties.

The resins of Group IV will not be treated in detail here for lack of space. The vinyl acetate resins find little applications in finishes but are widely used in adhesives. They are compatible with nitrocellulose and are sometimes used to increase its ease of heat-sealing in paper lacquers. The vinyl chloride-acetate resin of lower chloride content (VYCC resin) is manufactured for use in pyroxylin lacquers to increase resistance to alcohol, perspiration, and cold checking.

The acrylic ester resins are noted for their good color and color retention. In other properties and chemical resistance they resemble the vinyl chloride copolymers of Group I. Blends of vinyls and acrylics are often used. Clear finishes frequently are formulated around the acrylics, often with the addition of resin VMCH to improve air dry adhesion. They are also used in pyroxylin finishes where good color and color retention are important.

Solubility Characteristics of Vinyl Chloride Copolymers

The vinyl chloride copolymers classified in the first and second groups of resins require relatively strong solvents for solution. The resins of medium viscosity are usually prepared as 20 to 25 per cent resin base solutions. Solvents comprise about half the thinner and these are almost invariably ketones. For fast-evaporating thinners used on paper, cloth, or porous surfaces, methyl ethyl ketone or less frequently acetone is the solvent. Spray finishes are usually formulated around methyl isobutyl ketone. Methyl ethyl ketone may be used to modify the thinner for air-dry coatings over porous surfaces. Baking-type metal finishes are often

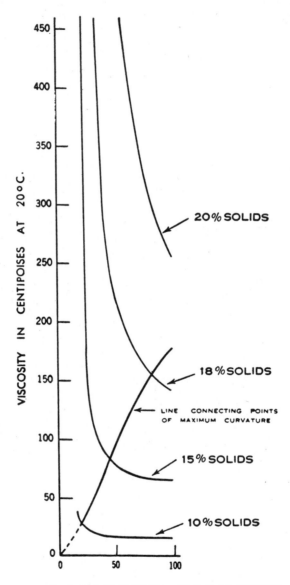

Figure 9.1. Equilibrium viscosities: "Vinylite" resin VYHH in methyl isobutyl ketone—toluene mixtures.

modified with slower ketones such as cyclohexanone or ethyl butyl ketone to improve the flow-out. Roller coatings are usually formulated around isophorone. Nitroparaffins are also excellent solvents for the resins, and esters which are free from alcohols are also used to extend the ketones or to modify the drying rate.

Aromatic hydrocarbons are used as diluents. *Aliphatic diluents are to be avoided since they are powerful precipitants for the vinyl resins.* Figure 9.1 indicates the manner in which the viscosity of solutions of resin VYHH varies as the methyl isobutyl ketone in the thinner is gradually replaced

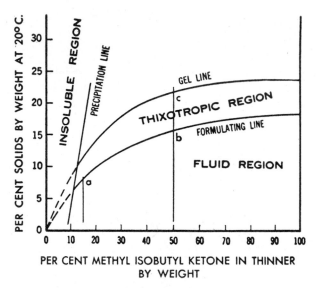

Figure 9.2. Phase diagram: "Vinylite" resin VYHH in methyl isobutyl ketone— toluene mixtures.

with toluene. Figure 9.2 shows the phase changes which occur as the resin content and the thinner compositions change. It will be apparent from a study of these diagrams that the resin has an apparently shifting dilution ratio. High solids solutions require richer thinners. For this reason base solutions are prepared at 20 to 25 per cent resin content from thinners containing about equal parts of ketone and aromatic hydrocarbon. Further thinning to spray viscosity can be accomplished with aromatic hydrocarbon alone. Usually, reducing thinners will carry 5 per cent ketone to prevent local precipitation during dilution. Figures 9.3 and 9.4 show similar data for isophorone. The sharp minimum viscosity is characteristic of the cyclic ketones.[7] Formulations containing more hydrocarbon than that corresponding to the minimum viscosity composition are often

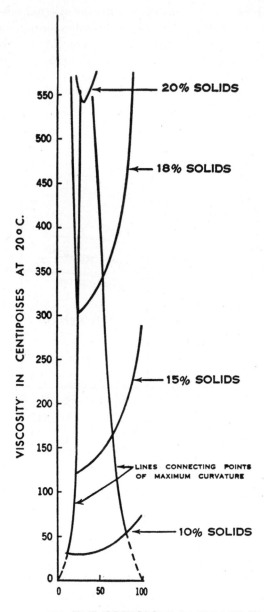

Figure 9.3. Equilibrium viscosities: "Vinylite" resin VYHH in isophorone—xylene mixtures.

used for roll coating. A certain measure of reflow of roll marks is obtained as the more volatile diluent evaporates and the composition approaches the viscosity optimum. The powerful solvent action of the cyclic ketones like cyclohexanone and isophorone is utilized to formulate novel baking finishes of better flow and gloss. Coatings are prepared with resin contents in the neighborhood of 25 per cent which utilize these high-boiling ketones as in the case of formulating for roll coating. These finishes will have a Ford Cup No. 4 viscosity of 200 to 400 seconds. Reduction to spray

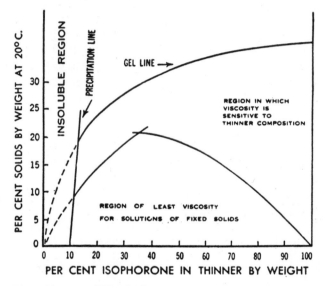

Figure 9.4.   Phase diagram: "Vinylite" resin VYHH in isophorone—xylene mixtures

is made with a very fast solvent such as acetone. In this manner the lacquer may be sprayed at 60 to 80 seconds viscosity using air pressures of 90 to 100 psi and fluid pressures of 20 to 30 psi. Surprisingly, the material does not sag despite the excessive amounts of high boilers, and with good air flow in the ovens it is possible to bake the coating free from solvents at temperatures of 250 to 300°F. A similar technique is just now showing promise in the pyroxylin lacquer field.

All the medium viscosity vinyl resins show similar viscosity behavior, with minor exceptions such as the increased tolerance of alcohol and glycol-ether solvents by resin VAGH. The vinylidene chloride-acrylonitrile resins differ to the extent that they do not tolerate as large percentages of aromatic hydrocarbons.[11]

The resins classified as high-viscosity types and many special vinyl resins of high vinyl chloride content and high molecular weight are formulated in thinners which are richer in ketones. Often hot solutions are used to reduce the viscosity, and the ketones of higher solvency such as the cyclic and unsaturated types are preferred.

The resins classed as low-viscosity types are used where it is possible to sacrifice some film strength in favor of higher solids solutions with resulting economies and better gloss. These resins can be prepared as base solutions with about 40 per cent resin in the conventional thinners used with the medium-viscosity grades. At solids contents of 20 to 25 per cent, weaker thinners can be used. With one resin, "Geon" 200 $\times$ 20, it is possible to prepare solutions in toluene alone.

In the preparation of solutions of the vinyl chloride resins it is common practice to include about 0.2 per cent propylene oxide in the thinner as a precaution against traces of acid in either the resin or the thinner which may result in corrosion of the container and the consequent discoloration of the resin solution.

Plasticizers for Vinyl Resins

The wide use of plasticized vinyl compounds has led to the development of a large number of excellent plasticizers for these resins. The most important of these are the phthalates, phosphates, and linear polyester types. Solution coatings generally require 10 to 20 per cent plasticizer based on the resin weight, although some of the thinner coatings utilize none. Di-2-ethylhexyl phthalate and tricresyl phosphate are the most widely used materials. Compatibility; color retention; nonvolatility; and resistance to water, oil, and chemicals are the properties generally required. Freedom from taste, odor, or toxicity is important for those plasticizers used in sanitary finishes.

Paper and cloth coatings and other highly flexible products require larger amounts of plasticizer. Flexibility at low temperatures, color, extractability, and heat and light stability are additional properties that are often important in these applications. The very extensive work of Dr. M. C. Reed[13,14,15] should be consulted for detailed information on the properties of plasticized films as a guide to the choice of particular plasticizers for a specific use.

Pigmented Vinyl Solutions

Pigmented vinyl finishes resemble pyroxylin lacquers in formulation and preparation. Pigments of maximum hiding power are preferred in order to prevent too great a change in film properties due to the bulk of the pigment in the film. Fillers and extenders are seldom used.

Most of the common pigments can be used in the vinyl chloride resins with the exception of those pigments containing iron and zinc. These latter pigments are avoided in finishes baked above 300°F because they catalyze the thermal degradation of the resin. Certain of the synthetic iron oxide pigments and zinc oxide pigments have been used successfully in air-dry and low-bake coatings, but the finishes must be formulated so as to have adequate opacity to ultraviolet light and enough basic pigment to insure that the film remains basic. With such precautions, zinc oxide improves the hardness of vinyl films and markedly retards chalking on Florida exposure.

The vinyl resins are neutral and nonreactive toward pigments with the exception of resins containing reactive acid groups. Nevertheless, dispersion of pigments in the resin is somewhat more troublesome than that in pyroxylin lacquers, because, as a class, the vinyl resins do not readily wet pigments. Since there is seldom enough plasticizer to serve as a dispersing medium, pigments must be dispersed in the vinyl resin. Intensive shearing forces are required to give glossy finishes. Best results are obtained if the pigment is dispersed in a fluxed mass of resin and plasticizer on a 2-roll rubber mill. Table 9.1 presents typical compositions ground in

TABLE 9.1. TYPICAL PIGMENTED BASES

Titanium dioxide	75	—	—	—
Chrome Yellow	—	80	—	—
Phthalocyanine Blue	—	—	25	—
Carbon black	—	—	—	20
Resin VYHH	17	15	65	65.8
Di-2-ethylhexyl phthalate	8	5	10	14
Amine 220	—	—	—	0.2
Per cent by weight	100	100	100	100.0

this manner. These pigment chips are converted to pastes by soaking in a small amount of solvent and then stirring until a smooth consistency is obtained.

Thinners with inadequate solvent power are to be avoided for dispersing the chips if the best gloss is desired. The pastes may be reduced with base solutions and plasticizers to prepare pigmented finishes.

Internal mixers are also effective in dispersing pigments in viscous resin solutions, and with whites the color may be better. Ball and pebble mills are effective in developing gloss with only a limited number of pigments. With some colors it is necessary to disperse the pigment in a thinner with wetting agent and then add a resin solution toward the end of the grind.

GROUP I RESINS:

Baking Coatings

The vinyl resins which do not contain carboxyl or other strongly polar groups require baking at high temperatures to develop adhesion to smooth surfaces. The resin must reach a temperature of 350 to 375°F during the bake. A long bake at a low temperature does not develop adhesion. The coating gels during the early stages of evaporation of solvent from the film. This gel shrinks during the latter stages of drying. The shrinkage presumably reduces the mechanical anchorage to the surface so that the film, which has a high cohesive strength, can be pulled off. It is believed that the bake at 350°F softens the gel to the extent that strains are released and it rewets the metal surface. These baked coatings exhibit excellent adhesion.

The temperature required to effect adhesion is in the range where the vinyl resin is thermally unstable and hydrogen chloride begins to split from the resin. Baked coatings must therefore be formulated to contain stabilizers. These are compounds which are capable of reacting with the liberated hydrogen chloride. This prevents attack on the metal substrate, as well as minimizing color development and film degradation. In the simplest case, lead pigments are used for a portion of the pigment. Sublimed white lead or blue lead are very satisfactory. Where lead pigments cannot be tolerated, urea-formaldehyde resins plasticized with nondrying alkyds are used to the extent of 2 to 5 per cent of the vinyl resin. In other instances epoxide compounds are often used. Many of the desirable stabilizers developed for calendering and extrusion of vinyls cannot be used in metal finishes because these stabilizers are often metallic soaps which detract from the adhesion to smooth surfaces.

When the baked system comprises two or more coats, it is necessary to bake only the primer at 350°F to establish adhesion. Subsequent coats knit well to the first and require baking only to speed the removal of residual solvents. This last bake need be only 250 to 300°F for which the topcoats require little stabilization.

The baked vinyl primer can often be replaced by a baked synthetic or oleo-resinous primer. While the adhesion of vinyls to these primers is usually adequate after a bake at 250 to 325°F, some improvement is obtained by blending vinyls containing hydroxyl groups in the formulation.

Baked vinyl finishes are preferred for applications where the maximum chemical resistance, hardness, and toughness are required. These finishes are widely used for cap and closure coatings, can and drum linings, appliance finishes, and chemical-resistant coatings.

Group II Resins:

Air-Dry Coatings

All the vinyl resins develop some measure of adhesion to porous or rough surfaces on air drying. Over smooth nonporous surfaces, however, it is important to formulate with one of the resins classified in Group II if adhesion must be obtained with air drying or low bakes. Smooth metal, glass, or ceramic surfaces require the use of resin with free carboxyl groups. As little as 10 per cent of the resin vehicle can be Resin VMCH, but common practice is to use 50 per cent or more. On surfaces containing old paint, on thermosetting plastic surfaces, and on cellulosic surfaces, the resins containing hydroxyl groups give somewhat better air-dry adhesion. Quite frequently air-dry coatings are formulated with blends of Resins VMCH and VAGH.

Resin Containing Carboxyl Groups

The formulation of air-dry coatings from Resin VMCH entails some care. *The solutions must be neutral.* Basic materials react with the carboxyl groups of the resin and destroy the ability to adhere. On the acid side, the solutions may corrode containers and often exhibit poorer adhesion. It is therefore particularly desirable to incorporate propylene oxide in the thinner formulation. Primers should be formulated with a pigment binder ratio on the low side of the normal range. For example, successful white primers will have 8 to 10 parts of titanium dioxide to 15 of resin. Basic pigments must be avoided in formulations containing Resin VMCH; otherwise livering, or gelation, will occur. These gels may be broken by the addition of certain acids such as maleic or citric but this destroys the ability of the resin to adhere without baking.

A certain amount of delay in the gelling of formulations containing basic pigments and Resin VMCH has been used to prepare insoluble coatings. Pigmented bases are prepared in neutral vinyl resins and these are thinned with a dilute solution of the reactive resin just before application. In this manner, certain rust-inhibitive pigments, otherwise unusable with VMCH resin, are incorporated into air-drying primers. The coating after drying becomes solvent-resistant.

When properly formulated and applied, coatings based on the maleic acid modified resin exhibit excellent performance on atmospheric exposure or immersion in fresh water. For salt water, the wash primer systems are preferred. Proper application entails the use of clean metal surfaces. Dirt, oils, grease, scale, or rust all detract from the ability of the resin to adhere.

Topcoats of any of the compatible vinyl resins can be applied over

VMCH resin primers without disturbing their bond to the underlying surface.

Vinyl Chloride-Acetate-Alcohol Resin

This is a new type of vinyl resin but one that has had a rapid growth. It differs from the other vinyl chloride copolymer resins in having a wider range of compatibility with oils, plasticizers, and other classes of resins. The hydroxyl groups present reactive positions through which the resin can be chemically modified or insolubilized. Furthermore, the polar groups aid in adhesion to certain classes of surfaces and resins.

An important class of air-dry, corrosion-resistant finishes has been developed by application of the hydroxyl-containing copolymer VAGH over the butyral wash primer. Here the VAGH resin is required to develop adhesion, although in some cases blends with VMCH are preferred. These finishes have been especially useful in applications where corrosion is quite severe. They have performed excellently in cases of salt water immersion and are the basis for the outstanding vinyl marine system. One of the principal features is the maintenance of adhesion around scratched areas, thereby preventing underfilm corrosion.

Formulation of these VAGH finishes is quite simple. Compositions contain resin with 10 to 20 per cent plasticizer and appropriate types and amounts of pigment. Table 9.2 shows a few typical formulations. Of these, the aluminum pigmentation gives the greatest resistance to moisture penetration and is therefore to be preferred for either fresh water immersion or atmospheric exposure. It has likewise shown excellent performance in salt water service, although red lead primers are generally used here.

Aluminum powders are dispersed by stirring into the vehicle. Other pigments are often pebble-milled into the resin solutions, but gloss reten-

TABLE 9.2. SOME TYPICAL VAGH FINISHES

"Vinylite" Resin VAGH	7.5	15.0	15.3
"Vinylite" Resin VMCH	7.5	—	—
Di-2-ethylhexyl phthalate	1.5	—	3.1
"Flexol" plasticizer TWS	—	1.5	—
Tricresyl phosphate	—	1.5	—
Aluminum powder	6.7	—	—
Red lead (98%)	—	22.0	—
Leaded zinc oxide (35%)	—	—	12.4
Titanium dioxide	—	—	6.1
Methyl isobutyl ketone	38.4	30.0	30.0
Toluene	38.4	30.0	33.1
	100.0	100.0	100.0

tion and freedom from chalking are improved if 2-roll mill chips are used. The special plasticizer combination in the red lead finish prolongs the color retention of this pigment over that obtained with conventional plasticizers. For underwater service it is often desirable to reduce the plasticizer proportions to about half those given in the table.

For atmospheric service, coatings of approximately 0.001 inch have given more than a year's service in industrial atmospheres and withstood 2,000 hours of salt spray testing. For rough surfaces or for more extreme service, coatings of 0.002 to 0.004 inch are preferred. These may be applied in multiple spray coats at intervals of 15 to 30 minutes.

Reacted Finishes Based on Hydroxyl Containing Resins

It is possible to produce varying amounts of insolubilization in vinyl resins containing hydroxyl groups through reaction on these groups. Resins such as ureas, melamines, or phenolics are quite effective. Diglycidyl compounds and the glycidyl resins will react to cause cross linkage under alkaline conditions. Blends of amine resins and glycidyl compounds with resin VAGH are used extensively to prepare vinyl finishes of better resistance to steam processing and to marring at elevated temperature.

Various other chemical reagents insolubilize resin VAGH, although these reactions have not been utilized commercially to any important extent. Many rubber accelerators, polybasic acids, glyoxal, dimethylol urea, and diisocyanates are a few of the compounds which are effective.

With VAGH resin it is possible to use vinyl resins to fortify other types of finishes. Alkyds and oleoresinous and phenolic varnishes dry tack-free in shorter times if the vinyl resin is present. The water, acid, alkali, and abrasion resistance of alkyds is improved in most instances, even in air-dry coatings. Gloss retention is also improved.

Baked alkyd finishes on caps and closures are improved in forming characteristics if 25 to 30 per cent VAGH resin is incorporated in the formulation. Three-component blends of alkyd, urea, and vinyl resins have also given good exposure service.

Group III Resins:

Vinyl acetal resins are secondary vinyl resins in that they are made from polyvinyl acetate by hydrolysis and reaction of some of the resulting hydroxyl groups with aldehydes. Commercially, two types of resin are important: the formaldehyde and butyraldehyde types. Neither resin has extensive use in coatings, but they are important for certain specific applications. The formaldehyde resin, manufactured under the name "Formvar," is widely used for wire enamels in admixture with phenolic resins. The butyral resin is manufactured primarily for safety glass under the names "Butvar," "Butacite," and "Vinylite." Low-viscosity grades are used with phenolic baking resins to improve flexibility and adhesion for applications such as wood sealers, can coatings, and adhesives. The butyral resins find their widest coatings use in a type of metal pretreatment called "wash primers."

Wash Primers

The wash primer technique is one of the most important postwar advances in corrosion protection. Mr. L. R. Whiting found that by pigmenting an alcoholic solution of vinyl butyral resin with a rust-inhibitive pigment, basic zinc chromate, and then diluting with phosphoric acid just before use, a primer was obtained which adhered to steel and provided an excellent rust-inhibitive base for subsequent finishes.[16] Coatings as thin as 0.0001 to 0.0003 inch were adequate to prevent underfilm creepage of rust. The primer is equally effective over other metallic surfaces such as aluminum, zinc, cadmium, tin, and stainless steel. While it is effective in improving the performance of almost all classes of finishes, the most spectacular corrosion protection is afforded if the wash primer is overcoated with a vinyl resin such as resin VAGH.

TABLE 9.3. TYPICAL WASH PRIMER FORMULATIONS

Basic zinc chromate	8.6	—	2.9
Lead chromate	—	8.6	5.7
Asbestine 3X	1.3	1.4	1.4
Lampblack	.1	—	—
Resin XYHL	9.0	9.0	9.0
Butanol	20.0	—	13.0
Isopropanol (99% grade)	61.0	53.0	53.0
Methyl isobutyl ketone	—	13.0	—
	100.0	85.0	85.0
Concentrated phosphoric acid	4.5	2.9	3.4
Water	4.0	2.9	3.4
Isopropanol (99% grade)	16.5	9.2	8.2
	25.0	15.0	15.0

Originally, the wash primer technique was developed for underwater finishes where it has given extraordinary service. The vinyl underwater finish on one test vessel inspected in October 1950, after completing five years' service was pronounced in excellent condition and left in service. This should be compared with the average prewar service of six months to one year for anticorrosive and antifouling coatings.

The wash primer technique has been explored further, especially to eliminate the necessity of adding acid just before use. While as yet there has been no single primer developed with the same versatility as the original wash primer (called WP-1), a number of types have been developed for special uses. Noteworthy is a method of treating butyral resin with chromic and phosphoric acids to develop a one-package clear primer. For service over steel under conditions of high humidity or fresh water immersion, especially at elevated temperatures, lead chromate or mixtures of lead and basic zinc chromates are preferred to the basic zinc chromate. All these special primers are subject to the limitation that they do not adhere well if applied at humidities above 75 per cent—a limitation that does not apply to the WP-1. Typical wash primer formulations are shown in Table 9.3.

Dispersion Coatings

Dispersion coatings represent one of the most important advances in coatings technology made during the last decade. By this technique resins, heretofore too insoluble to be applied from solution, are made available to the coatings industry. Rapid acceptance of the technique has created a market for two to three million pounds of dispersion resin per month in a relatively short time.[8]

The high viscosity which is characteristic of polymer solutions is avoided in dispersion coatings by the simple expedient of deferring solution until the coating is applied. Coatings are very simply prepared by dispersing a finely divided resin in organic media. Emulsion resins with particle diameters in the range of 0.02 to 1 microns are utilized. The resins contain 96 per cent or more of vinyl chloride. The dispersing media is a nonsolvent for the resin. It consists of a mixture of hydrocarbon diluents and dispersants which are polar liquids, such as esters, ketones, or glycol ethers. When volatile organic thinners are utilized, the dispersions are called organosols. In some instances the compositions contain sufficient plasticizer to impart fluidity without the use of volatile solvents. These compositions containing no volatiles are plastisols. Often dispersions are prepared and stored as plastisols, then reduced with thinner and applied as organosols.

The resins utilized for dispersions fall into two classes. Resins which consist of weakly bonded agglomerates of particles with diameters about 0.1 micron are preferred for organosols because of their better stability in suspension and easier fusion. These particles must be dispersed in a pebble or roll mill to obtain dispersions which are not grainy. Figure 9.5 shows an electron micrograph of such a resin.

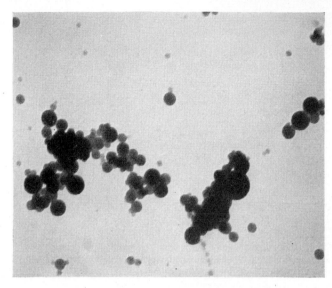

Figure 9.5. Electron micrograph of typical "Vinylite" resin VYNV (25,000 x).

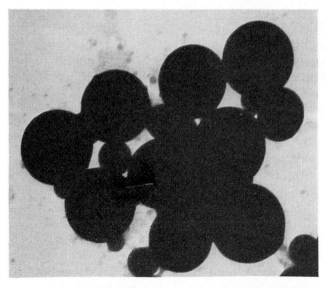

Figure 9.6. Electron micrograph of typical "Vinylite" resin QYNV (25,000 x).

Resins of particle sizes around 1 micron are preferred for plastisols since these can be prepared so that they may be merely stirred into plasticizers to form stable plastisols. Figure 9.6 represents an electron micrograph of such a resin.

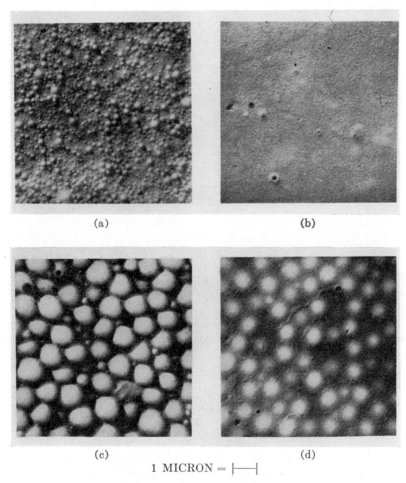

(a)　　　　　　　　　　　　　　(b)

(c)　　　　　　　　　　　　　　(d)

1 MICRON = |——|

Figure 9.7.　Fusion of "Vinylite" resin organosol films as shown by electron micrographs of shadowed surface replicas. (a) Resin VYNV.1, unfused; (b) resin VYNV.1, fused; (c) resin QYNV, unfused; (d) resin QYNV, fused.

After dispersions are applied it is necessary to apply heat to fuse the resin particles to a continuous film. This requires a temperature of 350°F. Figure 9.7 shows organosol and plastisol films in states of partial and complete fusion. The effect of incomplete fusion at low temperatures is reflected in lower tensile strength, as shown in Figure 9.8.

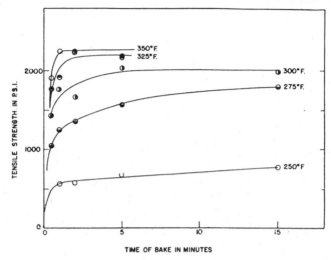

Figure 9.8. Effect of baking time on strength of films.

Formulation of Organosol Thinners

While the preparation of dispersions is quite simple, the formulation of the thinner requires considerable care, since the degree of dispersion, stability, viscosity, flow, and film-forming properties depend on achieving the proper balance in the suspending liquid. This thinner can be treated as a mixture of two kinds of liquids, called dispersants and diluents. The dispersants are liquids that contain polar groups capable of forming strong attachments to the resin. They serve as peptizing agents to wet the resin and suspend it in the thinner. Diluents, which are usually hydrocarbons, are blended with the dispersants to minimize the thinner cost, to decrease the viscosity of the resulting dispersion, and to control, if necessary, the solvating and swelling action on the resin by the dispersant.

Many of the dispersants have a strong swelling action on the resin, as do certain of the diluents which are aromatic in character. A certain amount of swelling and softening of the resin is desirable during grinding to assist in reducing the resin agglomerates to their basic particles and to attain a viscosity which prevents settling of those particles.

For each combination of diluent and dispersant, there is a range of compositions in which the resin can be ground to form an organosol. Within this range the viscosity, stability, and flow characteristics of the organosol are controlled by the balance between dispersant and diluent.

There is an optimum ratio of these two components which yields an organosol of lowest viscosity for a specific resin content. Addition of diluent to an organosol formulated at this optimum point causes agglomeration or flocculation of the resin particles, with an increase in consistency and, ultimately, settling of the resin. On the other hand, if excess dispersant is added, the viscosity is increased and the dispersion exhibits more pronounced pseudoplastic flow properties. Within reasonable limits, excess dispersant improves the stability of the system, but a larger excess may cause gelation. Organosols are generally formulated slightly richer in dispersant than indicated by the minimum on the viscosity curve to take account of a slow absorption of the dispersant by the resin.

The most satisfactory dispersants are plasticizers; they wet the resin well, yet they have a very slow rate of solvation at room temperature. Of the volatile dispersants, diisobutyl ketone is one of the best available. It is a poor solvent for many vinyl resins at room temperature, but it is an excellent solvent at elevated temperatures. It also wets the resin well. Methyl isobutyl ketone is a better solvent for vinyl resins at room temperature, but it yields organosols of higher viscosities because it swells the resin to a greater extent.

Aromatic hydrocarbons, such as xylene, have a strong swelling action on the resin and require but small proportions of dispersant to convert them to balanced organosol thinners. Aliphatic hydrocarbons, on the other hand, have little swelling or wetting action on the resin. They require a higher percentage of dispersant, but yield organosols of lower viscosity. The naphthenic hydrocarbons are preferred to the straight-chain compounds.

The rate of evaporation of the components of the organosol thinner is extremely important in controlling the performance, since the solvent release from organosols is so much faster than from solutions. For general use, even the medium-boiling solvents, such as methyl isobutyl ketone and butyl acetate, evaporate too quickly, resulting in excessive drying in open containers and cracking in films before they can be fused. While this rapid solvent release can be retarded somewhat by the use of oversolvated organosols and by the addition of soluble resins, the use of the higher boiling solvents and diluents is recommended.

Flow Properties of Organosols

The performance and the successful use of organosols are closely related to the flow properties of the dispersion. However, the measurement of these flow properties for control purposes is more difficult than in the case of solutions. While the viscosity of a solution can be characterized reproducibly by determining the time required for a measured volume to flow from a simple cup, this does not work with the dispersions. In the case of the organosols, the rate of flow varies with the force acting on the liquid, but the variation is not uniform in amount or in direction, especially

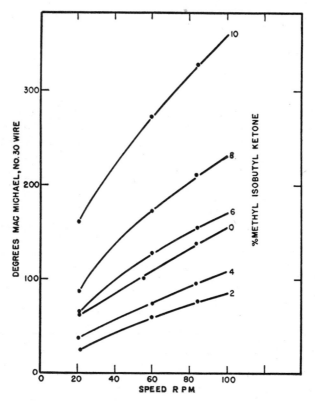

Figure 9.9.   Effect of dispersant-diluent ratio on viscosity.

Composition:
Resin VYNV.1   33.0
FLEXOL plasticizer DOP   6.6
Thinner   60.4
     Dispersant: methyl isobutyl ketone
     Diluent: xylene

                                                      ———
                                                      100.0

if the organosols differ widely in formulation. Because of this complex flow pattern, one must measure the rate of flow under varying conditions to determine the shape and position of the curve.

Extensive studies of the effect of composition on the flow properties have been made.[2] Figure 9.9 represents the typical flow curves obtained with a MacMichael viscosimeter. The deflection at some constant speed,

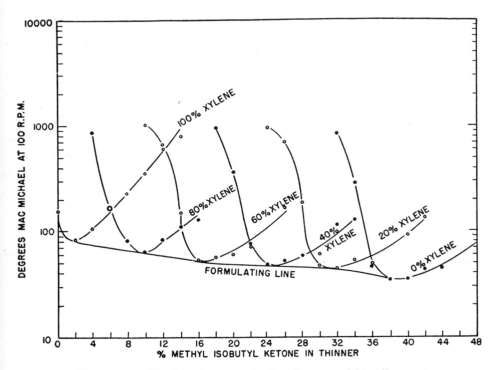

Figure 9.10. Plasticized organosol viscosity-composition diagram.

Composition:

Resin VYNV.1	33.0
FLEXOL plasticizer DOP	6.6
Thinner	60.4

  Dispersant: methyl isobutyl ketone
  Diluent: xylene and naphthenic thinner

——
100.0

Measurements at 26°C. Multiply values by 0.0336 to change to poises.

usually 100 rpm, is used to compare the effect of composition as shown in Figure 9.10. Similar data are obtained at higher plasticizer compositions (Figure 9.11), although here the latitude in formulation becomes considerably greater. At these higher plasticizer ratios it is the usual practice to prepare organosols with no volatile dispersant, but to obtain a balanced thinner by a variation in the ratio of aliphatic to aromatic diluent in the composition. This is illustrated by the comparison of plasticizers as shown in Figures 9.12 and 9.13.

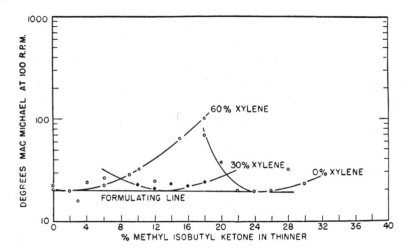

Figure 9.11. Plasticized organosol viscosity-composition diagram.

Composition:
Resin VYNV.1	33.0
FLEXOL plasticizer DOP	16.5
Thinner	50.5
Dispersant: methyl isobutyl ketone	
Diluent: xylene and naphthenic thinner	
	———
	100.0

Measurements at 26°C. Multiply values by 0.0336 to change to poises.

These dispersions have had extensive use in cloth coatings and in the preparation of unsupported film. They have been used for the preparation of flexible articles such as gloves or toys by dipping and slush molding techniques. Heavy coatings on metal have been quickly built up from plastisols for plating racks and for dish drainers.

The dispersion technique is important to the coatings industry because it opens markets for its products in completely new fields. Perhaps even more important on a long-term basis is the development of a new tool for handling the less soluble high polymers. In addition to the vinyl chloride resins, there have already appeared on the market even less soluble resins designed for application by the organosol technique. Vinyl chloride-

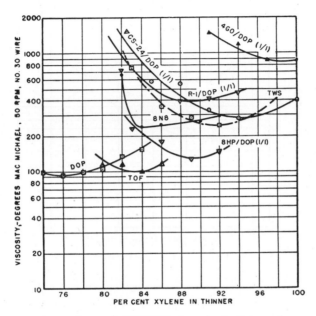

Figure 9.12. Comparison of FLEXOL brand plasticizers in organosols.

Composition:

Resin VYNV.1	40.0
Plasticizer (dispersant) indicated	12.0
Thinner	48.0
Diluent: xylene and naphthenic thinner	
	———
	100.0

acrylonitrile copolymers and fluorothene resins are examples of such materials which can be applied by the organosol technique and yet are not suitable for solution coatings. It is in this field where the greatest advances in vinyl resin coatings may be expected.

It is well to point out that many vinyl polymers are being made available in latices or in the form of powders readily redispersible in water. The technology of these is closely related to that of emulsion paints and

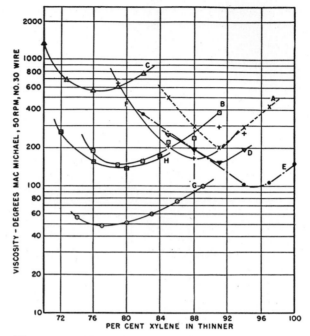

Figure 9.13. Comparison of plasticizers in organosols.

    Composition:

Resin VYNV.1	40.0
Plasticizer (dispersant) indicated	12.0
Thinner	48.0
Diluent: xylene and naphthenic thinner	
	100.0

(A) Plasticizer No. 4
(B) "Kronisol" plasticizer
(C) Tricresyl phosphate
(D) 1/1 KP 120/FLEXOL plasticizer DOP
(E) 1/1 Dioctyl sebacate/FLEXOL plasticizer DOP
(F) 1/1 "Paraplex" G-25/FLEXOL plasticizer DOP
(G) Dicapryl phthalate
(H) "Santicizer" 141

is a subject which requires a separate treatment, too lengthy to be
included.

References

1. "'Vinylite' Resins for Surface Coatings," Bakelite Corporation, New York, 1942.
2. "'Vinylite' Resins-Dispersion Coatings," Bakelite Corporation, New York, 1949.

3. Patton, C. W., "Vinyl Polymers in Surface Coatings," *Official Digest Federation Paint & Varnish Production Clubs* (May, 1948).
4. Quarles, R. W., "Vinyl Resins in Industrial Coatings," *Official Digest Federation Paint & Varnish Production Clubs* (October, 1949).
5. Powell, G. M., and Quarles, R. W., "A New Technique in Coatings—'Vinylite' Resin Dispersions," *Official Digest Federation Paint & Varnish Production Clubs,* **263**, 696 (December, 1946).
6. " 'Vinylite' Resin Organosols for Cloth Coatings," Carbide and Carbon Chemicals Corporation, New York, 1944.
7. Quarles, R. W., "Ketones as Solvents for Vinyl Resins," *Ind. Eng. Chem.,* **35**, 1033 (1943).
8. Patridge, G. E., and Jordon, G. O., "Plastisols and Organosols," *Rubber Age,* **67**, 553 (1950).
9. "Geon Polyvinyl Materials," B. F. Goodrich Chemical Company, 1946.
10. "Geon Paste Resin," Bull. 47–1, B. F. Goodrich Chemical Company, 1947.
11. "Saran F-120 Resin," Dow Chemical Company, 1946.
12. Doolittle, A. K., and Powell, G. M., "A New Vinyl Resin for Air Dry and Low Bake Coatings," *Paint, Oil, Chem. Rev.,* **107** (No. 7), 9 (1944).
13. Reed, M. C., "Behavior of Plasticizers in Vinyl Chloride-Acetate Resins" I, *Ind. Eng. Chem.,* **35**, 896 (1943).
14. Reed, M. C., and Conner, Leonard, II, *Ind. Eng. Chem.,* **40**, 1414 (1948).
15. Reed, M. C., and Harding, James, III, *Ind. Eng. Chem.,* **41**, 675 (1949).
16. Whiting and Wangner, U.S. Pat. 2,525,107 (October 10, 1950).

PART B: STABILIZERS FOR VINYL RESINS

R. E. LALLY

The Ferro Chemical Corporation
Bedford, Ohio

Stability problems of varying magnitude exist in the use of most synthetic resins. The field in which most studies have been made has been in stabilizing chlorinated polymers. Examples of such chlorinated polymers are polyvinyl chloride, copolymers of polyvinyl chloride, polyvinylidene chloride, chlorinated rubber, and the chlorinated paraffins. Since chlorinated vinyl resins exemplify the chlorinated polymers in general, this chapter will be based on the activity of stabilizers towards these vinyl resins.

While the first vinyl resin was prepared in 1838, commercial production in the United States did not take place until about 1938. Of course, a great deal was done in this one-hundred-year period, preceding large-scale production, to make possible the manufacture of some 400,000,000 pounds of vinyl resin per year at the present time. However, the greatest advances have been made in the last ten to fifteen years, and, although the technology of resin production has improved generally, the increasing growth in the use of such resins is due in no small part to the improvement of stabilizers for these resins.

Though vinyl resins may be processed by calendering, extrusion, molding, or coating operations, the basic formulations used are similar for most types of operations, inasmuch as they usually contain resin, plasticizer, stabilizer, and pigments. In addition, some formulations may require solvents, extenders, and secondary plasticizers, while, in the case of specially modified resins, the finished compound may consist of merely stabilizer and resin.

Theories of Degradation

All organic compounds may be decomposed by thermal or light energy, if the energy level is high enough. For many resins the processing temperatures are well below the point at which such decomposition becomes apparent. This, however, is not true in the case of most polymers containing chlorine. At their relatively high processing temperatures, there is a definite tendency to split off hydrogen chloride.

The polyvinyl chloride-containing resins are in this class, and degradation occurs when hydrogen chloride splits off, with the consequent formation of unsaturated bonds. These bonds may give rise to color increase as a result of conjugation or conjugation and oxidation, by which polyketonic groups are formed. The hydrogen chloride formed during initial degradation acts to catalyze further breakdown.

It should not be assumed that the process of degradation of such polymers takes place only at high temperatures. To illustrate that decomposition proceeds even at room temperature, a film was oven-heat tested, at 300°F, immediately after preparation. The degree of color increase of the film was taken as a measure of the degradation. Under the temperature conditions described, the film reached an amber color in one hour. After storing a portion of the same film at room temperature for six months between testing, an amber color was obtained after only forty minutes in the oven. Thus, in the case of polyvinyl chloride and its copolymers, some degradation may take place even at low temperatures, which renders the resin more sensitive to discoloration at high temperatures.

The action of light energy on chlorinated polymers is in some respects similar to that of heat, and in many cases heat stabilizers may aid in the prevention of degradation due to light. There is no doubt that a loss of hydrogen chloride from the resin molecule occurs under the action of light, but it takes place at a slower rate than in the case of heat degradation. Moreover, it is possible that the unsaturation, caused by the loss of chlorine, sets up a condition which, under the influence of light energy, yields some cross linkages between the resin molecules, which can cause embrittlement of the film. A secondary effect of cross-linking is the reduction in compatibility of the resin for some plasticizers, which results in a surface condition referred to as "spew" or tack.

Mechanism of Stabilization

The stabilization of polymers containing chlorine may be accomplished by the utilization of materials which have the following activities: (1) ability to accept hydrogen chloride; (2) ability to react with unsaturated bonds; (3) ability to act as an antioxidant; (4) ability to act as an ultraviolet screener. Of these requirements, the ability to accept hydrogen chloride is of prime importance, for, if it is not absorbed, the rate of degradation increases rapidly due to autocatalytic action.

Next in importance is the activity of materials which are capable of reacting with the double bonds formed when hydrogen chloride splits from the resin molecule. In this case minimization in degradation of the film is indicated by the reduction of both color and embrittlement. As mentioned earlier, oxidation of conjugated bonds may lead to color increase of the film due to the formation of polyketonic groups.

Effective antioxidants are not available for use as stabilizers because, in general, such antioxidants may break down to give color bodies themselves, and, in many cases, they are incompatible with resin compositions. However, it is believed that some stabilizers have antioxidant properties, as well as some capacity for combination with hydrogen chloride. An example of a stabilizer of this type is lead phosphite.

Finally we come to the consideration of ultraviolet screeners as stabilizers. Ultraviolet light screeners are those materials which when incorporated into the vinyl film will prevent the absorption of light energy. Many types of pigments will act as ultraviolet screeners, and in films containing substantial amounts of such pigments little additional light stabilizer is required.

Compounds Used as Stabilizers

Many of the compounds used as stabilizers are considered to have two or more of the activities listed above. It appears that nearly any metal salt of a weak acid will act as a stabilizer to some extent, and patents have been obtained covering most of the known salts of this type. Also, several types of organic compounds have found use as stabilizers. The discussion of such materials will be covered in the following order: (1) alkali metal salts; (2) alkaline earth metal salts; (3) heavy metal salts; and (4) organic compounds.

Alkali Metal Salts. Sodium and potassium were considered early in the quest for stabilizers for polyvinyl chloride. It was thought that their ease of reaction with hydrogen chloride could be used to advantage. At the present time sodium salts are used primarily as light stabilizers since, under the effects of heat, their presence in chlorinated vinyl films will in many cases actually accelerate the rate of decomposition. The most promising alkali salts are the alkali phosphates and alkali alkyl polyphosphates. Such salts will give excellent resistance to light deterioration.

Alkaline Earth Metal Salts. Calcium, strontium, and barium have been used as stabilizers and are today employed to a large extent. While calcium compounds are not as efficient as barium and strontium, calcium silicate, stearate, and ricinoleate are still quite important for the stabilization of films when low toxicity is required.

Strontium compounds, for a number of years, enjoyed a prominent place in the field of vinyl stabilization. In general, they show good compatibility with solvents and plasticizers, are relatively inexpensive, and give a fair degree of light stability.

Barium salts have recently displaced strontium compounds to a great extent, due, in part, to the fact that they offer better over-all heat stability, but mainly because they show a greater degree of synergism with other metal salts. This activity of barium compounds will be discussed more fully later in the chapter.

Heavy Metal Salts. Lead, cadmium, and tin are highly important in the consideration of stabilizers. Lead compounds were used quite early in the development of stable vinyl films, and today enjoy a strong position in the stabilizer field. Either neutral or basic salts of lead may be employed, but the basic types are more often used since, due to their high take-up of hydrogen chloride, on a weight basis, they are more efficient than neutral salts. While lead compounds offer excellent stabilizing action in some applications, they have the disadvantages of high toxicity, opacity, or discoloration in the presence of various sulfur-bearing compounds.

Cadmium salts are not considered as offering good stabilizing action in themselves, but in many cases are highly important when used with other materials. This point is covered more completely under the discussion of synergism.

Various types of tin salts are available as stabilizers, the most important being such dibutyl tin compounds as the dilaurate. Excellent clarity may be obtained using such tin salts, but the main disadvantages have been their relatively high cost and toxicity.

The question of the use of other heavy metals as stabilizers has often been considered. Manganese, copper, and mercury compounds have been proposed as stabilizers, but due to color, cost, or toxicity, little commercial application has been made of such materials.

Organic Compounds. Several types of organic compounds have been proposed and used as stabilizers, the important ones being those containing the amino, phenolic, or epoxy groups.

Amines have been used as stabilizers because of their ability to combine with hydrogen chloride, and in many cases they function as ultraviolet screeners. However, under severe processing conditions they may decompose to color the vinyl stock.

Phenolic compounds may act as antioxidants and ultraviolet screeners and therefore have been used as light stabilizers.

Epoxy compounds are organic materials containing the cyclic structure of two carbon atoms and one oxygen atom, thus:

$$\begin{array}{c} | \quad | \\ -\mathrm{C}-\mathrm{C}- \\ \diagdown \diagup \\ \mathrm{O} \end{array}$$

Such compounds have been used for a number of years to stabilize chlorinated organic compounds. Among these are ethylene oxide and propylene oxide. However, for most applications the low molecular weight epoxy compounds are too volatile and show poor compatibility with chlorinated polymers.

To obtain compounds of low volatility and improved compatibility it is possible to form condensation products of epichlorohydrin. Such condensation products are currently enjoying wide use as stabilizers for chlorinated polymers. Their activity may be twofold, since it is possible for the epoxide ring to open and react with either hydrogen chloride or with the unsaturated bonds formed in the resin molecule during degradation.

Synergism of Stabilizers

The discussion thus far has been limited to the use of single compounds. This was done to illustrate the fact that until quite recently a single material was expected to do the complete job of stabilization. It has been found, however, that the use of two or three compounds together may give unexpected results.

To illustrate this synergistic action of metallic compounds, if cadmium is used in a given resin-plasticizer system, a good initial color may be obtained, but under severe processing conditions the film may degrade more rapidly than it would if no stabilizer were present. On the other hand, barium will give some initial yellowing, which will hold over a long period of heat application. But if cadmium and barium are used together in this resin formulation, it is possible to obtain a good initial color which will hold over a long heat cycle. To show this more exactly we may mention the following examples of stabilizers used in films held for 2 hours at 300°F.

(1) 3% barium ricinoleate resulted in a dark brown film.

(2) 3% cadmium 2-ethylhexoate resulted in a black film.

(3) 1½% barium ricinoleate plus 1½% cadmium 2-ethylhexoate resulted in a colorless film.

A still more recent step in the application of synergism is the use of cadmium and barium with epoxy compounds. By the proper adjustment of the ratios of these three types of materials, improvement of 200 to 300 per cent in stabilization is possible over previous systems consisting of only cadmium and barium compounds.

As a result of the realization of the strong synergistic activity of cadmium and barium, there have appeared on the market a number of complex stabilizers containing these two metals as the active ingredients. Basically, the use of a single, premixed, multicomponent stabilizer would be the proper approach to the problem, were it not for the fact that few processors use exactly the same formulation under equal operating conditions.

Thus, while one ratio of cadmium-barium may be proper for the stabilization of a given resin-plasticizer-pigment combination, an entirely different ratio of stabilizer metals may be needed to obtain the best results if either the resin, plasticizer, or pigment is varied. In other words, when synergism is being employed, it is necessary to test each formulation under conditions representing plant production to arrive at the proper metal ratios.

Commercial Stabilizers

Amounts and Methods of Incorporation. There is no set rule as to the type or amount of stabilizer to be used in a given resin system. This is due mainly to the fact that changes in a single component, such as plasticizer or pigment, may affect the activity of stabilizers. Also, the processing conditions and conditions of use of the finished product must be considered. Thus, if the heat or light requirements are not severe or if a relatively stable resin is being processed, it may be practical to use a very small amount of a single stabilizer. However, stabilizers are generally used in amounts ranging from 0.5 to 5 per cent of the weight of chlorinated polymer. In solution coatings the amount is usually in the low range, from 0.5 to 1.5 per cent, while in plastisols and organosols an average of 3 per cent is used. There are cases, however, where unusual operating conditions have required the use of as much as 7 per cent stabilizer.

In the incorporation of stabilizers into the resin system, it is often desirable to use liquids which may be dispersed directly in the plasticizer. Furthermore, it is now possible to obtain in liquid form many of the really active stabilizer compounds, including cadmium and barium ricinoleates. When such materials as alkali phosphates are used for light stabilization, it is necessary to carry out a pre-milling operation of the stabilizer with a small portion of the plasticizer. The resulting paste may then be incorporated by simply mixing with the resin and remaining plasticizer.

Applications. There is a great deal of confusion in the commercial application of stabilizers for vinyl resins. The main factors contributing to this confusion are: (1) variations in raw material stability; (2) variations in processing methods; and (3) variations in end-product use.

Variations in Raw Material Stability. The subject of resin stability has already been discussed, but it should be emphasized that when dealing with a resin of lower stability, it is not simply a matter of using additional amounts of stabilizers, for resins of different structure often require a complete change in stabilizer formulation to obtain optimum results.

Changes in plasticizers and pigments may also require changes in type and amount of stabilizers. Some types of plasticizers reduce the stability of a given resin system by as much as 50 per cent, while others are available which act as stabilizers, especially in the presence of cadmium and barium compounds.

The surface action of stabilizers on pigments is most easily observed by noting their effect on the leafing properties of aluminum pigments. The deleafing of aluminum pigments by lead soaps is well known to the paint manufacturer. This condition results from the reaction between the lead compound and the coating of stearic acid present on the surface of leafing type particles. Once the pigment coating is converted to a soap, the individual particles lose their ability to orient themselves, thus destroying their otherwise shiny, metallic appearance. Manufacturers of cast film stock of vinyl chloride containing aluminum pigments may be confronted with this problem.

Tests of several types of stabilizers gave the following results after eight days of storage in the presence of a leafing type aluminum powder dispersed in plasticizer:

Modified barium ricinoleate........No loss of leafing

Modified cadmium ricinoleate......No loss of leafing

Strontium octoate ....15% loss of leafing

Modified calcium ricinoleate.......No loss of leafing

These were the only stabilizers which gave such results, all others tested caused complete loss of leafing after the eight-day storage period.

Variations in Processing Methods. To improve the ease of incorporation and the compatibility of stabilizers, modifications have been made in addition agents and solvents as well as in the anion portion of the stabilizer in the case of metallic soaps. While such changes have been necessary as new methods of processing have been evolved, they have increased the number of available stabilizers, and thus added, to some extent, to the confusion existing in stabilizer application.

Variations in End-product Use. The increasing use and variety of vinyl resin products has made it necessary to consider more critically the effect of stabilizers on the clarity, odor, water resistance, and toxicity of the finished product. Usually it is necessary to reach a compromise of these factors, but most requirements may be met by the use of metallic soaps, and it has been found that the use of organic acids of eight to eighteen carbon atoms give best results.

Since many of the stabilizers for vinyl compounds are the organic reaction products of the heavy metals, the use of such compounds brings up the question of toxicity. Most of these metals are handled regularly in many industrial applications, and when proper precautions are taken, are considered to offer little or no hazard to manufacturing personnel. Also, when once incorporated into vinyl films, the toxicity is considered nonexistent if the compound is not leached from the film under the conditions of use. For films coming in contact with foods, it is essential to test a new composition with respect to the degree to which components may be leached out or adsorbed from the particular film in question.

The toxicity of lead and its compounds is quite well known, and the fact that lead will accumulate in the body increases the danger involved in its use. Cadmium and tin are approximately equal in toxicity, but of a considerably lower degree than lead. They are readily eliminated from the body, and unless extremely large doses are involved they have little or no effect on body functions. No deaths have ever been reported from the use of cadmium salts. Next to sodium and calcium, which are considered nontoxic, barium is probably the least toxic of the stabilizer metals. Barium is nonaccumulative and is present in small amounts in some foods. For example, it may be present in table salt as the chloride, to the extent of 0.05 per cent, although large amounts taken into the body may be undesirable. Epoxy compounds of low molecular weight are considered toxic, but this is due to a large extent to their volatility. The condensation products mentioned earlier are considered nontoxic, although long contact with the pure stabilizer should be avoided due to possible dermatitic action.

Approximately thirty different basic types of commercial stabilizers are available on the present market. Each has been the result of an attempt to overcome some one of the variables mentioned above. Following is a list of the most common stabilizer metals and anions:

Metals	Anions
Sodium	Ricinoleate
Strontium	Laurate
Calcium	Stearate
Barium	Naphthenate
Lead	2-ethylhexoate
Cadmium	Phthalate
Tin	Salicylate
	Silicate
	Phosphate
	Phosphite

It is hoped that changes will be made in the future which will eliminate some of the variables and permit a simplification of stabilizer formulation and use. Of course the ultimate would be the universal stabilizer, but it appears to be a long way off at this time. However, as a better understanding of stabilizer activity is obtained, it may be possible to reach that goal.

PART C: RECENT DEVELOPMENTS IN THE THEORY AND USE OF PLASTICIZERS FOR VINYL RESINS

H. GRINSFELDER
Rohm and Haas Company
Philadelphia, Pa.

In greater part, we shall review in this chapter the developments in the field of plasticizers since 1945. A vast amount of study has taken place in this five-year period; in fact, more investigations into plasticizer action have been conducted during these years than during the entire period preceding 1945, and a greater number of researchers have become interested in this field than ever before.

One need not search far for the reasons motivating this interest and this research. A brief glance at the production figures for plasticizers in the United States shows for 1940, 28,500,000 pounds and for 1949, 166,000,000 pounds. One plasticizer, scarcely known in 1940, dioctyl phthalate, was produced in 1949 at a rate greater than that for all plasticizers in the year 1940.

Before proceeding further, it would be well to define the term "plasticizer." In Webster's Dictionary it is defined as "an agent added to certain plastics and protective coatings to impart softness and flexibility." Another definition, more often a desire, and rarely an actuality, is that a plasticizer is a substance capable of being incorporated into a paint, lacquer, or plastic, which, when so incorporated, improves it in most properties and injures it none. In line with this thought, the following definition has been given by Matiello:[1] "A plasticizer is a liquid or solid material added to plastic or semi-plastic compositions to increase the permanent flexibility. Through common usage, the term has been extended beyond its strict interpretation and is generally considered to cover the imparting of such qualities or combinations of qualities as elasticity, flow, distensibility, gloss, clarity, adhesion, resistance to water, solvents, and reduction of burning rate."

Properties of a Plasticizer

"An ideal plasticizer should be:[1]

1. Odorless
2. Colorless
3. Tasteless
4. Nontoxic
5. Nonhydroscopic
6. Nonflammable
7. Stable under heat and cold
8. Nonyellowing
9. Compatible
10. Inert to reactive pigments

"It should have:

1. High flash point
2. High boiling range
3. Low vapor pressure
4. High solvent strength
5. Low solvent retention
6. Dispersing power
7. Wettability for pigments

"It should impart:

1. Gelatinizing power with nitrocellulose
2. Free-flowing properties with fast-setting resins
3. Stability to consistency on aging
4. Distensibility to permit flow under stress without rupture
5. Distensibility without too great a loss in tensile strength
6. Toughness to film to withstand impact
7. Permanent flexibility and toughness to film on aging to avoid crumbling, stickiness, greasiness, and brittleness

It should enable the film to elongate and contract during temperature change and stay within the practical elastic limit.

It should control shrinkage during film formation to avoid pores and maintain a solid continuous film; and it should control shrinkage to increase the adhesion by reducing internal stresses within the film and enable the adhesion constituent of film to work freely."

Studies of the Mechanism of Plasticizer Action

Of the fields of research regarding plasticizers, by far the largest part has involved studies of the plasticization of polyvinyl chloride. A relatively few studies have appeared in the literature presenting data obtained for plasticizers in cellulosics. The studies of plasticizer action in polyvinyl chloride have been quite varied as to their approach and purpose. In general, however, the studies have been of three different types which may be classified as approaches to the mode of plasticization through consideration of either solvency properties, or of the chemical structure, or of the physical properties of the plasticized polymer.

Solvent Properties. In the group of solvent studies conducted since 1945, the work of Frith, Doty and Zable, Doolittle, Jones, Dyson, and Boyer are all excellent. Frith was the first to show that the questions of compatibility can be answered on the basis of the thermodynamics of the polymer-solvent systems. Frith[2] has described experiments which measure the viscosity of dilute polymer solutions in suitable mixed solvents containing the plasticizer in question. She has showed that the slope of the line obtained when plotting the viscosity per unit concentration against the concentration is related to the equilibrium extent of swelling of the polymer in the pure plasticizer. In general, the slope is a good measure of compatability; the steeper the slope the better the compatibility. The method has been criticized for the reasons that no values can be obtained for nonsolvents and also because the results are only valid in limited regions of concentration. For instance in very dilute solutions, higher viscosity corresponds to better solvents, whereas in concentrated solutions, higher viscosity corresponds to poorer solvents.

Doty and Zable[3] have reported on a novel method for determining μ, the semi-empirical constant, developed by Flory, Rehner, and Huggins in their treatment of the thermodynamics of polymer-solvent systems. The most important feature of their work is that not only has a new method for determining the polymer/liquid interaction constant μ been investigated, but it has been applied with great accuracy. This new method is based on swelling measurements which are much simpler than the classical osmotic pressure techniques.

What they did was to measure the swelling volume in a solvent for a cross-linked polymer and thus determine its average molecular weight between cross links. The values of μ for the noncross-linked polymer were determined by osmotic pressure measurements in the same solvent. In their particular experiments polyvinyl chloride was used, and to cross link it, heat was applied. The average molecular weight between cross links was determined in each of three different liquids with very good agreement. The cross-linked polymer was then used to determine the value of μ at two temperatures for fifty plasticizers. Phase separation or incompatability occurs as soon as μ exceeds a critical value of 0.5 or 0.55. In general, μ was found to increase and hence compatability decrease, as the temperature is lowered.

About this time, too, Doolittle[4] presented his studies on the mechanism of solvent action and translated his observations on solvents to plasticizers and plasticization. From his one study of dilution ratios of various classes of solvents and nonsolvents in homologous series, and another study of viscosity as related to concentration, he found the plots to approach asymptotically the same values. From this he reasoned that a resin solution is a dynamic equilibrium between the tendency of the solvent molecules to solvate the resin and the tendency of the resin molecules to unite with each other. He proposed that a plasticizer be viewed as a high-boiling solvent and that its performance be explained in terms of its concentration and solvent strength. However, he did not obtain agreement between plasticizer spue and solvent strength and attributed it to the difficulty of measuring solvency at the solids content as used. The dilution ratio method also has the weakness that the first portions of the diluent may actually improve the solvent ability of the plasticizer. Doolittle's approach is also handicapped by being restricted to homologous series of chemicals.

According to the viscosity theory of plasticizer actions of Jones,[5] the properties of a thermoplastic plasticized polymer are determined to a large extent by the viscosity of the plasticizer. The lower the viscosity of those plasticizers which are miscible with polymers, the softer is the plastic. He also stated that plastics containing those plasticizers having low temperature coefficients of viscosity will also have a low temperature coefficient. He attributed much anomolous data to the decrease in miscibility of the plasticizer as the temperature changed but also had difficulty applying his theory to polymeric plasticizers. Dyson[6] further criticized the Jones theory and reported results showing an unplasticized composition to be more temperature-sensitive than was one containing 25 dioctyl phthalate.

The development of the theory of plasticizer action on the basis of solvent properties was climaxed by the courageous effort of Boyer and his associates to interrelate the properties of compatibility, efficiency, and permanence. In the paper on this subject, which appeared in 1949, Boyer[7] discusses compatibility in terms of the Flory-Huggins thermodynamic approach to solutions where the smaller the value of μ becomes, the more compatible is the plasticizer. A relationship between efficiency and μ is shown, wherein for solvent type plasticizers, the lower the value μ the greater the efficiency. Efficiency in this case is measured by the number of degrees the brittle point is lowered. Boyer then goes on to show that loss of plasticizer into an air stream or to an oil bath surrounding the sample is dependent on either its effective vapor pressure or its internal diffusion. A linear relationship is found between the log of the diffusion constant and the brittle temperature, which indicates that the more efficient a plasticizer is, the more rapidly it can diffuse out of the polymer and be lost. He thus reached the significant conclusion that compatibility, efficiency, and permanence (to oil extraction) are in opposition. The difference between solvent and nonsolvent plasticizers is recognized. An attempt to solve this puzzle is suggested by way of polymeric plasticizers. In polymerics, it is pointed out, vapor pressure and diffusion rate are vanishingly small and efficiency is lower, but the differences between compatibility and incompatibility become less significant and hence are one practical solution to the cycle of properties portrayed and predicted for monomeric plasticizers.

Effect of Chemical Structure of Plasticizer. The work of Laurence and McIntyre[8] discusses the effect of the chemical structure of the plasticizer on its properties. They believe that compatibility can be controlled through functional groups—the carboxylic ester group being one of the strongest. They found that phosphate and amide groups are also strong solubilizers but that ether groups and double bonds are of little value. In their studies, efficiency was seen to be related to the functional groups and was highest when functional groups were the largest per cent of the molecule. Aliphatic groups were found to be more efficient than aromatic. They also found that factors promoting low temperature flexibility promoted migration. Ether groups were reported to promote water sensitivity and higher molecular weight reduces migration.

Effect of Physical Properties of Plasticized Polymer. The physical nature of plasticized polyvinyl chloride was studied and reported on in some detail by Alfrey, Tobolsky, and co-workers.[9] Previously, this team had investigated the creep behavior of plasticized "Vinylite" VYNW and had concluded that a three-dimensional network of great permanence was present. This, they believed, was necessary to explain the association of the small, long time creep with the large, short time compliance and the essentially complete recovery of films which had been stressed for long periods of time. On the basis of dilatometry, birefringence, and x-ray measurements which they conducted, it now appears to them that these materials contain a small fraction of a partially crystalline nature. The cross links which were deemed necessary to explain many of the physical properties found earlier are, therefore, considered to be crystallites. It is theorized that different plasticizers affect the microcrystalline structure differently. Partial melting of the crystal structure may be accomplished by application of heat or stress, but upon removal of the heat or stress, recrystallization may occur. They theorize that a plasticized stock consists of chains which are parallel bundles of micelles bound together. Each chain passes through one or more crystalline regions. The portion of the chain not in these micelles is amorphous. The plasticizer serves to solvate or shield these points of contact along the chain. The essential difference in the behavior of various plasticizers lies in their effect on the microcrystalline structure which they in turn produce.

Other investigators have more or less inadvertently encountered this highly likely possibility. For example, Jones in developing his viscosity/temperature theory stated that he often encountered anomalous data due to a decrease in miscibility with temperature. And Doolittle could not obtain agreement between solvent strength as he measured it and plasticizer spue. Boyer states that if the polymer crystallizes on aging, the compatibility may be altered for two reasons. Primarily, the crystalline areas may be physically inaccessible to the plasticizer molecules, so that an excess of plasticizer may be in existence for the remaining amorphous regions of the polymer. Secondly, the crystallites act as points of crosslinkage. The presence of cross links changes the effective value of μ, which would reduce compatibility and also limit the maximum amount of swelling of the network chains of the polymer.

Two other studies into the mechanism of plasticizer action are worthy of brief mention. One is that of Champetier[10] on cellulose nitrate and cellulose acetate, in which he tried to remove the plasticizer from the polymer by solvent extraction and application of pressure. He examined his stocks by x-ray diffraction and made a triaxular plot at various stages of extraction. The plot is a series of converging straight lines, each series starting with a definite proportion of plasticizer to polymer. Depending on where the lines converge (obtained by extrapolation), it may indicate whether preferential loss is solvent or plasticizer or neither. Champetier reasoned that if the preferential loss is solvent, a molecular combination must exist between polymer and plasticizer. By this approach he found tributyl phosphate to combine readily with cellulose nitrate. Tricresyl phosphate combined but to a lesser degree and required heat or strong solvents. By the same approach, tributyl phosphate does not combine at all with cellulose acetate.

The other was the work of Richards and Smith,[11] who conducted electron microscope studies on polyvinyl butyral stocks plasticized with various high density organo-mercury compounds such as those obtained by addition of mercuric acetate to various acrylate, methacrylate, and allyl esters. They reported observing submicroscopic phase separation in those cases where a plot of second order transition point against volume fraction of plasticizer deviated from a straight line.

Urea Resins

While such studies provide some insight into the theory of plasticization, we are still a long way from having a complete understanding of the mechanism and still further away from being able to predict plasticizer performance on the basis of chemical structure. However, this lack of knowledge has not hindered the use of plasticized polymers, nor has it apparently retarded the introduction of new plasticizers. The greater number of the new plasticizers have been principally offered for use in vinyl chloride.

One other development that deviates from the well beaten path of conventional plasticizers takes us into the field of nitrogen resin chemistry. Usually urea or melamine resins are extremely brittle and produce very poor adhesion by themselves. However, it is possible to formulate a urea formaldehyde that in itself is chemically plasticized and whose cured form is extremely flexible. Its function is then both one of plasticizing and of thermosetting. It is somewhat slower curing than conventional urea resins but produces a tougher, more flexible film with better adhesion. The resin is also more tolerant of aliphatic solvents, oils, long oil alkyds, varnishes, and other film formers. This, then, opens up several fields of possibility not heretofore considered for urea resins. An example of the particular resin is Rohm and Haas "Uformite" F240, which allows the possibility of utilizing the curing properties, alkali resistance, and color retention of urea resins in fields of coating previously inaccessible to them.

One of these fields is that of the thermosetting phenolics. An example of one of these alcohol-soluble phenolics is "Bakelite" BV1600, which forms on baking films of extreme hardness and considerable resistance to solvents and chemicals. The phenolic resin films are, however, deficient in adhesion when fully cured. "Uformite" F240 nicely complements this resin, plasticizes it, and improves the alkali resistance and the adhesion. Thus a film is possible which possesses excellent properties with respect to hardness, flexibility, adhesion, and superior resistance to attack by acids, alkali, and solvents. Optimum properties for many uses appear at about 70 per cent "Uformite" F240 and 30 per cent BV1600, when the enamels are baked for 30 minutes at 300°F.

Another field of usefulness of this new type of plasticizer is in vinyl coatings. With "Vinylite" VAGH, baking for one hour at 250°F "Uformite" F240 produces a film very much harder than either resin alone and one that is resistant to strong solvents and acids. It is probable that cross linking occurs. Films so cross-linked may need additional plasticizer other than the "Uformite," preferably polyester types such as Rohm and Haas "Paraplex" G-50 or G-60.

The field of metal decorating coatings offers one possibility for coatings of this type. As compared to conventional finishes, the following data are interesting.

	Conventional Urea/Alkyd	Metal Decorating Alkyd	Plasticized Vinyl*
Solids at coating viscosity	50%	54.5%	32%
Resistance to steam sterilization	Failed over tin and alkyd size coat	Failed over alkyd size coat	Very slight failure over tin only
Resistance to 200°F (2 hours)	O.K.	O.K.	O.K.
Resistance to 350°F (30 minutes)	Failed	Failed over vinyl size coat	O.K.
Resistance to ammonia fumes (24 hours)	O.K.	Discolors	O.K.
Gloss (% reflectance, 60°)	86	84	89

Solids Basis

*"Vinylite" VAGH	60
"Duraplex" ND77N	30
"Uformite" F240N	10
"Paraplex" G60	10

In the vinyl formula, "Paraplex" G-60 (a polymeric plasticizer) is used to provide heat stability and plasticizing action; "Duraplex" ND77N (a nonoxidizing type of oil-modified phthalic alkyd) is used to provide high gloss and solids; and "Uformite" F240N is used to produce higher solids at application viscosity and to improve film properties and chemical resistances.

Here we have discussed only some of the formulation possibilities for modification of a film which are referred to as plasticization, but which certainly are not such in the simple definition of the word. The advantages to be realized, however, when we permit our thoughts to stray from the conventional interpretation of the term, are considerable. Such thinking has influenced the art of formulation of films so that the practice has developed far ahead of theory, and when we speak of plasticizers in the most general sense of the practical art, there is only a very meagre theory to lead the way.

References

1. Matiello, J., "Protective Decorative Coatings," Vol. **3,** John Wiley and Sons, Inc., New York, 1943.

2. Frith, E. M., *Trans. Faraday Soc.*, **41,** 90 (1945).
3. Doty, P. M., and Zable, H. S., *J. Polymer Sci.*, **1,** 90 (1946).
4. Doolittle, A. K., *J. Polymer Sci.*, **2,** 121 (1947); *Ind. Eng. Chem.*, **38,** 535 (1946).
5. Jones, H., *J. Soc. Chem. Ind.*, **67,** 415 (1948).
6. Dyson, A., *J. Soc. Chem. Ind.*, **69,** 205 (1950).
7. Boyer, R. F., *J. Applied Phys.*, **20,** 540 (1949).
8. Laurence, R. R., and McIntyre, E. B., *Ind. Eng. Chem.*, **41,** 689 (1947).
9. Alfrey, T., Tobolsky, A., Wiederhorn, N., and Stein, R., *J. Colloid Sci.*, **4,** 211 (1949); *Ind. Eng. Chem.*, **41,** 701 (1949).
10. Champetier, G., *Official Digest Federation Paint & Varnish Production Clubs,* 77 (January, 1950).
11. Richard, W. R., and Smith, P. A., *J. Chem. Phys.*, **18,** 230 (1950).

10 : Aminoplast Resins for Organic Coatings

CHARLES H. PARKER and FRANK J. HAHN

Plastics Division
Monsanto Chemical Company
Springfield, Massachusetts

Fundamental Chemistry

Almost any resinous material has, by its very physical nature, a complicated chemical structure. Amino resins are no exception to this rule, so before considering their use in organic coatings, it will be well to review

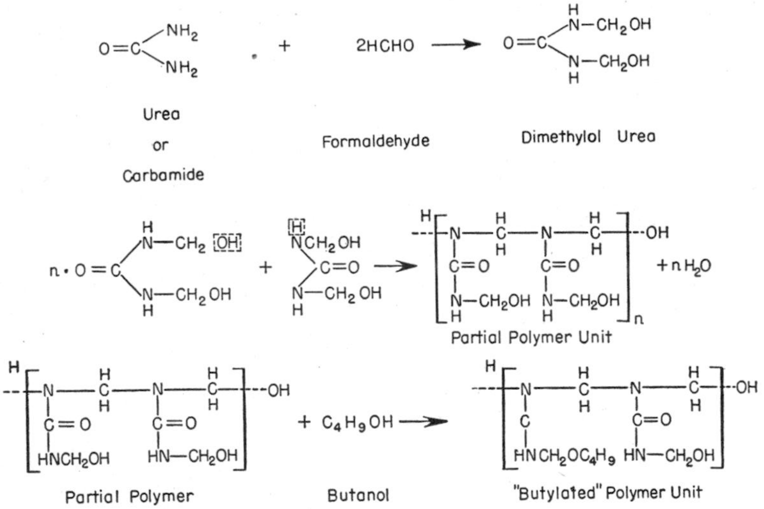

Figure 10.1. The reactions involved in the formation of butylated urea resins.

the fundamental chemistry involved. Figure 10.1 shows the methylol compound resulting from the union of one molecule of urea and two molecules of formaldehyde, and Figure 10.2 shows the methylol compound resulting from one molecule of melamine and one of formaldehyde. While the latter is not, to the best of our knowledge, an isolatable compound,

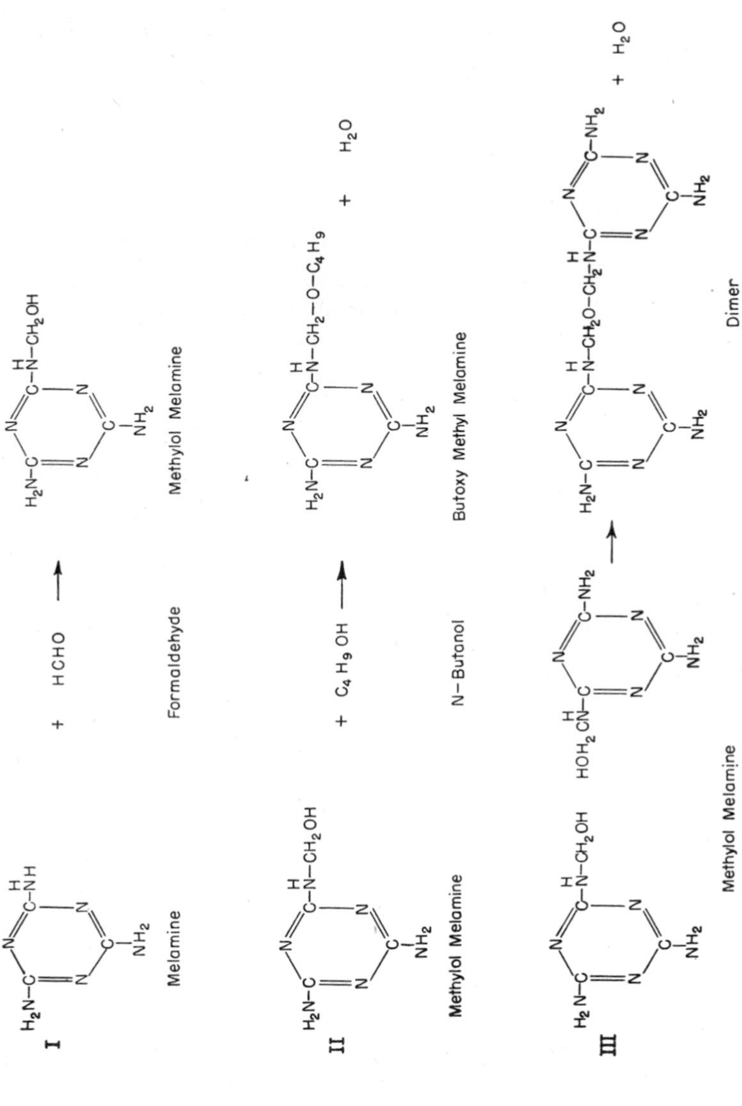

Figure 10.2. Some possible reactions in solutions containing equimolar quantities of melamine and formaldehyde and some butanol.

the ensuing discussion will be very greatly simplified by considering only a single reactive group. The urea molecule will accept and hold only two molecules of formaldehyde while the melamine molecule will accept, theoretically, six. Triazines other than melamine generally will accept fewer molecules of formaldehyde. Aceto-guanamine, an example of another triazine, will accept only four, since there are only two amino groups available. The "ether" resulting from the reaction of some of these methylol compounds with butanol and some theory regarding the mechanism of the resin-forming condensation reactions, are illustrated in Figures 10.1 and 10.2.

These reactions are the primary ones and are oversimplified for illustrative purposes, since only one reactive group is shown. Theoretically, any primary alcohol from methyl on up to those of 18 or more carbon atoms (and aromatic alcohols as well as heterocyclic types) can undergo this etherification. However, from a practical point of view, those having three to five carbon atoms are best because longer chain alcohols do not etherify sufficiently rapidly, although those with shorter chains complicate the recovery problem because of their ready solubility in water. The longer chain alcohols may be introduced by a transetherification reaction with an amino-methylol compound previously etherified with one of the shorter chain alcohols.

The physical and performance properties of the final resin may also be influenced by the initial aldehyde content and by the hydrogen ion concentration during the processing. It is the resin manufacturer's purpose to balance these factors to yield a desirable combination of properties in the final product.

Cure Mechanism

The transetherification reaction mentioned above may be a part of the mechanics by which amino resins cure in the presence of alkyds, as will be shown later. While the mechanism of cure of amino resins has never been conclusively demonstrated and is somewhat obscure, the following idealized statements might be made. Cure of these resins by themselves, particularly the melamine resins, is actually very sluggish, except at very high temperatures, but a *very* small amount of acid is sufficient to rectify this in normal baking ranges (200–400°F). Cure may take place by splitting out butanol from butoxy groups, formaldehyde from the portions of the resin not etherified by the alcohol, and possibly traces of water from residual methylol groups (Figure 10.3).

Curing of an amino resin in the presence of an alkyd resin allows the possibility of an additional mechanism which provides a new resinous structure in the film. Figure 10.4 illustrates a transetherification reaction

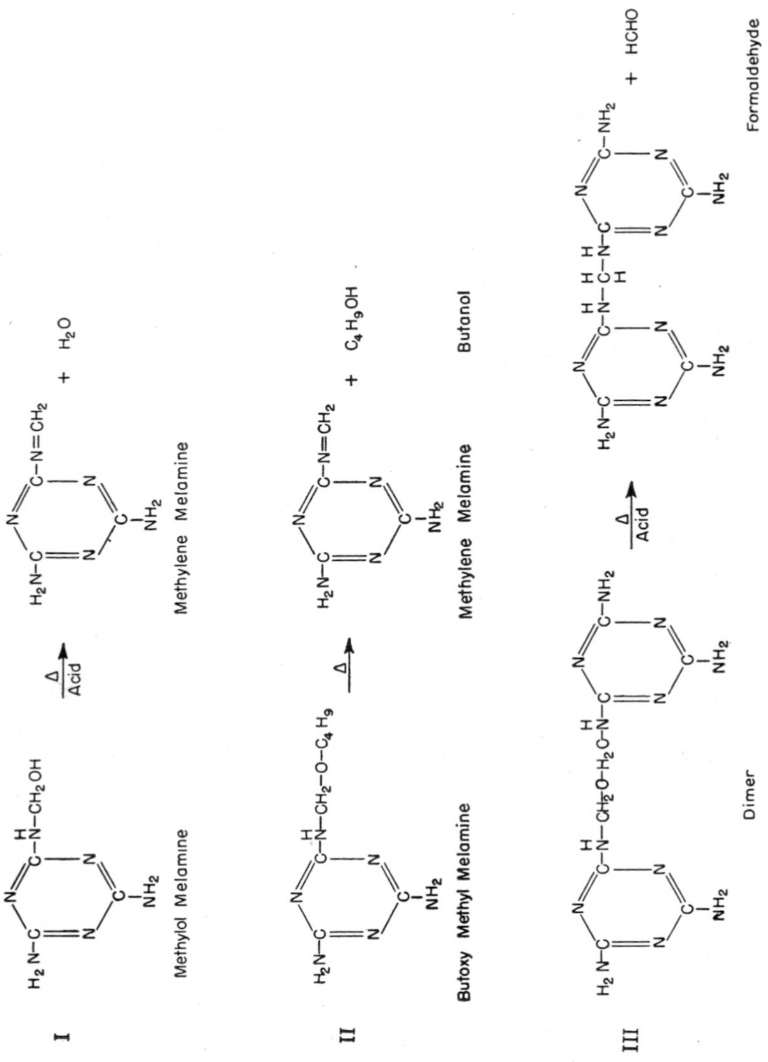

Figure 10.3. Some possible thermal decomposition reactions of butylated melamine resins.

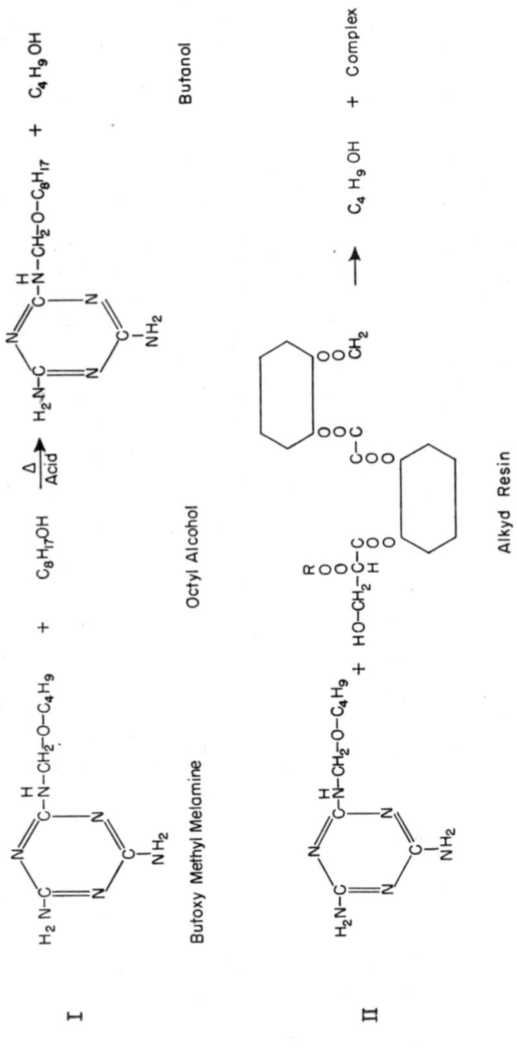

Figure 10.4. Reaction of butoxy methyl melamine with compounds containing free hydroxyl groups.

taking place in very simplified form. Alkyd resins that are high in hydroxyl content are very susceptible to this possible reaction with amino resins, and this may be one of the reasons why short-oil alkyds carrying a fair excess of hydroxyl over the stoichiometrically equivalent amount are more compatible with aminoplasts. In the baked film such alkyd resins yield films of higher gloss than do hydroxyl-deficient alkyds. The latter, in mixtures with aminoplast resins, frequently yield a cured film that lacks both gloss and toughness. The mild acidity of the alkyd in either case is sufficient to promote the curing reactions previously discussed.

Types of Aminoplast Resins

Since it does not seem possible to attain all the desirable properties of amino resins in a single product, there are several types available commercially, just as there are available many types of alkyd resins. The principal types of melamine coating resins may be classified according to the scheme of Table 10.1. Specifications for some typical resins are given in Table 10.2.

TABLE 10.1. CLASSIFICATION OF MELAMINE RESINS WITH RESPECT
TO SOME MORE IMPORTANT PROPERTIES

Type   I—Very fast curing; high color retention; limited compatibility and aliphatic hydrocarbon tolerance; good alkali resistance.

Type II—Slower curing; excellent compatibility, particularly with mineral spirits soluble alkyds; very high mineral spirits tolerance; high gloss; fair alkali resistance.

Type III—Good curing properties; excellent compatibility; very high gloss; best alkali resistance.

Type IV—Essentially same as Type III, but offers very wide latitude in active solvent selection.

TABLE 10.2. SPECIFICATIONS FOR SOME DIFFERENT TYPES
OF MELAMINE RESINS

	Resin No. 1	Resin No. 2	Resin No. 3	Resin No. 4	Resin No. 5	Resin No. 6
			Type			
	I	I	II	II	III	IV
Solids, %	50	50	50	60	60	65
Butanol, %	25	50	25	40	20	—
Xylol, %	25	10	(M.S.)25	—	20	35
Acid No.	−1	−1	−1	−1	−1	−1
Viscosity	L—P	G—M	L—M	S—W	L—P	Z—A_4
M.S. Tol.*	2.5–3.5	5.0	INF	10–1	3.0–5.0	0.6–1.6

* Measured with a naphtha having a Kauri-butanol value of 31–34. The figure represents cc's of naphtha per gram of solution.

The urea coating resins can be classified in a somewhat similar manner, as shown in Table 10.3. Examples of specification for some typical resin solutions are given in Table 10.4.

TABLE 10.3. CLASSIFICATION OF UREA RESINS WITH RESPECT
TO SOME MORE IMPORTANT PROPERTIES

Type I—High viscosity, fast cure, limited compatibility, general purpose use.
Type II—Low viscosity, slower cure, much better compatibility, better gloss.
Type III—Very high mineral spirits tolerance and excellent compatability, very low viscosity, rather slow cure and high gloss.
Type IV—Essentially same as Type III, but permits wide latitude in solvent selection.

TABLE 10.4. SPECIFICATIONS FOR SOME DIFFERENT TYPES
OF UREA RESINS

	Resin No. 1	Resin No. 2	Resin No. 3	Resin No. 4	Resin No. 5	Resin No. 6
				Type		
	I	II	II	II	III	IV
Solids, %	50	50	50	55	60	60
Butanol, %	30	30	30	30	24	—
Xylol, %	20	20	20	15	16	—
Other, %	—	—	—	—	—	40 (H.F. Naphtha)
Acid No. Solids	3—6	3—7	10.0 max.	2—4	3—8	3—8
Viscosity	X—Z	X—Z$_1$	N—P	S—U	L—Q	W—Z
M.S. Tol.*	1.5	1.5	3.0	3.0	8.0	2.5

* The figures represent average values and are expressed in cc's of 38 Kauri-butanol value minera spirits per gram of resin solution.

Rather distinct points of difference exist in the performance of melamine and urea resins in coatings formulations. These may be summarized in a very general way as in Table 10.5.

Applications

With a few possible exceptions, amino resins have applications only where coatings can be baked. Their actual applications are confined largely to metal substrata. In some cases where the cure can be catalyzed (applies to the urea types primarily), some find application in wood finishes which are force-dried at 100 to 150°F. Other more or less highly specialized applications would include certain textile and paper coatings. The following discussion will be confined largely to finishes for articles fabricated of metal.

Theoretical Considerations. Butylated melamine- and urea-formaldehyde resins should be considered as intermediate reactive resins rather than as film-formers in themselves. Both of these amino types, if attempts are made to use them alone, are relatively poor film-forming materials

TABLE 10.5. COMPARISON OF UREA AND MELAMINE RESINS WITH RESPECT TO PROPERTIES THAT ARE IMPORTANT TO PRACTICAL FORMULATION OF COATINGS

MELAMINE	UREA
1. Very much faster cure (esp. Type I)	1. Lower cost on pound per pound basis.
2. Much better alkali resistance.	2. Can be used with acid catalyst at low temperatures (125–160°F).
3. Much better color retention and gloss retention on overbaking.	3. Easier patching on rejects, probably because of poorer solvent resistance.
4. Less film shrinkage on curing, resulting in better build per coat.	4. Type I yields higher viscosity enamel at equal solids content.
5. Better initial gloss and flow.	5. Holds pattern better in hammertone finishes, esp. Type I.
6. Much wider baking range (200–500°F vs. 225–350°F).	6. Better adhesion on pound per pounP basis.
7. Much better cure in low amino ratios (5–15%) in resin mixtures.	
8. Better exterior durability (gloss retention, chalk resistance, and checking resistance).	

in that they are somewhat brittle and still possess reactive groupings, rendering them subject to attack in the later stages of their film life. Their effective use requires blending with other resins that are capable of interaction with the amino resin. After application of the mixed resin solution on a surface, and after evaporation of the solvent, the "curing" reactions occur at relatively high temperatures to form a hard, tough, chemically resistant film. The film formed is probably a new resin, possessing properties distinctly superior in many respects to those of either component resin. The modifying resin is frequently a flexible one in itself, but it need not necessarily be so, since two "brittle" resins (referring, of course, to the original physical state of each) may interreact to form an exceedingly tough, flexible film. As an example, the case might be cited of the combination of butylated melamine-formaldehyde resin with Epon resin. This latter is the polymeric reaction product of epichlorhydrin and bifunctional phenolic compounds (e.g., bisphenol-A). A resin suitable for modifying amino resins as described above must be soluble in a mutual solvent system, must be compatible (as judged by a perfectly haze-free film when the combination is baked out on glass), and must have sufficient hydroxyl functionality to allow for interaction with the amino resin. Under these conditions the reactive groups or "points of attack" of both resin components are combined, and a new resin is formed of superior properties during the process of film formation.

There are a number of modifying resins which meet the above requirements, but those most generally effective are the oil-modified alkyd resins;
polyvinyl butyrals; partially hydrolyzed polyvinyl chloride-acetate inter-
polymers; alcohol-soluble phenolic resins; and the "Epon" resins mentioned above. It is to be noted that all of these modifying resins contain
available hydroxyl groups, thus providing the necessary reactive points
essential to film compatibility. Of the modifiers mentioned, the alkyds
are by far the most common as well as the most generally satisfactory
types, and probably more than 85 per cent of the amino resin used in
this country at the present time is in such combinations. In passing, it
may be said that the introduction of the amino resins to the surface
coating industry was especially timely in that it was preceded by wide
acceptance of the alkyd resins. It is quite conceivable that had the amino
resins been introduced prior to this time, their good properties might
never have been understood, or at least their development would have
been very much retarded.

Practical Aspects. The alkyds constitute a class of synthetic resin
which enjoys greater volume usage in the surface coating industry of
today than any other single class of resin. Many of them are in themselves excellent film-formers and provide films of excellent quality on
either air-dry or bake applications when compared with the earlier oleoresinous varnishes (including those made with synthetic gums). The
alkyds are characterized by improved initial color and retention of color
under both light and heat; improved long-term gloss retention; adhesion;
flexibility; exterior durability; and speed of both air-dry and bake. The
introduction of the alkyds might be considered a major revolution in the
industry, since production schedules on line-finished articles were reduced
from baking time of 2 to 3 hours at approximately 250°F (the maximum
temperature considered safe at the time for most oleoresinous finishes)
to about one hour. When the amino resins were first used, baking schedules were reduced to levels theretofore considered impossible. Today,
baking schedules average around 5 to 15 minutes at 300°F, and many
applications employ bakes as fast as one minute or less at some higher
temperatures in excess of 450°F.

The use of amino resins imparts to an alkyd-amino resin finish
improved color, color retention, alkali-resistance, grease-resistance, sol-
vent-resistance, mar-resistance, and hardness. Naturally, the films are
less flexible than such as can be produced from alkyd resins alone.
With the urea resins, there is also some loss in exterior durability, but
with most melamine resins an *improvement* in durability is experienced.
Ordinarily, with the melamine resins the improvements in film properties
noted above are much greater than can be promoted by the use of urea
resins. Melamine resins do, however, detract from adhesion to a greater

extent than do most urea resins. Compensation for this deficiency may be made frequently by reducing the proportions of melamine resin in the combination, or by choice of an alkyd which compensates for this deficiency.

A considerable improvement in the initial color and in the color retention of baked films is effected by modifying even oxidizing alkyds with urea or melamine resins. These advantages are even more marked when amino resins are used with "nondrying" alkyds in baking finishes. The better resistance of such alkyds to discoloration under the influence of both heat and light contributes to the stability of the film. Such non-oxidizing alkyds would not form an impervious film if used as the sole film-forming resins. However, the "new resin" formed as the result of interaction with an amino resin is quite impervious to water and other chemicals, and possesses excellent physical properties. The resulting thermosetting film is cured largely by interaction of the alkyd and amino resins, and to a lesser extent by independent and separate condensation of the two resins. In contrast, a straight alkyd system of the oxidizing type depends to a greater extent on a much slower curing mechanism that involves both heat-induced polymerization and oxidation of its aliphatic unsaturation. To continue this contrast, a straight "nondrying" alkyd would be incapable of oxidation or polymerization of its aliphatic modifier and would, therefore, be unsuited as a film-former, unless it is baked in mixtures with aminoplast resins. Prior to the advent of amino resins, these types of alkyds were used almost exclusively as plasticizers for nitrocellulose lacquers.

Because of the above improvements imparted by amino resins, both melamine and urea types have enjoyed wide usage in modern baking finish formulations. Below are listed several types of finishes predominantly used in the industrial finishing of several articles encountered in everyday life:

Refrigerator enamel	Urea and/or melamine with alkyd
Washing machine enamel	Melamine with alkyd
Kitchen appliances	Urea or melamine with alkyd
Venetian blind (metal) enamel	Melamine or melamine-urea with alkyd
Automobile enamel-top coat	Melamine with alkyd
Automobile primer-surfacer	Urea with alkyd
Bicycle enamel	Melamine with alkyd
Exterior can coatings	Urea and/or melamine with alkyd
Brass articles	Urea with phenolic resin
Miscellaneous metal stampings ⎫ Metal furniture ⎭	Urea or melamine with alkyd
Wood furniture	Nitrocellulose lacquer or catalyzed urea with alkyd for low bake
Clear overprints	Melamine with polyvinylbutyral

Typical formulations for some of the above applications are shown in Table 10.6.

TABLE 10.6.   TYPICAL FORMULATIONS FOR VARIOUS APPLICATIONS

	Weight Per Cent
White Washing Machine Enamel	
Rutile titanium dioxide	25
Coconut oil modified (33%) alkyd (60% solids)	25
Dehyd. castor oil mod. (33%) alkyd (50% solids)	10
Type III melamine resin solution (60% solids)	10
Xylol	30
Black Automobile Enamel	
Carbon black	2.5
Soya-tung oil modified (41%) alkyd (50% solids)	54.0
Type II or III melamine resin solution (50% solids)	6.0
Xylol	37.5
White Enamel for Kitchen Appliances	
Rutile titanium dioxide	25
Soya oil modified (35%) alkyd (50% solids)	35
Type I urea resin solution (50% solids)	25
Xylol	15
White Refrigerator Enamel	
Rutile titanium dioxide	30
Undehyd. castor oil modified (47%) alkyd (60% solids)	18
Coconut oil modified (33%) alkyd (60% solids)	12
Type II urea resin solution (60% solids)	14
Type III melamine resin solution (60% solids)	6
Xylol	20
White Metal Venetian Blind Enamel	
Rutile titanium dioxide	25.0
Dehyd. castor oil mod. alkyd (33%) 50% solids*	40.0
Type I melamine resin solution (50% solids)	7.5
Type I urea resin solution (50% solids)	2.5
Solvent**	25.0

* In high-solvency, high-boiling aromatic solvent.
** Formulator to choose solvent blend of high, medium, and low boiling-range materials to suit bake schedule.

When formulating with amino resins, the amount to be used depends on the properties desired. In general, increasing amounts of amino resins impart the effects cited to an increasing degree. It is customary in formulating with urea resins not to exceed 50 per cent of the total binder, and in the case of melamines not over 40 per cent amino resin. However, recent data reveal that 65 per cent of Type III melamine provided a tough, durable film which showed negligible effects after weathering in Florida for one year. In addition, specialty applications can use as high as 90 per cent amino resin.

In addition to the broad choice between urea and melamine resins, from the viewpoint of formulation properties, a variety of selectives is

TABLE 10.7. PROPERTIES OF BUTYLATED MELAMINE RESINS IN ALKYD-AMINOPLAST ENAMELS

	Description	Alkyd Compat.	Cure Prop.	En'l Visc.	En'l Stab'y	En'l Gloss	Alkali Resis.	Min. Spts. Tolerance	Flexibility
Type I	(A) low CH_2O	short to med.	v. fast	high	fair	good	good	low	good
	(B) low CH_2O	short to med.	v. fast	low	v. good	good	good	med.	good
	(C) low to med. CH_2O	short to long	fast	low	exc.	v. good	good	high	v. good
Type II	(A) high CH_2O	med. to long	good	v. low	exc.	exc.	fair to good	ext. high	exc.
Type III	(A) med. CH_2O	short to long	v. good	low	good	exc.	exc.	low	v. good
Type IV	(A) med. CH_2O	short to long	v. good	*	*	exc.	exc.	v. low	v. good
	(B) med. CH_2O	short to long	v. good	med.	good	exc.	exc.	v. low	v. good

* Depends on solvent choice. Viscosity of enamel is, of course, very high with weak solvent or low with true solvent. Stability of enamel is poor with weak solvent but good with true solvent.

TABLE 10.8. PROPERTIES OF BUTYLATED UREA RESINS IN ALKYD-AMINOPLAST ENAMELS

	Description	Alkyd Compat.	Cure Prop.	En'l Visc.	En'l Stab'y	En'l Gloss	Alkali Resis.	Min. Spts. Tolerance	Flexibility
Type I	low CH$_2$O high visc.	short to med.	fast	v. high	fair	good	fair	low	good
Type II	high CH$_2$O low visc.	short to med.-long	med.	low	v. good	v. good	fair	med.	good
Type III	high CH$_2$O v. low visc.	short to long	slow	v. low	exc.	v. good	poor	high	exc.
Type IV	high CH$_2$O v. low visc.	short to long	slow	*	*	v. good	poor	low	exc.

* Same comment as for Type IV(A) melamine resin applies here.

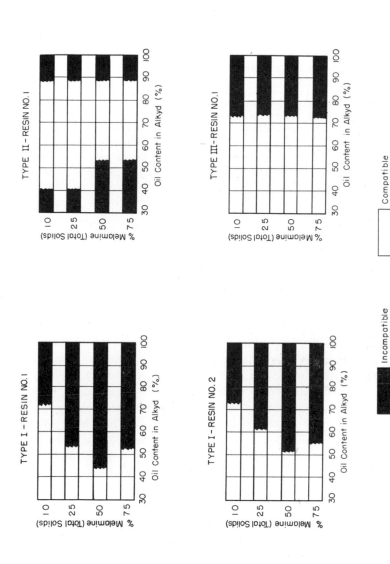

Figure 10.5. Compatibility of some melamine resins with soya oil alkyds.

possible within each group. Tables 10.7 and 10.8 illustrate some types that are used in formulations and suggest how advantage may be taken of their special properties according to the application intended.

In formulating with amino resins, certain precautions must be taken in order to avoid undesirable effects. Listed below are common troubles and effective means of overcoming them:

Blistering or popping	Allow adequate solvent evaporation prior to baking.
Oven flatting	Provide adequate ventilation in oven.
Oven crystallizing	Prevent chlorinated solvents from entering heating chamber.
Gelling of enamel	Select proper alkyd, amino resin, and solvent system. Enamels once gelled can often be recovered relatively easily.
Poor adhesion	Insure adequate cleaning of surface prior to coating.
Low gloss	Check compatibility of alkyd with amino resin. For example as in Figure 9.5.
Soft film	Inadequate bake time or temperature or alkyd too long in oil or insufficient amount of amino resin.
Sagging	Too much slow evaporating solvent in enamel.
Cratering or pinholing	Eliminate cause such as oil in air line, excessive antifoam agents, greasy surface.

Future Prospects. Future prospects for the use of amino resins in organic coatings will be along either or both of the following two lines: (1) new uses of present products, and (2) new amino resins for standard and new applications. Regarding the first, new applications for present products are being developed daily. Particular attention is being paid to reactive plasticizers other than alkyds. An excellent example is the "Epon" resin used with amino resins, and more particularly "Epon" in conjunction with alkyd and melamine. This latter three-component system provides a far better combination of hardness, toughness, adhesion, and chemical resistance than any alkyd-melamine systems. Another new application involves the use of melamine in air-dry lacquers and enamels to gain improved durability. Melamine provides interesting compounds when cured with blown linseed oil. The blown oil is both compatible and reactive, yielding a factice-like cured resin, and might find use in allied industries.

Regarding new amino resins, it appears that amino bodies other than urea and melamine are worthy of further study. In addition to improving present products, the goal of new resins would be to extend the use of amino resins into new fields. If the excellent durability provided by amino resins could be imparted to house paints and linoleum, the market could be tremendously increased and better products would result. Another approach involves the development of new reactive plasticizers to arrive at improved finishes through interreactive mechanisms.

Bibliography

1. Norris, W. C., and Bacon, T. C., "Chemistry and Application of Urea and Melamine Resins for Surface Coatings," *Off. Digest,* **285,** 785 (1948).
2. Burrell, H., "Development of Synthetic Resins for Protective Coatings," *Off. Digest,* **282,** 515 (1948).
3. Parker, C. H., "Review of the Fundamental Chemistry of and Applications for Some Amino Resins," *Off. Digest,* **315,** 237 (1951).
4. Glaser, M. A., "Formulation of Industrial Finishes," *Off. Digest,* **305,** 418 (1950).
5. Weed, F. G., and Beckwith, N. P., "Industrial Finishes and Finishing," *Off. Digest,* **280,** 383 (1948).
6. Thurmond, C. D., "Amino Resins," *Off. Digest,* **304,** 381 (1950).
7. Beckwith, N. P., Wint, R. F., and Parker, C. H., "High Resin Lacquers for Exterior Metal Finishing," *Off. Digest,* **331,** 518 (1952).
8. von Fischer, W., "Paint and Varnish Technology," Chapter X, New York, Reinhold Publishing Corp., 1948.

11 : Wood Properties that Affect Paint Performance*

F. L. BROWNE

Forest Products Laboratory,† Forest Service
U. S. Department of Agriculture

Five factors significantly affect the serviceableness of exterior paints on wood: (1) the kind and quality of the wood; (2) the effectiveness of the design of the building or structure in keeping the wood dry enough to hold paint; (3) the composition and quality of the paint; (4) the technique of application and the program of maintenance; and (5) the severity of the climatic and local conditions of exposure. This chapter deals chiefly with the first of these factors.

Achievement of the best possible service of paint on wood is complicated by the division of responsibility for the first four mutually dependent factors. The kind and quality of wood are determined, as a rule, before construction has been completed, usually by the designer, builder, lumber dealer, and often the owner.[3,23] The architect and builder are responsible for erecting structures adequately protected against entrance of water behind the painted woodwork.[2,33,34] The composition and quality of the paint are governed by its manufacturer, who may or may not disclose its ingredients.[16,22,25] The technique of application is fixed by the painter, often subject to limitation of the number of coats by the owner, and the program of maintenance is the responsibility of the owner.[7,17,26] The climatic and local conditions of exposure may need to be taken into account but ordinarily are not subject to control.[18] Many, if not most, of the disappointments so often experienced with paint service on wood stem from the difficulty in coordinating these factors.

Information about the performance of house paints on wood is derived from three sources. First, practical experience with paint on houses in

---

* Based on an illustrated lecture given to students in the course on paint technology at Case Institute of Technology, Cleveland, Ohio, December 5, 1950.

† Maintained at Madison, Wis., in cooperation with the University of Wisconsin.

service, particularly when troubles appear, affords a wealth of data otherwise unobtainable, including the consequences of renewing paint repeatedly over long periods of years.[15,35] The Forest Products Laboratory has kept records of more than 1,100 of the most instructive cases (one case often being a project containing hundreds of houses) examined by its staff during the past thirty years. In house service, however, the observer cannot control the variables or make tests in the systematic way needed for technical work. The second source, exposure of painted panels on test fences,[5,8] offers the experimenter wide freedom for orderly variation of woods, paints, technique, and place of exposure. Reports of some of the test fence studies made by the Forest Products Laboratory are listed in the bibliography.[1,3,4,9,10,11,12,13,19,21,27] But test fences fail to provide some of the conditions of moisture and temperature gradients that sometimes lead to troublesome paint behavior.[2,33,34] Special laboratory tests in which such conditions can be arranged under the control of the experimenter[8] have been designed as a third source of information.

PROPERTIES OF WOOD THAT AFFECT PAINTING

Lumber is cut from trees of many species. Grouping by species or closely related species is retained in merchandising because each species has characteristic average properties and finds uses accordingly. For some uses, paintability is a property of much importance, though other properties must usually be considered as well.

How a Tree Grows

In temperate climates, living trees grow only during the warmer part of the year and stand dormant during the colder weather. The trunk and branches of trees, the parts from which lumber is obtained, consist of woody tissue, technically called xylem, covered with a layer of bark. Terminal buds at the tips of the trunk and branches begin to advance each spring, but otherwise all growth of new woody tissue takes place at the junction between wood and bark, known as the cambium layer. Thus each year, a sheath of new wood is formed that completely covers all of the older wood in the trunk and branches. Each sheath in the trunk or in a branch has the shape of a gently tapering cone fitted snugly over the cone formed the year before. The wood formed during the early part of each growing season, called the springwood or early wood, is lighter in weight and coarser in texture than the summerwood or late wood formed near the end of the growing season. After most trees have reached a moderate age, the wood nearer the center of the trunk and branches undergoes further changes. It is then called heartwood to distinguish it from the unchanged wood, the sapwood. As a rule, heartwood is less readily permeable to liquids, contains less water, and is often darker in color than sapwood.

If the tree is cut down by sawing through the trunk just above the ground and the end of the trunk or the stump is smoothed sufficiently, most of the tree's history stands revealed. At the center is the pith, formed when the seedling sprang up or, in sections farther up the trunk, as the terminal bud advanced. In concentric rings about the pith, there are alternate layers of readily distinguishable springwood and summerwood. Each ring made up of the springwood and summerwood formed during one growing season is called an annual growth ring or annual ring. The number of these rings accurately reveals the age of the tree, and their relative thickness and proportions of springwood and summerwood tell much about the local climate during the life of the tree. When trees grow rapidly, the rings are wider than are those in slowly grown trees. It is customary to express rate of growth in terms of the number of rings to the inch along a radius of a cross section through the trunk. Cross sections through the trunk cut farther above the ground, of course, contain fewer rings because they lack all those for the years before the tree reached the height at which the section is cut. In most trees, the heartwood can be distinguished from the sapwood by its darker color. Sapwood is always light in color. Outside of the sapwood, there is a ring of bark.

When a tree trunk is cut into logs and the logs into boards, the two ends of each board lie in a cross section of the trunk and expose what is called end-grain wood, whereas the four sides lie in planes nearly parallel to the axis of the trunk. Two of the four sides of the board are apt to lie in planes tangent to the circular sections of the growth rings, in which case they are tangential faces and expose flat-grain wood. The other two faces then are approximately along a radius of the circular growth-ring sections and are radial faces exposing edge-grain wood. The board is said to be a flat-grain or an edge-grain board according as its two widest faces are flat grain or edge grain, respectively. On a flat-grain face, the annual rings form patterns of parabolas and ellipses and are much wider than they are on the cross section of the log. On an edge-grain face, the annual rings form a pattern of parallel lines in which each line is not much thicker than the width of a ring on the cross section of the log. Some boards can be cut so that the four faces are all much alike and have a grain pattern, called comb grain, about halfway between that of flat grain and edge grain. The two principal faces of an edge-grain board are essentially alike, but the two faces of a flat-grain board differ in that the growth rings lie with convex curvature toward the side nearer the bark of the tree (the bark side) and with concave curvature toward the side nearer the pith of the tree (the pith side).

Where branches emerge from the trunk of a tree, there is necessarily a disturbance of the normal arrangement of the wood cells, because within the branch, the longitudinal dimension is in the direction of the branch rather than in the roughly vertical direction of the trunk. In a growing tree, the new wood in the trunk must curve around the wood in the branch to fit snugly. As the tree matures in a forest stand, the lower branches generally die and drop off when they become too deeply shaded by the crowns of the trees. The wood of the trunk then closes over the gap left by the breaking off of the branch. When ready for cutting, the trunk then rises clear and unbroken for some distance above the ground, up to the first of the remaining branches. The outer portions of the lower logs from the tree, when cut into boards, contain only "clear" wood with the wood cells all arranged in their normal orientation. Nearer the center of the tree, however, there remain the butts of the branches that died and dropped off, and this branch wood forms areas of distorted grain in the boards cut through it. Such defects are called knots. In flat-grain surfaces, the knots present end-grain wood, whereas, in edge-grain surfaces, they present edge- or flat-grain surfaces with their longitudinal direction at a large angle to that of the clear wood of the tree trunk.

Lumber is graded for sale according to the number, size, and distribution of knots and other defects such as pitch pockets, heart rot, and imperfections of manufacture. The best and most expensive grades contain practically no defects. In softwood lumber, the four or five top grades are called select grades and are considered suitable for fine painting or finishing. The more knotty grades are called common grades.

Softwoods and Hardwoods

A sharp distinction is made between softwood lumber, which comes from coniferous or needle-leaved trees, and hardwood lumber, which comes from broad-leaved trees. The names have little to do with the actual hardness or softness of the wood, for such softwoods as southern yellow pine are harder than some hardwoods, such as cottonwood or yellow-poplar. In general, the greater its specific gravity, the harder the wood, whether the wood is classed as a softwood or as a hardwood.

As a class, the softwoods are more abundant, cheaper, more easily worked with tools, and better suited for the framework and exteriors of buildings than are the hardwoods. The best woods for exterior painting are all softwoods. Siding, shingles, exterior trim, and millwork are made predominantly from softwoods, though a few of the lighter weight hardwoods, such as yellow-poplar and basswood, were formerly used to some extent for such purposes. Heavier hardwoods, such as oak and birch, are sometimes used for front doors, door sills, and half-timbering.

Microscopic Structure of Wood

Wood is a complex structure made up of cells with rigid cellulosic walls and hollow centers; the walls of adjacent cells are cemented together with lignin. Softwoods are somewhat less complicated in structure than hardwoods.

In softwoods, the majority of the wood cells are tracheids, which are long, hollow cells (fibers) that are tapered and closed at the ends. The tracheids are roughly 2 to 4 mm long, less than 0.03 mm wide, and run vertically in the trunk of the tree. There are also ray cells, which run radially in the trunk and are shorter and blunter than the tracheids. The hollow centers of the tracheids and ray cells are not completely separated from one another because the cell walls contain small pits covered by membranes, some of which are known to have openings about 0.00002 mm in diameter. Air and liquids, if not too viscous, can pass through these small openings from one cell cavity to another, but the particles of nearly all paint pigments are far too large to do so. In the living tree, the tracheids and ray cells provide both mechanical strength and channels for movement of aqueous sap. In air-dry wood, the cells are empty except for air, which can move through the wood freely, though slowly. In some softwoods, such as the pines, spruces, larches, and Douglas-fir, certain openings called resin passages that run both vertically and radially are scattered between the cells. The true firs, hemlocks, cedars, baldcypress, and redwood normally have no resin passages.

Among softwoods, springwood and summerwood differ in the size of the cell cavities and in the thickness of the cell walls. In springwood, the cavities are large and the walls are thin; as much as 80 per cent of the volume of the air-dry wood may be air space. The springwood is therefore softer and lighter in both weight and color than the summerwood. In the summerwood, the tracheids are flattened radially, and have thick walls and small cavities; as little as 40 per cent of the volume of the wood is air space. Table 11.1 lists the specific gravity of springwood and summerwood samples whittled from the same annual growth rings of typical softwoods. Although summerwood has only half the capacity of springwood for holding liquids, liquids generally move through summerwood much more readily than through springwood. Contrary to popular expectation, paint oils penetrate deeper into the summerwood than into the springwood.

The weight of softwoods depends on the proportion of summerwood in their annual rings. A high proportion of summerwood makes the wood not

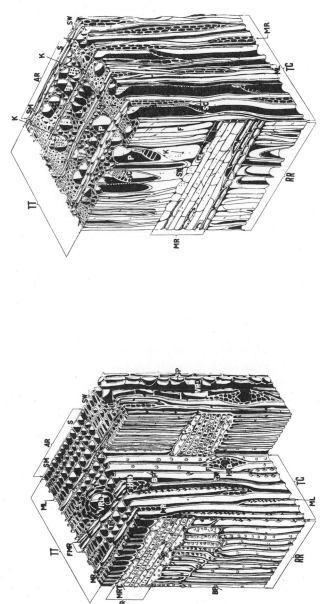

Figure 11.1.   Microscopic structure of a softwood (left) and of a hardwood with large pores (right). The top surface, *TT*, is transverse (end-grain); *TG*, tangential (flat-grain or plain-sawed); *RR*, radial (edge-grain or quarter-sawed); *AR*, annual growth ring; *S*, springwood; *SM*, summerwood; *MR*, wood ray; *ML*, middle lamella (lignin) which cements the cellulosic cell walls, *SW*, together. In the softwood, *TR* is tracheid; *MRT*, wood ray tracheid; *FMR*, fusiform ray containing horizontal resin passage *HRD*; *VRD*, vertical resin passage; *BP*, bordered pit; *SP*, simple pit. In the hardwood, *F* is fiber; *P*, pore or vessel; *SC*, open grid at spliced joint in a large pore; *K*, pits.

only heavy but strong and hard. The amount of summerwood in the annual growth ring may vary from more than half to an almost negligible proportion. There may also be great variations in the width of the annual growth rings, depending on the rate at which the wood grew. The number of rings may vary from less than two to more than one hundred per radial inch.

TABLE 11.1. SPECIFIC GRAVITY OF SAMPLES OF SPRINGWOOD AND SUMMERWOOD OF THE SAME ANNUAL GROWTH RING IN TYPICAL SOFTWOODS

Wood	Specific Gravity of:		Approximate Volume of Air Space*(%) in:	
	Springwood	Summerwood	Springwood	Summerwood
Baldcypress, 1st sample	0.332	0.941	78	37
Baldcypress, 2d sample	.282	.905	81	40
Douglas-fir	.469	.901	69	40
Fir (commercial)	.295	.901	80	40
Pine, ponderosa	.307	.843	80	44
Pine, southern yellow	.291	.953	80	37
Redwood, 1st sample	.317	.831	79	45
Redwood, 2d sample	.263	.768	82	49

* Computed by considering that the entire weight of the oven-dry wood is wood substance of specific gravity 1.5. This introduces an error, usually small in that the extractives in the wood are assumed to have the same specific gravity as wood substance.

In hardwoods, the functions of the tracheids are assumed by two types of wood cells: the fibers, which chiefly provide mechanical strength, and the vessels, which serve as the main channels for movement of sap in the living tree. In general shape, the fibers resemble the softwood tracheids; that is, they are long, tapered cells and closed at the ends, but, as a rule, are much smaller in size than the tracheids. Interspersed among the hardwood fibers are the vessels, which may be described as long pipelines extending longitudinally through the wood. In sapwood, the vessels afford clear passageways for fluids, but in the heartwood of some hardwoods, they are blocked by foam-like growths called tyloses. The vessels are approximately cylindrical and are open and spliced together at the ends; they are considerably larger in diameter than the fibers and are usually the elements that give characteristic appearance or "grain" to the hardwoods. The openings where the vessels intersect a surface are commonly called pores. It is convenient to classify the hardwoods on the basis of size and distribution of pores into:

(1) Hardwoods with relatively large pores
  Ring-porous hardwoods
  Diffuse-porous hardwoods
(2) Diffuse-porous hardwoods with relatively small pores

In ring-porous hardwoods, such as oak, chestnut, and ash, the pores are larger in the early springwood than in the summerwood, which has comparatively small pores. In diffuse-porous hardwoods, such as walnut, birch, and gum, the pores are more nearly uniform in size and distribution throughout the annual growth ring. In ring-porous hardwoods, the variation in size of the pores makes the summerwood denser and harder than the springwood. In diffuse-porous hardwoods, there is usually far less contrast in density between summerwood and springwood than there is in softwoods.

Chemical Nature of Wood

The walls of the wood cells consist chiefly of cellulose and closely related carbohydrates and some lignin. The cellulose of all woods is similar and possibly identical in chemical composition. By careful dissection, the walls can be seen to consist of a number of thin layers, much like the layers of an onion. Each layer can be further separated into fibrils, which are slightly spiraled about the long axis of the cell or, in some cases, wrapped around the cross section of the cells. The fibrils can be broken down into still smaller units. Most of the lignin occurs in the middle lamella, which is the cementing material between cells. The lignin is chemically very similar in all woods. For convenience, the cellulose and lignin together are called the wood substance.

Wood substance is a hygroscopic material that absorbs water and swells; its moisture content and volume come to equilibrium with the relative humidity of the surrounding air. At saturation, wood substance contains roughly 30 per cent by weight of water and is fully swollen. Green wood always contains more than enough water to saturate the wood substance, the excess remaining as liquid water or water vapor in the air spaces within the wood. As the wood dries, the free water is removed first. The moisture content when free water is absent but the wood substance is saturated is called the fiber saturation point. Further drying causes the wood substance to shrink, but only part of the shrinkage appears in changes in external dimensions of the board because part is taken up by change in the volume of the cavities in the wood cells. External shrinkage is greatest tangentially to the annual growth rings, somewhat less radially, and very slight longitudinally. Thus edge-grain boards shrink less in width than flat-grain boards, and neither kind changes much in length during drying, unless the boards contain an abnormal type of wood known as compression wood. When in the air-dry condition, wood is in a partly shrunken state in which its moisture content and dimensions are subject to change in response to changes in the relative humidity of the air. In their effects on the dimensions of wood, changes in relative humidity are usually much more important than changes in temperature.

The common paint liquids are taken up by wood only as free liquids in the air spaces and do not cause any change in dimensions of the wood. Alcohol, however, causes wood to swell slightly.

In addition to wood substances, wood contains extraneous constituents which can be removed fairly easily by extraction with suitable solvents and which are quite variable in nature and in amount, differing not only between species but often between heartwood and sapwood and in the heartwood in different parts of the same tree. The extraneous constituents are conveniently classified into those soluble in organic liquids, such as ether and alcohol, and those soluble in water.

The ether-soluble extractive of longleaf and slash pines is a resin containing turpentine and rosin. Rosin is a substance of acid reaction capable of forming soaps by reaction with basic paint pigments. The other pines, both white pines and yellow pines, contain similar resins in material amounts. Western redcedar, redwood, the true firs, Douglas-fir, hemlocks, spruces, and larches ordinarily contain only small amounts of ether-soluble extractives except for resins that occur in local deposits in the tree, such as pitch pockets. Hardwoods do not contain resins like those in the pines. Baldcypress and some of the cedars contain characteristic oils soluble in ether and some which are soluble in linseed oil. These oils are quite different chemically from the piny resins and contain very little material of acid reaction. Alcoholic extracts from wood usually contain most of the ether-soluble substances and some of the water-soluble ones.

The water-soluble extractives include tannins and other complex organic substances often of an aromatic nature; highly colored carbohydrates; organic acids like formic, acetic, and their homologs; traces of organic nitrogen compounds; and mineral constituents of wood ash. Woods in which the heartwood is strongly colored, such as redwood, redcedar, and walnut, owe their color chiefly to extractives of this class.

Table 11.2 shows the average content of extractives found in boards of different softwoods. The boards were used in test panels for a series of exposure tests started in 1924.[1,3] When the paint tests were completed, the boards provided the material for the analytical study.

Painters often call the bands of summerwood in softwoods "pitch streaks," because they attribute their darker color and hardness to the presence of resin. True pitch streaks, however, do not follow the annual growth rings and affect both springwood and summerwood. Moreover, the summerwood of softwoods that are relatively free from resin is often just as hard and dark in color as that of resinous species (Table 11.1). Summerwood and springwood of the same growth rings were whittled out of

boards of ponderosa pine and southern yellow pine and their content
of extractives determined with the results shown in Table 11.3. Boards of

TABLE 11.2. AVERAGE CONTENT OF EXTRACTIVES IN THE BOARDS OF SOFTWOODS
USED FOR THE 1924 SERIES OF PAINT TESTS

| | Per Cent Dry Wood Soluble in: | | | | Potassium Hydroxide (mg) Required to Neutralize Extract from 1 Gram of Dry Wood by: | |
Wood	Cold Water	Hot Water	Ethyl Alcohol	Ethyl Ether	Ethyl Alcohol	Ethyl Ether
Baldcypress	1.6	2.0	9.0	5.5	2.3	1.4
Douglas-fir	3.7	5.8	4.3	1.0	5.5	.7
Fir (commercial)	2.0	3.1	2.7	.6	1.4	.5
Hemlock, eastern	2.9	4.2	5.0	1.2	3.5	1.0
Hemlock, western	2.7	3.8	3.4	.4	4.7	.4
Larch, western	14.9	17.0	4.0	1.1	4.6	1.0
Pine, eastern white	2.9	5.1	8.0	4.0	6.7	3.7
Pine, ponderosa	2.4	5.0	5.7	3.3	6.9	3.9
Pine, southern yellow	3.5	6.2	8.5	5.2	8.2	7.1
Pine, sugar	4.5	7.2	9.0	4.3	8.5	5.9
Pine, western white	2.8	4.3	6.5	3.3	5.6	3.0
Redcedar, western	8.0	11.5	13.2	1.4	7.5	1.4
Redwood	6.4	10.9	11.8	.7	.6	.5
Spruce, eastern (com.)	1.3	2.4	2.2	.7	1.6	.7
Spruce, Sitka	2.7	4.6	3.6	.6	2.7	.8
White-cedar, Port Orford	2.5	4.0	3.8	.8	2.7	.4
Yellow-cedar, Alaska	2.8	3.9	4.0	1.3	2.9	.8

TABLE 11.3. CONTENT OF EXTRACTIVES FOUND IN SPRINGWOOD AND SUMMERWOOD
OF THE SAME ANNUAL GROWTH RING IN PONDEROSA PINE AND
SOUTHERN YELLOW PINE

| | Per Cent Dry Wood Soluble in: | | |
Description of Wood	Cold Water	Hot Water	Ethyl Alcohol
Ponderosa pine, springwood	1.8	3.0	3.53
Ponderosa pine, summerwood	1.6	2.8	3.08
Southern yellow pine, springwood	1.6	5.3	4.76
Southern yellow pine, summerwood	1.2	3.3	4.36
Southern yellow pine, springwood	2.0	6.3	25.42
Southern yellow pine, summerwood	1.1	3.9	17.71
Southern yellow pine in which the resin was evident to visual inspection, springwood	1.3	6.3	37.10
summerwood	1.2	4.1	24.42

high resin content had more extractives in the springwood than in the
summerwood, whereas those of low resin content had a fairly uniform
distribution of resin between springwood and summerwood.

Behavior of Paint on Woods During Application

The first coat of paint applied to new wood is very largely consumed in filling the cavities of those wood cells that were cut open in planing the surface of the boards. Much of the liquid of the priming-coat paint penetrates deeper into the wood because it can pass through the pit membranes

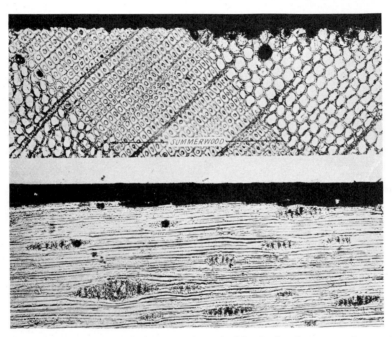

Figure 11.2. Photomicrographs of a coating of white lead paint on southern yellow pine, by transmitted light. The upper view is a transverse (end-grain) section and the lower view a longitudinal section. The paint appears black because it is opaque. The paint penetrates into the cavities of only those tracheids that open into the painted surface because the pigment particles are far too large to pass from one cavity to another. Linseed oil from the paint, however, penetrates far deeper into the wood. Under the microscope, oil can be seen filling some of the tracheid cavities in the summerwood below the painted surface, but this oil does not show in the photographs because it is transparent.

in the cell walls and reach the cavities in wood cells beneath the surface. Since woods vary in the volume of cavities presented at the surface and in their absorptiveness for liquids, they likewise vary somewhat in consumption of priming-coat paint. In comparison with porous materials like plaster, concrete, and stucco, however, wood consumes relatively little paint because its structure is cellular rather than labyrinthine or sponge-like.

Consumption of Paint by Different Softwoods

During the exposure tests on different softwoods started in 1924, careful record was kept of the amount of paint consumed.[1] There were forty-four panels of each wood. Sets of panels were painted by each of eleven painters, of whom four were professional painters and seven were technical men

TABLE 11.4. SPECIFIC GRAVITIES AND SPREADING RATES FOUND FOR PRIMING-COAT PAINT ON SOFTWOODS WHEN NEW AND AFTER WEATHERING FOR 1 YEAR

Wood	Specific Gravity of Wood	Approximate Volume of Air Space in Wood* (%)	Average Spreading Rate of Priming-Coat Paint on: (sq ft/gal)	
			New Wood	Wood Weathered for 1 Year
Woods with spreading rates below 640 sq ft/gal				
Fir (commercial)	0.362	76	612	379
Hemlock, eastern	.375	75	†601	411
Spruce, Sitka	.395	74	620	398
Hemlock, western	.473	68	625	400
Pine, sugar	.362	76	614	283
Redcedar, western	.330	78	618	396
Redwood	.370	75	588	312
Woods with spreading rates between 640 and 700 sq ft/gal				
Douglas-fir	.495	67	666	319
Pine, eastern white	.374	75	682	360
White-cedar, Port Orford	.444	70	†673	424
Woods with spreading rates above 700 sq ft/gal				
Baldcypress	.408	73	738	410
Larch, western	.520	65	752	360
Pine, ponderosa	.421	72	768	415
Pine, southern yellow	.531	65	790	398
Pine, western white	.402	73	742	349
Spruce, eastern (commercial)	.388	74	†770	394
Yellow-cedar, Alaska	.432	71	766	457
Average for all woods tested			685	380

* Computed by considering that the entire weight of the oven-dry wood is wood substance of specific gravity 1.5. This introduces an error, usually small, in that the extractives in the wood are assumed to have the same specific gravity as wood substance.
† Eastern hemlock, Port Orford white-cedar, and eastern spruce were not represented by full sets of test panels so that the data for these woods are not fully comparable with those for the other woods.

or laboratory aids in paint-testing laboratories. The average spreading rates for priming-coat paint (square feet covered by one gallon of paint) on the different woods and the average specific gravities of the woods are given in Table 11.4. In general, the spreading rate varied directly with the specific gravity; that is, the lower the specific gravity the lower the spreading rate. Low specific gravity, of course, indicates a relatively large proportion of springwood with its larger cavities in the tracheids. There are, however, other factors affecting spreading rates, because redwood, Sitka spruce, western hemlock, and Douglas-fir had somewhat lower spreading rates than would be indicated by their specific gravities. Paint seems to wet these woods very quickly, and the oil is absorbed while the brush sweeps over it, thus encouraging the painter to apply more paint.

It should be emphasized that the extent of the variation in paint consumed is too small to be of much practical importance. Redwood took about 11 per cent more and southern yellow pine about 13 per cent less priming paint than the average wood. The spreading rates of second-coat and third-coat paint were independent of the nature of the wood so that the variations in total paint consumed amounted to roughly plus or minus 4 per cent of that required for the average wood. By mixing the priming paint for redwood with slightly more and that for southern yellow pine with slightly less liquid, the variations could be offset entirely.

Personal variations among painters exert far more effect on spreading rates than variations between woods. In the experiments of the 1924 series, the average spreading rate at which the different painters applied priming-coat paint varied from 561 to 869 square feet per gallon. The experienced painters applied paint more generously than the technical men and the laboratory aids, because the former had an average spreading rate of 604 and the latter 751 square feet per gallon. For three-coat painting with the paints commonly used in 1924, the priming coat was properly spread at approximately 600 square feet per gallon for best results. All of the spreading rates for new wood in Table 11.4 should be regarded as too high, though they probably were representative of much practical painting at that time, and in any case they reveal the extent of variation between species reasonably well. In more recent years, the composition of paints underwent important changes. The connection between these changes in paint and the desirable spreading rates has been discussed elsewhere.[21]

The discussion so far refers to smoothly planed wood, such as the planed side of house siding. Rough surfaces, such as the sawed side of bevel siding, take much more paint. Weather-beaten wood becomes rough and consumes much paint if subsequently painted. The last column of Table 11.4 presents data for smoothly planed woods exposed vertically facing south at Madison, Wisconsin, in 1924 and painted one year later after they had become greatly roughened. After weathering, all woods seem to be greedy for paint and no relation can be discovered between spreading rate and specific gravity of the wood.

Hardening of Paint on Different Woods

Ordinarily the time of hardening of paint depends almost entirely on the composition of the paint, the intensity of sunlight, and the temperature and relative humidity of the air. Extractives present in certain woods, however, may retard hardening under certain circumstances.[19,28,29] In full sunshine and at temperatures above 70°F, paints made with sufficient drier should harden promptly on all native woods, provided that the wood is reasonably dry and the relative humidity of the air is not unusually high. Exceptionally oily boards of baldcypress, however, may retard the hardening of linseed oil paints that contain no white lead or zinc sulfide pigments. On redwood and baldcypress containing much more than 20 per cent moisture, priming-coat paint may remain liquid for days, especially in the absence of sunshine, at temperatures well below 70°F, and with paints that contain no white lead or zinc sulfide pigment. Unverified reports from industrial sources point to difficulty with hardening of paint under similar conditions on some of the hardwoods that are relatively rich in tannins, such as the oaks, chestnut, and walnut. The identity of the extractives in woods that are responsible for retarded hardening of paint is not yet known. It has been proved that the responsibility lies with some of the extractives because water-soluble extract of redwood and alcohol extract of baldcypress have been transferred to white pine and eastern hemlock and imparted to those woods the property of retarding hardening under the circumstances described.[19]

Filler Necessary on Hardwoods with Large Pores

Ordinary painting by hand brushing or spray application does not succeed in filling the large pores in hardwoods that have pores larger than those in birch. The largest pores remain as observable depressions

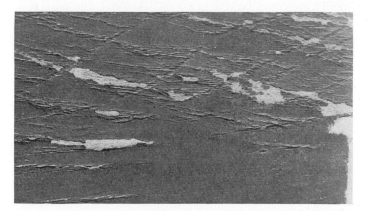

Figure 11.3. Large pores in hardwood, unless properly filled with wood filler, cause early failure of paint or enamel coatings. The illustration shows failure of a green enamel finish on the back of a chair made of elm after about 6 months exposure in a baseball park. The same enamel gave good service on metal parts of the chair. Failure on the elm began at the depressions in the coating over the large pores, which were not filled.

or as holes in the coating even after three substantial coats of paint have been applied. As time passes, the disintegration of the coating sets in abnormally early at these points of weakness and shortens the life of the coating. Apparently paint that is fluid enough for application by brush or spray gun is too fluid to plug or bridge large pores adequately. If the large-pored hardwoods must be used under paint coatings, they should first receive a wood filler, that is, a pigment paste thinned with volatile thinner for convenient application and then rubbed into the pores shortly after the volatile thinner has evaporated. A smooth, level surface for the reception of subsequent coats of paint can be produced in this way, but the extra cost of the filling operation makes the proper painting of large-pored hardwoods relatively expensive.

Defects in Lumber of Low Grade

When lumber is to be cut into smaller pieces for use, it is sometimes economical to buy lumber of a common grade, cut out the defects, and obtain clear lumber for the important surfaces. Even then the wood may be somewhat inferior for painting to lumber of the same species in a select grade, because the common grades come in considerable proportion from parts of the tree that grew rapidly, have wider growth rings, and do not hold paint quite so well as the wood of somewhat later growth. In building construction, however, where nearly all of the lumber is used with as little cutting as possible, defects in common grades must be covered with paint.

Very small knots may be concealed satisfactorily and may retain paint about as well as the clear wood. Knots are often unusually absorptive of the oils in paint and therefore tend to make the paint lose its gloss over the knots. Large knots can rarely be concealed because they do not follow the clear wood in swelling and shrinking with changes in moisture content, and on weathering they often crack open, breaking the coating over them. Over knots in both white and yellow pines, paint often becomes promptly discolored with a yellow substance that appears to be soluble in linseed oil, and the coating over the knot soon becomes brittle and scales off. For that reason, and to keep the knots from taking too much oil from the paint, it is common practice to shellac knots. The shellac is most effectively applied after putting on the priming-coat paint, not before. Unfortunately shellac is not so durable for exterior exposure as a good paint, but somewhat longer life over the knot can be obtained by adding 5 or 6 ounces of castor oil to a gallon of the shellac varnish. The Western Pine Association recommends in place of shellac a special knot sealer made of synthetic resins. When aluminum priming paint is used, an extra application over the knots may prove more satisfactory than

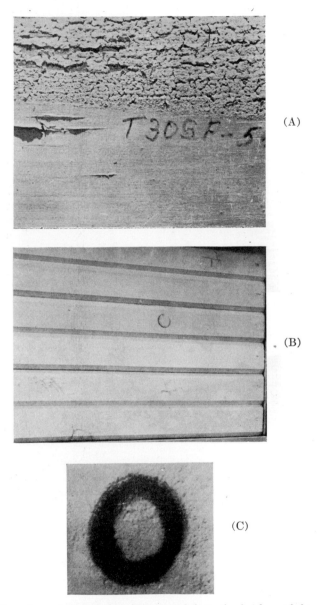

(A)

(B)

(C)

Figure 11.4. Premature failures of paint over defects in lumber of low grade. (A) cracking and flaking of the coating over a pitch streak while the coating is still reasonably sound over the clear wood below the pitch streak. (B) unsatisfactory appearance over knots and raised grain even though the coating remains intact over the knots (although the knots themselves crack badly). (C) discoloration and flaking of paint over a knot in one of the pines long before the coating over the clear wood has begun to disintegrate.

TABLE 11.5. CLASSIFICATION OF NATIVE WOODS FOR ABILITY TO HOLD AGED COATINGS OF HOUSE PAINTS

Paints of type A are those that fail by checking and crumbling, such as pure white lead paint and most red barn paints; those of type B fail by cracking, curling, and flaking, such as paints containing zinc oxide in the pigment or much hard resin in the vehicle.

Group No.	Description of Group	Forest Service and Other Common Names	Botanical Name	Representative Specific Gravity[1]
1	Woods on which paints of types A and B disintegrate slowly.	*Softwoods:*		
		Baldcypress (southern cypress)	*Taxodium distichum*	0.42
		Alaska yellow-cedar (Alaska cedar)	*Chamaecyparis nootkatensis*	.42
		Atlantic white-cedar[2]	*Chamaecyparis thyoides*	.31
		California incense-cedar[2]	*Libocedrus decurrens*	.35
		Northern white-cedar[2]	*Thuja occidentalis*	.29
		Port Orford white-cedar (Port Orford cedar)	*Chamaecyparis lawsoniana*	.40
		Western redcedar	*Thuja plicata*	.31
		Redwood	*Sequoia sempervirens*	.41
2	Woods on which paints of type A disintegrate slowly but those of type B disintegrate somewhat more rapidly than they do on woods of group 1.	*Softwoods:*		
		Eastern white pine (northern white pine)	*Pinus strobus*	0.34
		Sugar pine	*Pinus lambertiana*	.35
		Western white pine	*Pinus monticola*	.36
3	Woods on which paints of types A and B disintegrate more rapidly than they do on woods of group 1.	*Hardwoods:*		
		American basswood[2]	*Tilia americana*	0.32
		Aspen	*Populus* sp.[3]	.35
		Cottonwood[2]	*Populus* sp.[3]	0.32 to 0.37[3]
		Magnolia[2]	*Magnolia* sp.[3]	.40 to .46[3]
		Yellow-poplar (Yellow poplar)	*Liriodendron tulipifera*	0.38
		Softwoods:		
		Fir	*Abies* sp.[3]	.35

	Eastern hemlock	*Tsuga canadensis*	.38
	Western hemlock	*Tsuga heterophylla*	.38
	Lodgepole pine[2]	*Pinus contorta latifolia*	.38
	Ponderosa pine	*Pinus ponderosa*	.38
	Eastern spruce	*Picea* sp.[3]	.37
	Engelmann spruce	*Picea engelmannii*	.31
	Sitka spruce	*Picea sitchensis*	.37
4 Woods on which paints of types A and B disintegrate more rapidly than they do on woods of group 3.	*Hardwoods:*		
	American beech[2]	*Fagus grandifolia*	0.56
	Birch	*Betula* sp.[3]	0.45 to 0.60[3]
	Maple	*Acer* sp.[3]	.44 to .57[3]
	Sweetgum (red gum)	*Liquidambar styraciflua*	0.44
	Black tupelo[2] (blackgum)	*Nyssa sylvatica*	.46
	Water tulepo[2] (tupelo gum)	*Nyssa aquatica*	.46
	Softwoods:		
	Douglas-fir	*Pseudotsuga taxifolia*	.45
	Western larch	*Larix occidentalis*	.48
	Red pine (Norway pine)	*Pinus resinosa*	.44
	Southern yellow pine	*Pinus* sp.[3]	0.45 to 0.64[3]
	Tamarack[2]	*Larix laricina*	.49
5 Wood unsuitable for conventional house painting because wood filler is required to fill the pores properly.	All hardwoods with pores larger than those in birch, such as ash, chestnut, elm, hickory, oak, walnut.		

[1] Average specific gravity for the species (based on oven-dry weight and volume when green) listed in U. S. Dept. of Agriculture Technical Bulletin No. 158, "Comparative Strength Properties of Woods Grown in the United States." Within any species individual boards may vary widely from the average specific gravity.

[2] Species not included in comparative paint tests but classified according to similarity in properties to one or more of the species that were tested.

[3] More than one species of the family known by the same common name. In many cases commercial shipments of lumber bought under the common name will contain boards from two or more of the species. For example, southern yellow pine lumber may contain boards from one or more of the following: loblolly (*Pinus taeda*), longleaf pine (*Pinus palustris*), pitch pine (*Pinus rigida*), shortleaf pine (*Pinus echinata*), and slash pine (*Pinus caribaea*).

shellac. It is seldom desirable to shellac knots in any wood other than pine, because knots in such woods do not discolor or embrittle paint and often hold paint longer than the clear wood.

Pitch pockets are best painted by cutting them out with a chisel and filling the cavities with good putty after the priming-coat paint has been applied. Knot holes should be puttied in the same way. Pitch streaks may mar the painted surface by exuding resin and embrittling the coating, but the writer knows of no method of dealing with them satisfactorily except by rejecting the board or at least that part of it containing the pitch streak. Loose grain likewise is beyond remedy. Wood checks or cracks should be puttied after priming to keep them from acting as centers of early disintegration of the coating.

By the time that proper attention has been given to the defects in common grades of lumber, the extra costs usually make it more expensive than the select grades that are better suited to uses calling for painting. For uses in which good paint service is important, select grades of the woods of groups 1 and 2 of Table 11.5 are best; but if cheaper woods must be chosen, it will often be better to buy a select grade of a cheaper species than a common grade of a wood of group 1 or 2.

EFFECT OF WOODS DURING EARLY LIFE OF PAINT

As a rule, the nature of the wood has little effect on the behavior of paint during its early life, say during the first year or two after application. The composition of the paint, the adequacy of the technique of application, and the local and climatic conditions are usually much more important during this period than the kind of wood.

Undesirable early developments over defects in lumber of low grade have already been discussed. Exudation of resin through paint coatings over clear wood sometimes occurs early without impairing the integrity of the coating.[28] It is observed on the pines more often than on other softwoods, but has been found occasionally even on softwoods that contain relatively little piny resin. Such exudation is most likely to occur when the lumber has been seasoned at low temperatures and is used soon after manufacturing. Lumber kiln dried at higher temperatures or stored for some time before use is less likely to exude resin because less of the turpentine is left in the resin to make it soft enough to move freely. The oils in Alaska yellow-cedar, Port Orford white-cedar, eastern redcedar, and baldcypress may come through paint and collect in a sticky mass on the surface if there is no circulation of air over the surfaces, as when boards are stacked on top of one another.[28] There is no such occurrence if air circulates over the surfaces because the oils are slowly volatilized.

Colored water-soluble extractives in western redcedar, redwood, and some of the hardwoods do not come through sound paint coatings unless free water in some way gets into the wood behind the coating. If cracks appear in the coating, the coating at the edges of the cracks may be discolored for a short time immediately after a rain storm, but the writer has never seen enough discoloration so produced to affect materially the good appearance of the coating.

Occasionally, flat-grain boards of softwoods exposed to the weather and painted on the pith side will develop loose grain and crack the coating within a few months, even though there was no evidence of loose grain when the paint was applied. The bark sides of such boards rarely, if ever, develop loose grain. The pines seldom show loose grain even on the pith side except on floors or other places of severe mechanical wear.

If long life of paint coatings is to be assured, the moisture content of lumber must remain always well below the fiber-saturation point. When free water accumulates within the wood, early failures of paint may occur. These failures are discussed in detail elsewhere.[2, 33, 34]

EFFECT OF WOOD PROPERTIES ON DISINTEGRATION OF PAINT

The deterioration of paint coatings proceeds in successive but overlapping stages as follows:[14]

(1) *The soiling stage.* The coating gradually becomes dirty.

(2) *The flatting stage.* The coating loses its gloss.

(3) *The chalking stage.* Dirt may be thrown off more or less completely, but colors appear to fade.

(4) *The fissure stage.* Fissures are of two general types, depending upon the nature of the paint:

(a) Checking. The fissures are at first superficial but later may penetrate entirely through the coating.

(b) Cracking. The fissures pass entirely through the coating when first observed. The coating at the edges of the cracks sooner or later comes loose from the wood and curls outward. As a rule, cracking comes at a more advanced stage of deterioration than checking.

(5) *The stage of disintegration.* Behavior in the fissure stage determines the form in which disintegration takes place:

(a) Erosion, which is the gradual wasting away of the coating from its surface until it becomes too thin to hide the wood satisfactorily. Crumbling or flaking usually sets in before sufficient erosion occurs to uncover the wood.

(b) Crumbling, which develops from checking and is the falling away of tiny fragments of coating cut off when the fissures become interwoven (reticulate) and penetrate entirely through the coating.

(c) Flaking, which develops from cracking and curling. The loosened edges of coating that curl outward finally fall off, after which the newly formed edges curl and the process continues progressively. Flaking is usually a more rapid form of disintegration than crumbling.

The soiling, flatting, and chalking stages may be considered the early life of the coating, the fissure stage the later life, and the stage of disintegration the period of paint neglect. Good practice in paint maintenance calls for repainting before the coating has passed far into the period of neglect but not before erosion has become well advanced.[35]

The effect of the wood on the life of the coating usually appears first after the fissure stage is reached and, if the coating is not too thick, dominates further developments by the time disintegration sets in. Up to the fissure stage, the coating seems to remain tough and adherent enough to stay intact. Fissures appear when these properties are lost and the coating becomes brittle, loses its adherence to the wood, and remains clinging to the surface chiefly through mechanical anchorage to the cavities of the wood cells at the surface of the boards.[6] The situation might be expressed by saying that in its early life the coating sticks to the wood, but when the paint has become embrittled with age the wood holds the coating as best it can.

In softwoods, the springwood holds the aged coating to better advantage than the summerwood because of the larger cavities in the wood cells (Table 11.1), not because of a difference in resin content (Table 11.3). At any rate, disintegration proceeds much more rapidly over the summerwood than it does over the springwood, and the amount and distribution of summerwood in softwood boards very largely determine how long the coating lasts. On hardwoods, the principal factors seem to be the size and distribution of the pores and the specific gravity of the wood. Repainted coatings behave in much the same way as initial coatings, except that the fragments of coatings that fall off may be somewhat larger and may not begin to fall off quite so soon.

Specific Gravity of Wood

Since the proportions of summerwood and springwood very largely govern both the specific gravity and the rate of disintegration of aged paint on softwood boards, a definite relation between specific gravity and paint durability on softwoods is to be expected. Such a relation is shown in Figure 11.5, in which the average durability of the paint coatings on the softwoods tested in the 1924 series is plotted against the average specific gravity of the boards of those species used in the tests. In general, the woods that held aged paint well were the woods of low specific gravity, and those that held it poorly were high in specific gravity. The relation is by no means exact, however, because paint was held better by redwood, baldcypress, Alaska yellow-cedar, and Port Orford white-cedar and more poorly by fir than indicated by the specific gravity of these woods. Reasons for these discrepancies are suggested in subsequent paragraphs.

Figure 11.6 presents similar data obtained in the 1930 hardwood series. If hardwoods with large pores, hardwoods with small pores, and softwoods are considered separately, the general relation between specific gravity and rate of disintegration of coatings applies for the woods within each group, but the relation differs for the three groups. On the hardwoods

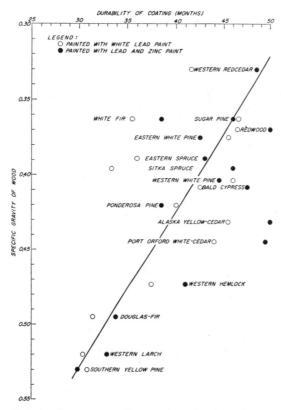

Figure 11.5.   Relation between specific gravity of softwoods and durability of coatings of house paint.

with small pores, the coatings lasted longer than they did on wood of equal specific gravity in the other two groups. The endpoint of the useful life of a coating occurs very early in the stage of disintegration, however, and if disintegration is allowed to proceed very far before repainting, the comparison between softwoods and hardwoods with small pores changes in favor of the softwoods. On the softwoods, the disintegration of the coating remains for a long time confined to the bands of summerwood, but on the hardwoods with small pores, the relatively uniform texture throughout the annual growth ring permits disintegration to spread fairly rapidly over the entire board. For that reason, only the lightest hardwoods with small pores should be considered as acceptable as the softwoods for

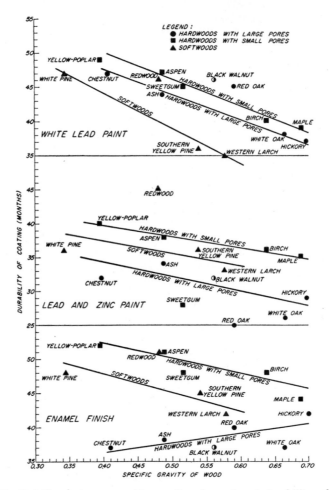

Figure 11.6. Relation between specific gravity of wood and durability of paint for (a) softwoods, (b) hardwoods with small pores, and (c) hardwoods with large pores. The enamel finish on hardwoods with large pores failed prematurely because of a faulty combination of pigments in a wood filler used on those woods only; consequently the normal relation of durability to specific gravity was not realized on those woods.

conventional house painting. None of the hardwoods with large pores can be regarded as satisfactory for such purposes because conventional painting leaves the pores unfilled.

Figure 11.7. Paint wears longer on some woods than on others. The appearance of a good house paint is shown after 8 years of exposure to the north on western redcedar (two upper boards at left), eastern white pine (two lower boards at left), Douglas-fir (two upper boards at right), and southern yellow pine (two lower boards at right).

Figure 11.8. Characteristic forms of paint disintegration on softwoods and on hardwoods with small pores. Upper view, badly neglected coating of lead and zinc paint on southern yellow pine. Disintegration is still largely limited to the bands of summerwood. Lower view, similarly neglected coating of lead and zinc paint on yellow birch. Disintegration of the coating has laid bare much larger areas of the wood.

Width of Annual Growth Rings in Wood

Among softwoods, the distribution as well as the amount of summerwood affects the disintegration of paint. For the same ratio of summerwood to springwood, the individual bands of summerwood are narrower the greater the number of annual growth rings per radial inch; that is, the less rapidly the wood grew. In Figure 11.1, the departures from the general relation between specific gravity and durability are largely attributable to such differences in width of annual rings. Many of the boards of fir used in the 1924 series of tests contained compression wood, which is an abnormal type of wood with a high proportion of summerwood but which is lighter in weight than normal summerwood. The fir likewise tended to have few annual rings per inch. These facts account adequately for earlier disintegration of the coatings on the fir than the specific gravity indicated. On the other hand, all of the boards of Alaska yellow-cedar and Port Orford white-cedar had many annual rings per inch, as did many of the boards of redwood and baldcypress. These woods therefore would be expected to hold paint longer than woods of similar specific gravity but fewer rings per inch.

Among the diffuse-porous hardwoods, the width of the annual growth rings seems to have very little bearing upon the rate of disintegration of coatings as would be expected from the fact that there is little difference in texture between springwood and summerwood. On the ring-porous hardwoods, all of which have large pores, the width of the growth rings likewise seems to be of minor importance.

Grain of Wood

Edge-grain boards of softwoods present much narrower bands of summerwood on the painted surface than flat-grain boards of similar specific gravity and rings per radial inch. For that reason, coatings last longer on edge-grain boards of softwoods.[20] Among the hardwoods, however, there seems to be less difference in the rate of disintegration of paint on edge-grain and flat-grain boards, especially among the hardwoods with small pores.

Variation within Species

Different boards of the same species, even different boards from the same tree, may vary widely in specific gravity and in number of annual growth rings per inch. The durability of paint varies correspondingly. Account is not taken of such variations in the commercial grading of lumber, except in structural timbers of some species where mechanical strength rather than paintability is the object in view. Whenever it is practicable to buy lumber on special specifications or to cull over a large supply of boards for those best suited for painting, it is possible to take advantage of the variation in specific gravity, grain, and rings per inch to select boards materially better for painting than the general average for the species.[23]

Results of tests on Douglas-fir begun in 1929 illustrate the possibilities in selection of lumber for painting. Five shipments of Douglas-fir siding were obtained, four representing so-called "red" and "yellow" Douglas-

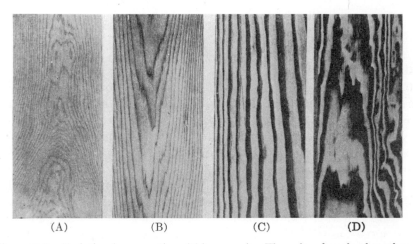

(A)   (B)   (C)   (D)

Figure 11.9. Variation in properties within a species. These four boards of ponderosa pine were taken from test panels after the paint coatings had worn out and were resurfaced to reveal the wood. Boards A and B held paint well, boards C and D poorly. Board A had 36 annual rings per inch, specific gravity 0.40; B had 27 rings, specific gravity 0.48; C had 6 rings, specific gravity 0.48; and D had 15 rings, specific gravity 0.73.

fir and with each subdivided into "soft" and "dense" types, and the fifth representing a special selection of Douglas-fir for good painting characteristics. "Red" and "yellow" Douglas-fir in "soft" and "dense" types are traditional classifications by lumbermen, but they are not recognized in the present methods of grading for sale. When the specific gravity and ring count of the boards were determined, the average values and ranges in these properties were much the same for the four groups, and the average durability of the coatings was likewise much the same. On the group specially selected for painting, however, the durability of the coatings was better than the average for the other four shipments, being forty-four months as compared with thirty-eight months. When the boards of all shipments were reclassified according to the measured specific gravity and further subdivided into flat-grain and edge-grain boards, the data of Table 11.6 were obtained. Edge-grain boards held paint longer than flat-grain boards of similar specific gravity, and boards of low specific gravity held paint longer than boards of the same grain but high specific gravity.

TABLE 11.6. VARIATION IN DURABILITY OF PAINT COATINGS ON DOUGLAS-FIR CLASSIFIED BY GRAIN AND BY SPECIFIC GRAVITY

Specific Gravity of Wood	Average Durability (months) of Coatings on:	
	Flat-grain Boards	Edge-grain Boards
Below 0.5	41	44
0.5 to 0.6	38	39
Above 0.6	29	37

Extractives in Wood

Certain extractives in wood of some species undoubtedly affect the durability of coatings, but in general the effect of such extractives is small in comparison with the effects of such physical characteristics as specific gravity, ring count, grain, and grade. This fact should be emphasized because the importance of extractives in wood is grossly exaggerated in much of the literature on painting.

It is difficult to account for the position of redwood, baldcypress, Alaska yellow-cedar, and Port Orford white-cedar in Figure 11.5 and of redwood in Figure 11.6 wholly on the basis of the high ring count in the lumber of those species used in the 1924 series and the 1930 hardwood series of tests. Some of the boards of redwood and baldcypress had relatively few annual rings per inch and yet held paint longer than the specific gravity indicated. In the 1930 extractive series, the cold-water extract of redwood and the alcohol extract of baldcypress were transferred to boards of eastern hemlock before painting. Disintegration of the coatings was definitely retarded by the redwood extract, but the results with the baldcypress extract were not so conclusive. It is possible that the ingredient in redwood responsible for the good effect on paint retention is the same one that retards hardening of paint under poor drying conditions. If so, the close botanical relation between redwood and baldcypress suggests that the same substance, or one similar to it, may occur in baldcypress among its water-soluble extractives rather than its alcohol-soluble ones, and that more significant results might have been obtained with the water rather than the alcohol extract of cypress.

Figure 11.5 reveals a difference between the pines and softwoods other than the pines in the relative durability of pure white lead paint and of lead and zinc paint. On each one of the pines, the pure white lead paint outlasted the lead and zinc paint, but the lead and zinc paint outlasted the white lead paint on all other softwoods. The same tendency appears in Figure 11.6, in that redwood and white pine held white lead paint about equally long, but redwood held lead and zinc paint much longer than white pine; the tendency is not so clearly shown, however, for southern yellow pine and western larch. With the two latter woods, the high proportion of summerwood dominates paint disintegration so much that minor effects of extractives are often obscured, but the tendency for paints containing zinc oxide to disintegrate faster on the pines of lighter weight than on other softwoods of similar specific gravity has run consistently through many series of tests. The data of Table 11.2 strongly suggest a connection between the ether-soluble extractives of acid reaction present in the pines and the relative rate of disintegration of paints that do and do not contain zinc oxide. The suggestion was confirmed in the 1930 extractive series of tests when it was found that transfer of the alcohol extract of ponderosa pine to eastern hemlock impaired the durability of lead and zinc paint but did not affect that of white lead paint. It is further in line with an opinion prevailing among paint experts that paints containing zinc oxide should be made with linseed oil in which there is no more than a very moderate amount of free acids, although linseed oil of materially higher acid number is considered suitable for making white lead paste paint.

The effect of the extractives in the pines seems to be due chiefly to the nature rather than to the amount of extract present in the wood. Since a very small volume of paint is placed on a relatively large volume of wood, it may well be that the least resinous boards of a pine contain enough of the reactive substance to complete whatever reaction takes place in the paint, in which case boards containing still more resin would act no differently. In a series of tests started in 1927, boards of southern yellow pine were sampled for determination of their content of ether-soluble extractive and then painted for observation.[27] The variations in durability of white lead and of lead and zinc paint followed closely the variations in specific gravity and ring count of the boards, but were independent of the content of ether extract, which varied from about 1 to nearly 20 per cent by weight of the wood.

CLASSIFICATION OF WOODS FOR PAINTING

Table 11.5 presents a classification of native woods according to their desirability for exterior house painting by conventional methods. Most of the woods are classified on the basis of the 1924 softwood series[3] and the 1930 hardwood series[13] of tests, together with observations of the woods in use on houses or other practical service. Changes made in commercial house paints in more recent years have not altered the effects exerted by the wood on paint behavior. A few less important woods that were not tested are classified according to their physical and chemical properties and their similarity to some of the woods tested. Average shipments of lumber of a select grade in mixed flat and edge grain are assumed. Lumber specially selected for superior painting characteristics, as pointed out in the preceding discussion, may be entitled to a higher rating than that given the species in Table 11.5

TABLE 11.7. PRODUCTION OF SOFTWOOD LUMBER IN THE UNITED STATES IN 1947 AS RELATED TO THE CLASSIFICATION OF WOODS FOR PAINTING

Woods Arranged by Groups According to the Preference for Painting	Production of Lumber in 1947	
	Total Quantity (million board feet)	Proportion of Total Softwood Lumber (%)
Group 1:		
Cedar	366	1.31
Cypress	240	0.86
Redwood	529	1.89
Total	1,135	4.06
Group 2:		
White pine	1,370	4.90
Sugar pine	343	1.23
Total	1,713	6.13
Group 3:		
Balsam fir	27	0.10
White fir	673	2.41
Hemlock	1,244	4.46
Spruce	392	1.40
Ponderosa pine	3,839	13.75
Lodgepole pine	100	0.36
Total	6,275	22.48
Group 4:		
Douglas-fir	9,042	32.35
Larch	292	1.05
Yellow pine	9,473	33.91
Total	18,807	67.31
All other	7	0.02
All softwoods	27,937	100.00

Table 11.7 shows that nearly 90 per cent of the softwood lumber supply of the United States consists of woods of groups 3 and 4. More than 67 per cent falls in group 4. There has been little change in the distribution among the groups as classified for painting during the past quarter of a century, and the changes that can be foreseen in the future will not decrease the predominance of group 4 woods. There are, therefore, strict limitations to the extent to which preference can be given in practice to

the best woods for painting. Much wood of group 4 is and must continue to be used for purposes in which painting is important.

It was found in tests started in 1925 and in other tests[11] that the difference between woods of groups 1 and 2 on the one hand and groups 3 and 4 on the other in their effect on durability of paint cannot be reduced materially by altering the proportions of pigments, linseed oil, and turpentine in the conventional priming-coat paint or by substituting special volatile thinners for the turpentine. The generous use of volatile thinners in priming coats for woods like southern yellow pine and Douglas-fir, though often recommended, is distinctly bad practice.[4,24] Numerous tests,[4,10,12,21] however, have shown that certain special priming paints used in place of the conventional priming paint add materially to the durability of paint on woods of groups 3 and 4. When such woods are to be painted, results more nearly comparable to those obtainable on woods of groups 1 and 2 will be obtained if one of these special priming paints is used.

The most satisfactory special priming paint so far discovered for this purpose is aluminum priming paint. It consists of 1¾ to 2 pounds of dry aluminum powder of standard varnish grade in 1 gallon of very long-oil spar varnish. If desired, 2 pounds of commercial paste aluminum or 1½ pounds of dry aluminum powder of standard lining grade may be used in place of the standard varnish powder. Aluminum priming paint, if properly applied so that the grain of the wood is entirely concealed, greatly retards crumbling or flaking of paint from the bands of summerwood, thereby minimizing the discrepancies in durability between different woods. Graphite priming paint made by adding 1 pound of flake graphite to 1 gallon of long-oil spar varnish seems to have much the same effect as aluminum primer, but graphite primers have not been widely used on wood. Next to aluminum primers, the zincless primers with so-called controlled penetration serve best to improve paint durability on woods of groups 3 and 4.[21,23]

MODIFICATION OF WOOD TO IMPROVE PAINTING

Many unsuccessful efforts have been made during the past twenty-five years to alter wood or the surfaces of woods of groups 3 and 4 so as to improve the performance of paint. Treatments with chemicals, resins, water repellents, sealers, or other additives have proved of little or no benefit. There have been a number of significant developments, however, that have succeeded in improving paintability, though not all of them came into use primarily with that result in mind.[36]

Perhaps the most radical way of modifying wood is to separate it almost, if not quite, into its fibers by suitable processing and then to reform it into fiberboard bound together with its own natural resins or added binders. Southern yellow pine, for example, is converted into large sheets of fiberboard in which the specific gravity can be controlled within reasonable limits and the troublesome alternations of hard summerwood and soft springwood give place to an approximate uniformity of texture. Although such fiberwood is not as strong for its weight as wood, it presents a surface that holds paint fully as well as do the woods of group 1.

Plywood and laminated wood, because of the greatly improved weather resistance of modern glues, afford an important means of making the limited supply of preferred woods and high-grade wood go further. For wall coverings such as siding, for example, clear wood of group 1 or 2 need be used only for one face veneer to provide good paintability, and the core and second face can then be of cheaper quality. Plywood is now made not only in large sheets but in patterns that may be erected to give either the appearance of bevel siding or that of flush siding. There is also available laminated material in which, for example, cedar lumber of low grade is covered on the exposed face with a thin veneer of clear, edge-grain cedar. The product, of course, has the paintability of its face veneer.

Plywood may be covered on one or both faces with ground wood or wood pulp bound together with suitable weather-resistant resin. Such products are now on the market. The paintability of the covered face is then similar to that of fiberboards, that is, equal to that of woods of group 1.

Paper impregnated and attached with weather-resistant resin may be used as a covering for the exposed faces of plywood or of lumber. Suitable impregnated papers for the purpose and also plywood so covered are commercially available. Impregnated papers are made in varying thicknesses, densities, and proportions of resin for different purposes. Some but not all of them have been tested for paintability when used as coverings for plywood. Excellent paintability, fully equal to that of woods of group 1, is obtained with papers of moderate density and resin content. Papers with too high a density or resin content, particularly those with highly glossy surfaces, probably are undesirable for best paintability.

Softwood plywood faced with veneers of wood in group 4 that were cut by the economical rotary method presents a surface with wide bands of summerwood and therefore ranks low in paintability. Under many conditions of use, particularly when exposed to the weather, it often tends to become seriously face-checked, even when well protected by paint. By grooving one or both of the face veneers with parallel grooves about $\frac{1}{32}$ inch deep, spaced about 8 or 9 grooves to the inch, the bands of summerwood at the surface are cut to very narrow widths, and both paintability and resistance to face checking are very greatly improved. Plywood striated in that way has been commercially available for some time. The paintability of such plywood is thereby raised from group 4 to at least the level of group 2, perhaps to that of group 1. About 11 per cent more of paint is needed to paint such a striated surface, corresponding to the increase in area of surface to be covered. Lumber, of course, can be striated with similar benefit to its paintability.

Although impregnation of wood with resins does not improve paintability and may impair it, significant improvement can be effected by impregnating the wood with certain resins which are in an early stage of resin formation and still of low molecular weight, and then completing the resin formation by applying heat. The resulting product, called "Impreg,"[30] swells and shrinks very little with changing moisture content, and it holds paint better than untreated wood of similar density and grain structure. Plywood or laminated wood, of course, may be made with "Impreg" for the face plies only. In a further modification of the process, the wood may be compressed while it is being heated to effect the final curing of the resin in the wood. The resulting product, called "Compreg,"[31] can be made in a range of densities up to that of wood substance itself, about 1.5. "Compreg" can be polished to a highly glossy, lustrous finish of great durability. Although "Compreg" may be painted, it would rarely be used for purposes requiring painting.

The hygroscopicity of wood, which gives rise to swelling and shrinking, resides largely in the hydroxyl groups of the glucose residues in the cellulose molecules. Water that causes swelling evidently attaches itself to such hydroxyl groups and possibly to similar polar groups in the lignin. By effecting stable chemical reaction between the hydroxyl groups and an organic radical of small size, such as an acetyl group, the active hydroxyl groups can be kept preoccupied to the exclusion of wood-swelling water. Acetylated wood has been made on a pilot scale for experimental purposes.[32] It has been found to be dimensionally very stable. There was some concern lest the blocking off of the polar hydroxyl groups might impair the adhesion of paint, but tests of the paintability of acetylated wood prove that it holds paint better than untreated but otherwise similar wood. The successful painting of acetylated wood suggests that if paint clings to wood by specific adhesion,[6] the polar hydroxyl groups of the wood are not essential for such adhesion.

The classification of woods for painting and the present knowledge of the wood properties that affect painting make it possible to select the best woods for the purpose when paintability can be made the dominant consideration in choice. Moreover, there are several ways in which paint performance on woods with less desirable properties for painting can be improved. As a general rule, however, other matters besides paintability must be considered in deciding upon the kind of wood to use in a given case. Even when the most satisfactory wood can be selected, it still remains necessary to see that the building is designed and used properly, to choose paint of suitable kind and quality, and to apply and maintain the paint correctly with due thought for the climatic and local conditions under which the painting must serve. The paintability of the wood is only one of the factors on which good paint service depends.

References

Single copies of the publications marked with an asterisk (*) are obtainable free on request from the Forest Products Laboratory, Madison, Wis., as long as the supply lasts. Publications of the Department of Agriculture are purchasable from the Superintendent of Documents, Washington 25, D. C. Other publications must be consulted in files of the journals in which they appeared.

1. Browne, F. L., "Spreading Rate of Outside White House Paints on Different Woods," *Drugs, Oils, & Paints*, **42**, 230, 268 (1927); *Painters' Magazine*, **54**, 10 (1927).
*2. ———, "Some Causes of Blistering and Peeling of Paint on House Siding," *Forest Products Lab. Rept. No. R6*, Revised (1933).
3. ———, "Properties of Wood That Determine the Service Given by Exterior Paint Coatings," *Official Digest Federation Paint & Varnish Production Clubs, No. 95*, 106 (1930); *Am. Paint J.*, **14**, 22 (April, 1930).
4. ———, "Effect of Priming-Coat Reduction and Special Primers upon Paint Service on Different Woods," *Ind. Eng. Chem.*, **22**, 847 (1930).
5. ———, "Procedure Used by the Forest Products Laboratory for Evaluating Paint Service on Wood," *ASTM Proc.*, **30** (2), 852 (1930).
6. ———, "Adhesion in the Painting and in the Gluing of Wood," *Ind. Eng. Chem.*, **23**, 290 (1931).
*7. ———, "When and How to Paint Homes and Farm Buildings," *Forest Products Lab. Rept. No. R962*, Revised (1938).
*8. ———, "Testing House Paints for Durability," *J. Chem. Education*, **10**, 529 (1933); *Forest Products Lab. Rept. No. 1011* (1933).
9. ———, "Durability of Paint on Longleaf and Shortleaf Pine," *Southern Lumberman*, **146**, 20 (Feb. 1, 1933).
10. ———, "Effect of Aluminum Priming Paint on the Durability of House Paints on Wood," *Ind. Eng. Chem.*, **26**, 369 (1934).
11. ———, "For the St. Paul Test Fence Committee, Fourth Progress Report, Priming Coat at Reductions for Painting New Wood Surfaces," *Am. Paint J.*, **19**, 7 (Dec. 10, 1934).
12. ———, "Special Priming Paints for Wood," *Ind. Eng. Chem.*, **27**, 292 (1935).
13. ———, "Painting Characteristics of Hardwoods," *Ind. Eng. Chem.*, **27**, 42 (1935).
14. ———, "The Effect of Change from Linoxyn Gel to Xerogel on the Behavior of Paint," *Colloid Symposium Monograph*, **11**, 211 (1935).
15. ———, "Repainting Paint Neglected Frame Houses," *Natl. Painters Mag.*, **2**, 15 (Apr., 1935), 14 (May, 1935), 6 (June, 1935); *Forest Products Lab. Rept. No. R1135* (1935).

16. ———, "A Proposed System of Classification for House Paints," *Ind. Eng. Chem.*, **29** (9), 1018 (Sept., 1937). Discussion by P. D. Buckminster, *Am. Paint J.*, **22** (3A), 7 (Oct. 6, 1937); reply by F. L. Browne, **100** (13), 24 (June 23, 1938). Discussion by F. L. Browne, *Nat. Paint Bull.*, **3** (5), 8 (May, 1939). Editorial comment, *Paint Ind. Mag.*, **55** (1), 9 (Jan., 1940); reply by F. L. Browne, **55** (3), 79 (Mar., 1940).

*17. ———, "The Program of Paint Maintenance for the Frame House," *Forest Products Lab. Rept. No. R1127* (1937).

18. ———, "Effect of Climatic Differences on Paint Behavior," *Pacific Purchaser*, **20** (2), 13 (Feb., 1938).

19. ———, "Effect of Extractive Substances in Certain Woods on the Durability of Paint Coatings," *Ind. Eng. Chem.*, **28**, 416 (1936).

20. ———, "Discussion of W. W. Kittelberger's Paper on 'Influence of Variation in Wood Graining Angle upon the Accelerated Weathering Testing of Exterior House Paints,'" *ASTM Bull. No. 107*, 34 (1940).

*21. ———, "The Two-Coat System of House Painting," **33**, *Forest Products Lab. Rept. No. R1259,* Revised (1950).

22. ———, "Classification of House and Barn Paints, as Recommended by the U. S. Department of Agriculture," *U. S. Dept. Agr. Tech. Bull. 804* (1942).

*23. ———, "Wood Properties and Paint Durability," *U. S. Dept. Agr. Misc. Pub. 629* (1947).

24. ———, *et al.*, "Round-Table Discussion of the Painting of Southern Yellow Pine," *Official Digest Federation Paint & Varnish Production Clubs*, **268**, 283–301 (1947).

25. ———, "Quality Standard for House Paint," *Miss. Valley Lumberman*, **80** (10), 13, 24 (Mar., 1949); *Western Bldg.*, **28** (3), 4, 6, 8, 10 (Mar., 1949); *Wood Working Digest*, 111–123 (Apr., 1949); *Buildings*, **49** (3), 37–38 (Mar., 1949).

26. ———, "Painting the Farm and City Home," *U. S. Dept. of Agr. Yearbook of Agriculture*, **1949**, 625–630.

27. ———, and Hrubesky, C. E., "Effect of Resin in Longleaf Pine on the Durability of House Paint," *Ind. Eng. Chem.*, **23**, 874 (1931).

*28. ———, and Rietz, R. C., "Exudation of Pitch and Oils in Wood," *Forest Products Lab. Rept. No. R1735* (1949).

29. Schmitz, F. C., and Palmer, F. C., "Drying of Exterior Paints under Various Weather Conditions and over Different Woods," *Ind. Eng. Chem.*, **22**, 84 (1930) (comment by F. L. Browne, p. 400).

*30. Stamm, Alfred J., and Seborg, R. M., "Forest Products Laboratory Resin-Treated Wood (Impreg)," *Forest Products Lab. Rept. No. 1380,* Revised (1950).

*31. ———, "Forest Products Laboratory Resin Treated, Laminated, Compressed Wood (Compreg)," *Forest Products Lab. Rept. No. 1381,* Revised (1951).

*32. Tarkow, Harold, and Stamm, Alfred J., "Acetylated Wood," *Forest Products Lab. Rept. No. 1593,* Revised (1950).

*33. Teesdale, L. V., "Condensation Problems in Modern Buildings," *Forest Products Lab. Rept. No. R1196,* Revised (1941).

*34. ———, "Remedial Measures for Building Condensation Difficulties," *Forest Products Lab. Rept. No. R1710* (1947).

*35. Browne, F. L., and Laughnan, D. F. "How Often Should a House be Painted," *J. Forest Products Research Soc.*, **2** (5), 173–93 (1952); *Paint, Oil, Chem. Rev.*, **115** (16) 16, and (17) 26 (1952).

*36. ———, and Laughnan, D. F. "Modification of Wood and Plywood to Improve Paintability," *J. Forest Products Research Soc.*, **2** (3), 3–24 (1952); *Forest Products Lab. Rept. No. D1926* (1952).

12 : Hot Spray Lacquers

R. F. WINT and F. E. PIECH

Hercules Powder Company
Wilmington, Delaware

Ordinarily it is a new raw material or a new formulation which is the basis for influencing trends in the lacquer industry. However, in the cellulosic lacquer field it is the hot-spray process which is creating the greatest interest at the present time. The chief advantage of this process is that it offers a more economical method of applying lacquer, and it follows that the less costly the use of lacquer becomes, the greater the quantity of lacquer which will be consumed and the more the lacquer manufacturing business will grow. This process is of special interest to the furniture industry,[1] as lacquer has long been the preferred finish because of its beauty, durability, long life, and ease of application. The hot-spray process is economical for the following reasons:

(1) **Lacquer Solids Content Is Higher.** The bars in Figure 12.1 illustrate the manner in which lacquer solids content varies at spray viscosity with application temperature. The shaded portion of the "Hot Lacquer" bar represents the increased solids obtained with hot spray. This is equivalent to 43 per cent (9 parts in 21).

When lacquer is warmed or heated, it can be sprayed at higher concentrations. A lacquer designed to be sprayed at room temperature at 21 per cent solids can be sprayed at 30 per cent solids when heated.

(2) **Solvent Waste Is Lower.** Obviously, a higher per cent of solids at spraying consistency means less solvent is needed. A typical cold lacquer at 21 per cent solids requires 3.76 pounds solvent per pound solids applied. A comparable hot lacquer at 31 per cent solids requires only 2.33 pounds solvent per pound solids applied. Therefore, 61.4 per cent of the solvent needed at 30 per cent solids with the hot lacquer process is wasted by continuing to spray cold at 21 per cent solids.

(3) **Coverage per Gallon Is Increased.** If one gallon of lacquer, applied cold at 21 per cent solids, will finish 100 units, then one gallon of lacquer sprayed hot (30 per cent solids) will finish 143 units (with the same

thickness of film). The extra coverage obtained by hot spray is illustrated by the black dots in Figure 12.2.

(4) **Fewer Coats Are Needed.** Frequently three coats are required to obtain sufficient finish to beautify and protect a product. Experience has

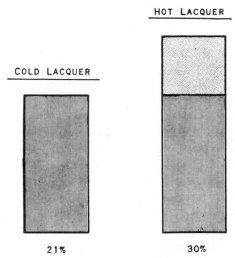

Figure 12.1. Lacquer solids are higher.

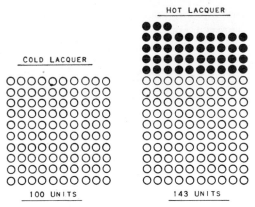

Figure 12.2. Coverage per gallon is increased.

shown that by spraying hot, at high solids (30 per cent instead of 21 per cent), two coats of lacquer will give the same satisfactory amount of finish.

(5) **Plant Capacity Can Be Increased.** Reduction of a three-coat to a two-coat finishing schedule is equivalent to adding 33 per cent extra plant capacity (which would mean one-third more floor space, more spray guns,

more operators, more compresser capacity). Similarly, reduction in the number of coats from two to one, which frequently becomes possible, is equivalent to adding 50 per cent to the existing finishing capacity.

In addition to the above economic advantages, the hot-spray process produces improved quality in lacquer finishes because:

(1) **The Finish Has Better Flow.** Existing evidence indicates that films applied heavily flow out better than thin ones. The hot-spray technique not only makes heavy films possible, but encourages this. There is a natural tendency to apply heavy coats, as a result of the inherent higher solids. Better flowout means reduced orange peel and fewer expensive sanding operations. Rubbing and polishing requirements are, therefore, sharply reduced.

(2) **The Finish Has Less Tendency to Sag.** Lacquers applied hot, at correspondingly higher solids, have less tendency to sag than lacquers thinned for application at room temperatures. For example, one lacquer applied to a vertical surface at room temperature sagged when a film thicker than 0.001 inch was applied. The same lacquer solids, applied at 160°F in a hot-spray solvent formulation, did not sag when 0.002 inch of film was applied. Sag resistance was more than doubled.

(3) **Blushing Is Eliminated.** In some environments, blushing is a major problem, particularly during humid weather. Moisture condenses on the freshly sprayed lacquer droplets which have been cooled below room temperature by the rapid evaporation of solvent, and clouds the film. When lacquer is sprayed hot, instead of at room temperature, it is virtually impossible for blushing to occur.

The hot-spray process was first investigated in the late thirties, but until recently the lack of adequate mechanical equipment—circulating spray guns and heating units—made the process of little practical value. In other words, hot lacquer was ready for its initial trials as early as ten years ago, but the proper equipment to apply it economically wasn't. With the end of World War II, however, equipment makers were able to devote more time and attention to development, and so today the situation is entirely different. A number of people have applied their imagination and ambition to develop highly efficient equipment that delivers lacquer to the gun with negligible temperature drop. They have also developed the types of guns best adapted to handling and spraying with least loss of heat and material. The cost of this equipment is surprisingly low in terms of the production economies it makes possible.

Some interesting sidelights on the extent of these equipment problems, and the ingenious ways by which they have been solved, are disclosed in recent literature.[2]

"It was necessary to develop a thoroughly practical, simple and safe lacquer heater, one that was not too complicated for the sprayers to operate. This we now have. In fact, there are a number of efficient lacquer heaters on the market. We also had to develop a practical, trouble-free circulating mechanism to circulate the lacquer through the heater to the spray gun and return. The noncirculating paint heater is not adaptable for lacquer use except in rather isolated cases. However, to develop a circulating mechanism was not a simple thing. Pumping hot lacquer presents a number of problems beyond that of pumping cold lacquer. For example, to keep the pump's shaft seal properly lubricated was quite a problem, due to the heat generated and the hot solvents coming in contact with the seal. Also, a circulating system had to be devised to enable the pump to operate slowly, because the hot lacquer does not have the lubricating property that cold lacquer has. Another critical problem to be licked was finding a fluid hose which would stand up to the hot solvents. This, too, has been overcome."

Prior to and during the promotion of the hot-lacquer process by the Hercules Powder Company in 1950–1953, different types of commercially available heating equipment were tested extensively in the company's development laboratories as to their suitability for commercial spray requirements. Comments pertaining to those units which illustrate different mechanical principles involved in the hot spray operation, such as hot air, hot water, steam, heated metal, air motor, electric motor, and heater position relative to the spray gun, are as follows. Because of rapid developments, new manufacturers of heating units have appeared and older models are being improved.

Heating Equipment Tested

High-Capacity Units for Large-Scale Production

*Arvins-Viscolator Paint and Lacquer Heater.** This heater consists of an aluminum casting which contains two 1,000-watt heating elements. The fluid is circulated by an air-driven gear pump from the spray tank, through the heater to the spray gun and back to the heater. The unit is constructed with a steam chamber so that either steam or electricity can be used for heating. It can be converted to use either method without disturbing the steam and electrical installation. This unit is sold with an Underwriters' Laboratories, Inc. label attached.

"Dualheet" Paint and Air Heater.† The unit consists of a 2,500-watt

---

* Manufactured by the Arvins-Viscolator Corporation, 123 DeKalb Avenue, Brooklyn 1, New York.

† Manufactured by the Beck Equipment Company, 10,118 Detroit Avenue, Cleveland 2, Ohio.

electric heating element embedded in an aluminum casting. An air-driven pump for circulating the lacquer from the feed tank, through the heater and to the spray gun is mounted on the front of the heating unit. The lacquer is heated in a coil contained within the casting. A thermostat through which temperature can be regulated is built into the unit. Temperature and pressure gauges are provided on the effluent lacquer line leading to the spray gun. This unit is sold with the Underwriters' Laboratories, Inc. label attached.

*Bede Paint and Air Heater.** The unit consists of an aluminum casting insulated from a sheet-metal container by glass wool. The casting is heated electrically by 2,000-watt heaters on 110-volt current. The lacquer, supplied from a feed tank, is heated in a coil within, and in direct contact with the aluminum casting which is the heat-transfer medium. The thermostat control is in a well at the top of the casting. An air-motor pump provides for circulation of the hot lacquer to the spray gun. The pump is powerful enough to draw cold lacquer out of an open container without the use of a pressure tank. A ball-and-spring valve on the return line to the pump can be regulated to adjust the pressure and flow rate. A thermometer and a pressure gauge are provided at the heater in the lacquer line leading to the spray gun.

DeVilbiss-Type QBH-5001 Steam Unit.† This is a complex, but simple-to-operate, self-contained unit for heating lacquer and maintaining it at a predetermined temperature. It has all the controls (air-activated) that might be desired for regulating and indicating temperature and pressure. Cold lacquer is forced from a pressure tank into a steam-heated chamber through a coil in which it is heated to the desired temperature, and is circulated to the spray gun by means of an air-motor pump. The unit does not heat air for atomization. Low-pressure steam (maximum of 15 pounds) is used to heat the lacquer.

This unit is not portable. It is fairly bulky and has to be connected to a steam supply line. The unit can supply heated lacquer for several guns at production-line spraying speeds.

Thermatic Spray Painting Unit, Model A.‡ This unit is electrically heated and is mounted on a steel base provided with casters. Cold lacquer is forced under regulated air pressure from the feed tank into an electrically heated hot-water tank through a copper-alloy coil, in which it is heated to the desired temperature. The lacquer is then circulated to the

---

* Made by Bede Products, Inc., 1110 Brookpark Road, Cleveland 9, Ohio, and protected by U. S. Patent 2,481,813, issued to James A. Bede on September 13, 1949.

† Made by The DeVilbiss Company, 296 Phillips Avenue, Toledo 1, Ohio.

‡ Made by the M & E Manufacturing Company, 2571 Winthrop Avenue, Indianapolis 5, Indiana.

spray gun by means of a belt-driven electric-motor pump. The unit does not heat air for atomization. In Hercules test work the hot-water tank was set for 185°F, which is the temperature found to give a lacquer temperature of 160° F. A thermometer and pressure gauge are provided in the lacquer line leading to the gun.

Therm-O-Spray Heater Type SPC-4*. The unit consists of an electric air heater with 1,400-watt capacity which provides thermostatically controlled air temperatures between 170 and 300°F. It also includes a heat exchanger provided with a thermometer for lacquer and air temperature as well as an automatically regulated valve which distributes hot air to the heat exchanger and to a special air-heated fluid hose during interruptions in spraying.

Spee-Flo Pressurematic (Circaflo) Heater.† This unit consists of two 1,000-watt heating coils enclosed in a circular heater through which lacquer passes between the spray tank and the spray gun. A gearless centrifugal electric pump circulates lacquer to the spray gun. The unit can be mounted directly on the wall of the spray booth or can be obtained mounted or fastened to a dolly, making it readily portable.

Small-Capacity Units for Intermittent Spraying

Study of these heating units showed that adequate and satisfactory commercial heating equipment is available. The lacquer user may choose the type of unit most suitable for his needs. Comparison data for the hot-spray units used in this investigation are given in Table 12.1. A pump for circulating hot lacquer is advisable with all the high-capacity heating units for large-scale production in order to maintain the close temperature control (within 10°F) essential in taking advantage of the decrease on viscosity produced by heating.

Pol-Flo Heated Paint Cup.‡ This is a thermostatically controlled quart-size heating unit. It operates on 110–120 volts and has an electric input of 300 watts. Approximately 8 minutes are required to raise the temperature of a lacquer to 160°F.

Thermalflo Heater.§ This unit consists of a common pressure pot which has been modified with a heating unit and jacket. It operates on 110–120

* Manufactured by Svenska Maskin AB Greiff, Stockholm, Sweden. The American distributor is Special Equipment Corporation, 26 W. Putnam Avenue, Greenwich Connecticut.

† Manufactured by The Spee-Flo Company, 3603 Harrisburg Blvd., Houston 3, Texas.

‡ Manufactured by Pol-Flo Paint Sprayer Corporation, 1200 S Street, Sacramento, California.

§ Manufactured by Thermalcup, Incorporated, 10,118 Detroit Avenue, Cleveland 2, Ohio.

TABLE 12.1

HIGH-CAPACITY HEATING UNITS FOR LARGE-SCALE PRODUCTION

	Arvins-Viscolator Corp, 123 DeKalb Ave., Brooklyn 1, New York	Beck Equipment Co., 10,118 Detroit Ave., Cleveland 2, Ohio	Bede Products Co., 1110 Brookpark Rd., Cleveland 9, Ohio	DeVilbiss, 296 Phillips Ave., Toledo 1, Ohio	M & E Mfg. Company, 2671 Winthrop Ave., Indianapolis 5, Ind.	Special Equip. Corp., 26 W. Putnam Ave., Greenwich, Conn.	The Spee-Flo Co., 3603 Harrisburg Blvd., Houston 3, Texas
Model	Model PESC	Dualheet	Model U	QBH-5001	Thermatic A	SPC-4	Pressurematic 600 A & C
Time to heat up lacquer (70 to 160°F)	15–20 min.	15–20 min.	15–20 min.	15 min.	90 min.	15 min.	15 min.
Holdup in unit and lines*	—	2 qt	2 qt	2.5 gal	1.5 gal	approx. 1 qt	approx. 1 qt
Temp. drop* from unit to spray gun	10°F	10°F	10°F	10°F	10°F	—	10–15°F
Air temp. for atomization	line temp.	line temp.	line temp.	line temp.	line temp.	approx. 100°F	line temp.
Heating medium	electrically or steam heated Al metal	electrically heated Al metal	electrically heated Al metal casting	5 to 12 lb steam	electrically heated water	electrically heated air	electrically heated Al metal
Circulating system	air motor pump	air motor pump	air motor pump	air motor pump	electric motor pump	none	reciprocating air pump
Heating unit	2100 watts 110 volts	2500 watts 110–220 volts	2000 watts 110–220 volts	lacquer coil in steam chamber	lacquer coil in hot water (185°F)	1400 watt air heater 110–220 volts	2000 watt pump 110 volts

* 10 feet of 3/8 inch I.D. hose to and from unit and spray gun.

SMALL-CAPACITY HEATING UNITS FOR INTERMITTENT SPRAYING

	Bede Automotive Products, Inc., 1110 Brookpark Rd., Cleveland 9, Ohio	Pol-Flo Paint Sprayer Corp., 1200 S Street, Sacramento, Calif.	The Spee-Flo Co., 3603 Harrisburg Blvd., Houston 3, Texas	Thermalcup, Inc., 10,118 Detroit Ave., Cleveland 2, Ohio
Model	Model C (3 wells, water as heat-transfer medium)	Pol-Flo Cup Model 13-B	Spee-Flo	Thermalcup
Time to heat up lacquer (70 to 160°F)	35 min.	7 min.	30–40 min.	12 min.
Capacity	3 1-qt units	1 qt	1 gal	1 qt
Heating unit	650 watts, 110 volts	300 watts, 110–120 volts	330–660 watts, 110 volts	250 watts, 110 volts

volts and has a capacity of 6 quarts of material. It does not provide temperature control between the heating unit and the spray gun.

*Spee-Flo Heater.** This unit has two parts: the heater itself, which is a hot plate with a surface especially designed to fit the bottom of a gallon paint can, and a collar which fits into the groove in the top of the paint can. The material to be heated is placed on the hot plate, the collar is placed on the top of the can, and thinner, if needed, is added. The advantage of this unit is that the material is heated in its original container and, therefore, clean-up is minimized.

APPLICATION, FORMULATION, AND PROPERTIES OF HOT LACQUER

The current and rapidly growing interest in the hot-lacquer process has introduced many questions about the formulation, application, and properties of hot lacquers. Many of the questions which arose while the process was going through a "growing pains" stage are tabulated below, along with information and answers which have been obtained both from experimental data and actual experience.

Application

(1) *What is the best temperature for applying hot lacquers?*

Generally, 160°F is recommended. Lacquers can be held at this temperature for 8 to 12 hours with no noticeable effect and for several days without marked degradation of properties. Furthermore, the decrease in viscosity obtained as lacquer temperature is increased above 160°F is relatively small. Table 12.2 shows experimental data on the viscosity, color stability, and cold-check resistance of a lacquer heated continuously for the indicated time. These tests, representing a drastic mistreatment of the lacquer, are a proof that lacquers have good stability against the ordinary conditions of commercial hot-spray work. It is believed that in commercial operations, even with intermittent spraying, the lacquer would be used fast enough to permit at least one complete change every hour.

(2) *When hot lacquer is being sprayed, what is its temperature when it hits the surface?*

Lacquer applied at 160°F has been found to be at room temperature when sprayed on an object 8 inches from the spray gun. This is in contrast to regular lacquers which are at approximately 20°F below room temperature, 8 inches from the spray gun. This is illustrated by the data in Table 12.3.

* Manufactured by The Spee-Flo Company, 3603 Harrisburg Blvd., Houston 3, Texas.

TABLE 12.2. STABILITY OF LACQUER* TO HEAT

(Summary of data on viscosity, color stability, and cold-check resistance of a lacquer heated in each of four commercial hot-spray units. No differences shown in lacquer heated in different units.)

Heating Time at 160°F	Per Cent Loss in Viscosity	Gardner Color	Cold-Check Resistance No. of Cycles to Fail
Cold—no heating	—	4	20
Up to temp (160°F)	3.3	4	20
1 hour	6.3	5	20
2 hours	8.8	7	20
3 hours	8.1	8	—
4 hours	7.3	8	20
8 hours	11.5	9	20
After shutdown, overnight	12.0	9	13
16 hours	17.7	12	8
24 hours	13.6	13	—
32 hours	20.0	13	7

Composition:

31 Per Cent Solids

RS Nitrocellulose, ½-second	33.30
Aroplaz 905	30.00
Lewisol 33†	20.00
Dibutyl phthalate	8.35
Castor oil, raw	8.35
Total	100.00

69 Per Cent Solvent

Butyl acetate	37.5
Ethanol	10.0
Butanol	12.5
Xylene	40.0
Total	100.0

Reg. U.S. Pat. Off.

TABLE 12.3. SURFACE TEMPERATURES OF LACQUERS SPRAYED COLD AND HOT

Lacquer Used	Lacquer Temp at Spray Gun (°F)	Air Temp at Spray Gun (°F)	Room Temp (°F)	Surface Temp of Lacquer After Spraying (°F)
20 per cent solids; standard cold-spray solvent	75	80	75	55 to 61
26 per cent solids; high-solvency solvent	75	80	75	57 to 59
33 per cent solids; hot-spray solvent	160	80	73	68 to 79
	160	180	77	79 to 82
32 per cent solids; hot-spray solvent containing methyl isobutyl ketone in place of butyl acetate	160	80	72	68 to 79

Cold-sprayed lacquers were cooled 15 to 20°F below room temperature, while hot-sprayed lacquers were cooled to approximate room temperature. The fact that the temperature of hot-sprayed lacquer solids does not drop below room temperature is probably the reason why such lacquers do not blush. Another advantage, apparently, of this higher temperature of freshly laid lacquer films is the better opportunity given for the improved flowout that helps to eliminate orange peel, and the faster solvent release that reduces sagging.

Figure 12.3 shows the rate at which the hot lacquer, while being sprayed, was found to cool at various distances from the spray gun. Essentially, the hot lacquer (160°F.) was cooled to near room temperature

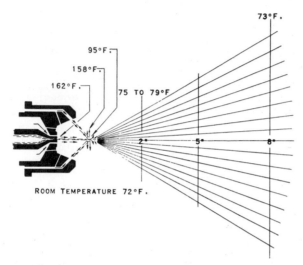

Figure 12.3.   Lacquer temperature at various distances from spray gun.

at the focus for the air and lacquer coming out of the gun. Both the room temperature and the temperature of the air for the spray gun were 72°F. Readings were taken at various distances from the spray gun nozzle.

(3) *Is it an advantage to use hot air to atomize hot lacquer?*

The effect of the air temperature on atomization was studied, and data are listed in Table 12.4. Room temperature air (75 to 100°F) was found

TABLE 12.4.   EFFECT OF AIR TEMPERATURE ON ATOMIZATION*

Air Temperature (°F)	Dry-Film Thickness Range Sprayed (mils)	Flowout	Tendency of Wet Film to Bubble
75	1.0 to 4.0	good	none
100	0.8 to 4.5	good	none
125	1.0 to 3.8	fair	none
150	1.0 to 4.5	poor	much
200	1.2 to 4.2	very poor	very great

* Lacquer used: Base, RS Nitrocellulose, ½-second viscosity; 31 per cent total solids; and 160-second viscosity by Ford No. 4 cup at 25°C. Hot-sprayed at 160°F using MBC gun, FX tip, No. 765 air cap and a lacquer flow rate of 20 ounces per minute.

preferable for hot-spraying lacquers containing low-boiling solvents. However, if high-boiling solvents, such as those used in European practice, are employed, hot atomization air is desirable. In fact, this study indicated that it was not advisable to use hot air for atomization of lacquer because it gave poor flowout and caused bubbling of the sprayed film. The lacquer temperature 5 inches from the spray gun nozzle is reported to be 68°F. This temperature is lower than that reported for lacquer 2 and 8 inches from the nozzle. All the temperatures shown were determined experimentally. The variations (68 to 73°F) shown in Figure 12.3 are believed to be within experimental error and, therefore, insignificant.

(4) *Is pinholing more troublesome with hot lacquers than with room-temperature lacquers?*

Pinholes in lacquer films applied hot or cold appear when the top of a bubble of air trapped in a lacquer film breaks. Lacquer solvents must be blended in such a manner that air which is trapped between particles of atomized lacquer when it strikes the surface to be coated can rise to the surface and be released before the surface of the film dries to a typical film.

It has been reported that difficulty with pinholing is encountered occasionally when hot lacquer is applied to certain open-grain woods. In certain instances, this trouble has been traced to the filler employed. If pinholing develops when trials are made with hot lacquer, the filler should be examined as a source of trouble.

(5) *Is it beneficial to heat the object being sprayed when using hot lacquer?*

TABLE 12.5. EFFECT OF TEMPERATURE OF OBJECT BEING SPRAYED
ON ATOMIZATION*

Panel Temperature (°F)	Dry-Film Thickness Range Sprayed (mils)	Flowout	Tendency of Wet Film to Bubble
32	1.5 to 2.7	average	none
75	1.8 to 2.7	good	none
100	1.8 to 3.9	good	none
125	1.6 to 3.8	fair	none
150	1.8 to 3.9	poor	great

* Lacquer used: Base, RS Nitrocellulose, ½-second viscosity; 31 per cent total solids; and 160-second viscosity by Ford No. 4 cup at 25°C. Hot-sprayed at 160°F using air at room temperature for atomization.

Laboratory work has shown that best results with hot lacquer are obtained when the object being sprayed is at room temperature or slightly higher. Extreme cooling or heating is not desirable. The data appear in Table 12.5. The panels sprayed at 32°F and 125°F showed slightly poorer flowout than did those sprayed at 75°F and 100°F; otherwise, no harmful effects were observed. Panels sprayed at 150°F gave poor flowout and considerable bubbling.

(6) *Is the spraying technique the same for hot lacquer as for room-temperature lacquer?*

It is essentially the same. Because of the higher solids content of hot lacquer, build-up is somewhat more rapid and fewer gun strokes are required. In general, hot lacquer makes it possible to obtain with lacquer the spraying qualities of competitive finishes such as varnish or synthetic enamel, while still retaining the advantages that can be obtained with lacquer.

Formulation

(1) *How do hot lacquers differ from lacquers made for room-temperature application?*

The nonvolatile portion of a lacquer, the part which forms the film, need be no different in a hot lacquer than in a room-temperature lacquer. The solvent ingredients, however, must be changed. To spray at 160°F, it is advisable to eliminate fast-evaporating solvents such as acetone, ethyl acetate, and methyl alcohol from the blend.

(2) *Are hot lacquers formulated at higher solids than room-temperature lacquers?*

Yes, lacquers prepared for hot application generally contain 40 to 55 per cent more solids than room-temperature lacquers.

(3) *Can certain resins, plasticizers, or solvents be selected which will produce exceptionally low viscosities in hot lacquers?*

Tests were made to determine the effect that changes in solids and solvents compositions in lacquer formulation would have on temperature-viscosity relationships. The results of these tests indicate that for a given change in temperature—say, from 77 to 158°F—the percentage change in viscosity is roughly the same whether the viscosity at the low temperature is relatively low or relatively high. Furthermore, the data presented indicate that viscosities may be run at room temperatures where control is simple instead of at the lacquer hot-spray temperature where viscosity control offers considerable difficulty.

Effect of Solids. In Table 12.6 are tabulated solids composition and viscosity data for fourteen lacquers, the viscosities of which were run at four temperatures: 77°F, 104°F, 131°F, and 158°F. The solvent used in each case was the same. The main differences in the lacquers were that (1) different resins were used with one and the same type nitrocellulose (RS, ½ second) and (2) different ratios of nitrocellulose:resin were used.

TABLE 12.6. LACQUER SOLIDS COMPOSITION—EFFECT ON VISCOSITY-TEMPERATURE RELATIONSHIP

(Solids Composition—Proportional Parts and Test Data)

Formula No.

	1	2	3	4	5	6	7	8	9	10	11	12	13	14
Solids Ratio in Lacquer														
RS Nitrocellulose, ½-sec	1	1	1	1	—	1	1	1	1	1	1	—	2	40
RS Nitrocellulose, 30–35 cps	2	—	—	—	—	—	—	—	—	—	—	1	—	—
Aroplaz 905	—	—	—	—	1	—	—	—	—	—	0.9	0.9	—	—
Aroplaz 906	—	2	—	—	—	1	—	—	—	—	—	—	—	—
Resin X4000-15 (Cellolyn* 502)	—	—	—	—	—	—	—	—	—	—	—	—	—	—
Glyptal 2477	—	—	2	2	—	—	—	—	—	—	—	—	—	—
Rezyl 99	—	—	—	—	2	—	1	1	—	—	—	—	—	—
Melmac 245	—	—	—	—	—	—	—	—	3	3	—	—	3	—
Cellolyn 95	—	—	—	—	—	—	—	—	0.3	0.3	—	—	—	—
Cellolyn 102	—	—	—	—	—	—	—	—	—	—	—	—	—	—
Cellolyn 104	—	—	—	—	—	—	—	—	—	—	—	—	—	40
Lewisol* 33	—	—	—	—	—	—	—	—	—	—	0.6	0.6	—	—
Dibutyl phthalate	—	—	—	—	—	0.2	0.2	0.2	—	—	0.25	0.25	—	—
Raw castor oil	—	—	—	—	—	—	—	—	—	—	0.25	0.25	—	6.7
Baker's No. 15 castor oil	—	—	—	—	—	—	—	—	—	—	—	—	—	13.3
Total per cent by weight	30	30	30	30	34	27	27	31	36	38	35	38	33	33
Lacquer viscosity in centipoises (Ubbelohde)														
at 25°C (77°F)	592	562	792	298	444	563	598	410	750	392	999	525	442	691
at 40°C (104°F)	279	294	386	149	199	301	300	199	338	179	494	247	236	353
at 55°C (131°F)	152	138	197	81	103	148	160	105	160	90	254	134	136	188
at 70°C (158°F)	89	81	—	50	61	87	95	61	85	51	135	77	84	112
Viscosity decrease, 25 to 70°C, per cent	85.0	85.6	—	83.3	86.3	84.5	84.2	85.2	88.8	87	86.4	85.4	81.1	83.8

Solvent Formulation. All lacquers contained the same solvent, as follows:

	Per cent by Weight
Butyl acetate	37.5
Butanol	12.5
Ethanol	10.0
Xylene	40.0
Total	100.0

* Reg. U.S. Pat. Off.

As would be expected, viscosities at room temperature varied from lacquer solution to lacquer solution. Solids contents ranged from 27 to 38 per cent. The most significant data recorded, perhaps, are those showing the close equivalency in percentage drop in viscosities, approximately 85 per cent, which occurred when lacquer solution temperatures were raised from 77 to 158°F. The lowest percentage drop was 81.1, while the highest was 88.8.

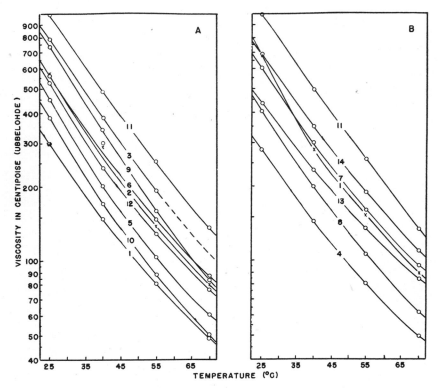

Figure 12.4. These curves were plotted from the viscosity-temperature data in Table 12.6 showing the effect of lacquer solids on viscosity-temperature relationships. It will be noted that the curves are essentially parallel, indicating no abnormal solvation effects. It will also be noted that curves 4 and 11 appear on each chart as reference curves.

Viscosity-temperature curves for each of the fourteen formulas are shown in Figure 12.4, A and B. The plottings (on semilogarithmic, coordinate paper) were divided between two sheets in order to prevent overlapping. It should be noted that the lowest and highest viscosity curves are duplicated on the two sheets. These two curves are for lacquers 4 and 11, Table 12.6.

Effect of Solvents. The data in Table 12.7 show what can be expected to happen to viscosity-temperature relationships when solvents are changed and solids are held constant relative to composition and amount. The total viscosity drop, percentagewise, on raising the lacquer solution temperature from 77 to 158°F was of the same general magnitude as that found when solids compositions were changed and solvents were held the same. However, the average was a bit lower, that is, 83 instead of 85 per cent. When these data are plotted as in Figure 12.4, the curves tend to be parallel, indicating no probability of abnormal solvency effects of great magnitude.

TABLE 12.7.   LACQUER SOLVENT COMPOSITION—EFFECT ON
VISCOSITY-TEMPERATURE RELATIONSHIP*

Materials	Composition—Parts by Weight						
	1	2	3	4	5	6	7
Butyl acetate	37.5	37.5	30.0	—	—	—	—
Cellosolve acetate	—	—	—	37.5	—	—	—
Diethyl maleate†	—	—	—	—	37.5	—	—
Methyl isobutyl ketone	—	—	—	—	—	37.5	31.0
Ethanol	10.0	—	10.0	10.0	10.0	10.0	10.0
Butanol	12.5	22.5	15.0	12.5	12.5	12.5	12.5
Methyl isobutyl carbinol	—	—	—	—	—	—	6.5
Xylene	40.0	40.0	45.0	40.0	40.0	40.0	40.0
Total	100.0	100.0	100.0	100.0	100.0	100.0	100.0
	Viscosity in Centipoises (Ubbelohde)						
Viscosity at 25°C (77°F)	349	501	437	417	508	205	263
Viscosity at 40°C (104°F)	172	240	212	200	262	109	141
Viscosity at 55°C (131°F)	93	120	107	110	129	63	76
Viscosity at 70°C (158°F)	56	66	61	63	79	42	46
Viscosity decrease, 25 to 70°C, per cent	81	86.8	85.5	85	84.5	79.5	82.5

* Lacquer solution composition, parts by weight:

RS Nitrocellulose, ½-second	9
Aroplaz 905	18
Solvent	73
Total	100

† Diethyl maleate is not a normal lacquer solvent. It was used here as a means of widening the series range.

All these data, Tables 12.6 and 12.7, and their plottings in Figure 12.4 clearly indicate that the reduction in viscosity of a lacquer solution on being heated is primarily a temperature effect which follows the temperature-viscosity correction equation shown in Table 12.8. In Table 12.8 are shown also the values of the equation constant K at four temperatures. These values were calculated using experimentally determined viscosity data for both V and V_1.

These K values show a difference of about 12 per cent between 25 and 70°C. Despite this apparent variation in K value with temperature, it is believed that these values are sufficiently accurate to be used in calculating high-temperature viscosities when room-temperature viscosity is

TABLE 12.8. TEMPERATURE-VISCOSITY CONSTANT

(For a nitrocellulose lacquer at four temperatures)

$$\text{Log } V = \text{Log } V_1 + K(t_1 - t)$$
Where V = Viscosity at spraying temperature
(usually 25°C (77°F),
V_1 = Viscosity at temperature t_1
K = Constant

Then:

if t = 25°C (77°F),	K = 0.0207
if t = 40°C (104°F),	K = 0.0202
if t = 55°C (131°F),	K = 0.0196
if t = 70°C (158°F),	K = 0.0182

TABLE 12.9. CALCULATED VISCOSITY VALUES—COMPARISON WITH DETERMINED VALUES

(Determined values are those reported in Table 12.8)

Tests	Viscosity in Centipoises (Ubbelohde)						
	Lacquer 1	Lacquer 2	Lacquer 3	Lacquer 4	Lacquer 5	Lacquer 6	Lacquer 7
Determined viscosity at 25°C	349	501	437	417	508	205	263
Determined viscosity at 40°C	172	240	212	200	262	109	141
Calculated viscosity at 40°C	174	249	217	207	253	102	131
Difference	+2	+9	+5	+7	−11	−7	−10
Determined viscosity at 55°C	93	120	107	110	129	63	76
Calculated viscosity at 55°C	88	126	110	105	128	52	66
Difference	−5	+6	+3	−5	−1	−11	−10
Determined viscosity at 70°C	56	66	61	63	79	42	46
Calculated viscosity at 70°C	53	76	66	63	77	31	40
Difference	−3	+10	+5	0	−2	−11	−6

known. This is illustrated in Table 12.9. Here are given the determined viscosities for the seven lacquer solutions already reported in Table 12.8. Along with these determined viscosities are the calculated viscosities using the equation and K constants shown in Table 12.8. Some few of the calculated values differ widely, percentagewise, from the determined values. These differences probably stem from the difficulty encountered in exercising sufficient control at the high temperatures to achieve as high a degree of accuracy at the high temperature as at room temperature.

(4) *Can all pigments and dyes used in room-temperature lacquers also be used in hot lacquers?*

Generally, yes. Some care must be taken in selecting pigments to eliminate highly reactive types. The catalytic effect of heat encourages acidic or alkaline pigments to react. Dyes which are not heat-stable should be avoided.

Properties

(1) *Does the application of lacquer at elevated temperature impart different properties (cold-check, print, rubbing and polishing, sanding, and shrinkage) to a furniture lacquer film than would be obtained if the same quality lacquer were applied at room temperature?*

In carrying out tests to determine the answer to this question, three lacquers were sprayed, each to give films of three different thicknesses of approximately 1, 2, and 2.5 mils. The solids composition for each lacquer was the same; the lacquer solutions applied differed only in nonvolatile amount and volatile make-up.

Data on the compositions of the lacquer solutions applied and test data obtained appear in Table 12.10. The nonvolatile composition formula appears under *A;* the solvent formulas appear under *B;* and the test data obtained appear under *C*. The data indicate that lacquer films of equivalent composition and thickness should show no significant differences in properties because of being applied by these different methods.

In addition to the tests already cited, these three lacquers were sprayed on stained, filled, and sealed mahogany panels. Then, after an overnight air-dry, the lacquers were sanded, rubbed, polished, and allowed to age for six months. Here again the qualities of depth, gloss, and shrinkage of the hot-sprayed, one-coat films, 2 mils thick, were as good as or better than those of cold-sprayed films of equivalent thickness.

(2) *Does the hot-lacquer process make possible the formulation of lacquers of improved quality?*

When heating a lacquer results in decreasing the viscosity of the lacquer below that of the normal spraying range, nitrocellulose of a higher viscosity type or a larger proportion of nitrocellulose can be used in formulation. Either of the above procedures produces lacquers with improved cold-check resistance, toughness, flexibility, and print resistance.

From present indications, the hot-spray lacquer process shows every indication of proving of definite value to the furniture industry in reducing over-all finishing costs with no sacrifice of quality. It makes use of the same basic types of lacquer, with the elimination of most of the low- and medium-boiling solvents, and the same solids composition, with the resulting same high-quality finish. By spraying the lacquer hot, a much thicker coating is applied. In fact, in many instances, "Now, Once Around

TABLE 12.10. COMPOSITION OF HOT-SPRAYED VS. COLD-SPRAYED LACQUERS

A—Lacquer Solids Formulation		B—Lacquer Solvent Formulation			
Materials	Parts by Wt	Materials	Cold-Spray Lacquer	High-Solvency Lacquer	Hot-Spray Lacquer
RS Nitrocellulose ½-sec	33.30				
Aroplaz 905	30.00	Ethyl acetate		10	
Lewisol 33*	20.00	Butyl acetate			37.5
Dibutyl phthalate	8.35	Methyl ethyl ketone		25	
Castor oil, raw	8.35	Methyl isobutyl ketone	30	20	
		Ethanol	10	10	10.0
Total	100.00	Butanol		5	12.5
		Toluene	60	30	
		Xylene			40.0
* Reg. U.S. Pat. Off.		Total	100	100	100.0

C—Test Data on Lacquer Films

	Standard Cold-Spray Lacquer			High-Solvency Lacquer			Hot-Spray Lacquer			
Nonvolatile as sprayed →	20%			26%			31%			
Film thickness, mils, dry	1	2*	2.5	1	2*	2.5*	1	2†	2	25
Drying speed, minutes										
Cotton-free	9	26	—	6	23	22	11	—	25	25
Foil-free	12	34	—	7	26	31	16	—	33	40
Tack-free	13	36	—	8	27	35	20	50	40	50
Hardness, Sward (% of glass)										
At end of 1 hr	14	4	—	16	6	2	11	2	4	2
At end of 2 hr	22	8	—	18	8	6	13	6	6	6
At end of 3 hr	22	10	10	20	12	6	16	10	9	8
At end of 24 hr	28	20	22	24	20	18	24	20	20	18
Sanding quality (no. of double rubs)										
At end of 1 hr	11	4	—	10	8	4	8	5	6	3
At end of 2 hr	13	10	—	12	10	7	10	6	9	6
At end of 3 hr	12	11	—	12	10	9	11	8	9	8
At end of 24 hr	13	13	12	13	13	12	13	13	13	14
Print test (after overnight air-dry)										
Under 2 psi	none	mod.	mod.	none	mod.	mod.	none	mod.	mod.	bad
Under 5 psi	slight	bad	bad	slight	bad	bad	slight	bad	bad	bad
Cold-check cycles to fail	20+	20+	20+	20+	20+	20+	20+	20+	20+	20+
Sag point, mils	0.7	0.7	0.7	1	1	1	2.2	2.2	2.2	2.2
Shrinkage at end of 2 months	slight	slight	slight	slight	slight	slight	slight	slight	slight	slight

* Two coats sprayed 10 minutes apart to give the film indicated.
† In this case the lacquer was diluted to 20 per cent solids and with two coats being cold-sprayed 20 minutes apart to give a final film of 2-mil thickness.

Is Enough." The result is an over-all saving of 25 to 30 per cent in finishing costs without any sacrifice in quality.

The following case histories of current satisfied users of the hot-spray process indicate the increasing acceptance by the furniture industry of this method of lacquer application.

(a) A California furniture factory reports: "The finishing foreman is very enthusiastic about the use of hot lacquer and stated that he is saving 50 per cent of the rubbing costs which they had when they used cold lacquer. One coat of lacquer is being applied over sealer on furniture made from all wood except mahogany, walnut, and oak. These woods receive two lacquer topcoats because of their large pores."

(b) A lacquer producer to the furniture industry says: "Yesterday, we observed the wooden panels finished in January and measured the film thickness of the metal panels prepared at the same time. Insofar as the wood panels are concerned, it still shows that one coat of hot-spray lacquer is equal in fullness to two coats of cold-spray. We feel confident that the after-shrinkage of hot-spray lacquers will not be excessive. The next day all cabinets were rubbed, and they dried to the entire satisfaction of all concerned, which frankly, we didn't expect. The owner of this furniture plant was entirely satisfied with the build on one coat of cold and one coat of hot and has since decided that one coat of hot over sealer will give him the results that he needs. They also were satisfied with the luster of the cabinets after rubbing."

(c) Another satisfied user of hot-spray lacquer states: "We thought you should know the excellent results we are having with the hot-spray process in applying lacquer finishes to our products. We have doubled our production on the spray line. With the cold-spray process we applied six coats of lacquer. With the hot-spray process we apply two coats and get better coverage. We also use 50 per cent less thinners, and on top of this, we have also reduced re-work to a minimum."

(d) A large furniture company recently reported: "Obtaining a coverage of 408 square feet per gallon of hot lacquer, whereas formerly we averaged only 335 square feet with a gallon of varnish."

(e) Another furniture lacquer manufacturer states: "We are getting some very satisfactory results with hot lacquer and have several customers now using it. Our customers who are now using hot lacquer apparently are having no difficulty whatsoever. We believe hot lacquer will continue in its acceptance by other firms as it becomes more widely known and will take its place as a permanent finishing material."

(f) A prominent lacquer producer writes as follows: "We have been selling a considerable quantity of hot lacquer over a period of a year. As you know, varnishes generally run from 40 to 50 per cent solids, are rather heavy in body, and give good build in one coat. These varnishes, however, dry fairly slowly, do not have very good hot-print resistance, and pick up considerable lint, dust, and dirt before they set up, so that it is necessary to have a dustproof room to get a clean finish for furniture. These varnish finishes also do not have the tensile strength of nitrocellulose lacquers. Nitrocellulose lacquers dry fast and hard in a number of minutes and are tack-free in a few minutes so that they do not pick up lint."

All of the positive advantages of cold lacquer are retained through the use of the hot-spray method of application. It is estimated that at present 75 per cent of all wood furniture is finished with lacquer because of the following well-recognized advantages: lacquer lasts longer; the natural beauty of the wood is retained and enhanced; there is no other way to obtain the rich effect that sells furniture on sight; and repairs and minor touch-up jobs are less costly and more satisfactory. When necessary, the lacquered finish can be completely removed by solvents, and the operation is uniquely simple. Lacquer is more stable in storage than other finishing materials, and no catalysts or other products which do not contribute to the ultimate value of the coating are needed to make the lacquer finish dry.

References

1. Hercules Powder Company, *A Report on a Study of the Hot-Spray Application of Lacquer,* October, 1950.
2. Bede, James R., *Organic Finishing,* Vol. 12, No. 1, January, 1951.

Bibliography

1. Carlson, N. K., U.S. Patent 2,378,184 (to Sherwin-Williams Co.), June 12, 1945, Heater and Circulating Unit—Apparatus for Applying Coating Material.
2. Cowlard, T., "Progress in the Finishing Shop," *Decorator,* 45, 46, 63 (May, 1946).
3. Ericsson, R. L., "Application of Hot Lacquers and Dopes," *Am. Paint J.,* **27** (32), 40, 44, 46, 48–9, 52 (1943); "Hot Lacquers and Their Solvent Requirements," *Paint Ind. Mag.,* **59,** 345–7 (1944); *Am. Paint J.,* **29** (5B, Convention-at-Home-Daily) 30–32 (1944); *Can. Paint & Varnish Mag.,* **19** (6), 18, 32–34 (1945).
4. Fisk, N. R., "Hot Application of Coatings," *Paint Technol.,* **8,** 112–14 (1943).
5. Frey, E. F., "New Developments in Spray Equipment for Hot and Cold Nitrocellulose Lacquer," *Paint, Oil, Chem. Rev.* (Nov. 2, 1944).
6. Glasbeek, H., Jr., Dutch Patent 58,412, Oct. 15, 1946, Apparatus for Heating a Liquid (Lacquer).
7. Hopkins, A. C., Jr., "The Hot-Lacquer Process," *Paint, Oil, Chem. Rev.,* **107** (17), 9–11, 26 (1944).
8. Klinkenstein, G., "Developments in Lacquers, Enamels for Industrial Finishing During 1939," *Product Finishing,* **4** (4), 34–6 (1940); "Review of Progress in the Industrial Finishing Field," *Product Finishing,* **5** (4), 42–4 (1941).

9. Kraus, A., "High Temperature Application of Nitrocellulose Lacquers," *Farben-Ztg.*, **44**, 160–1 (1939).
10. Ledwith, R. J., "Developments in Cellulose Lacquers," *J. Oil & Colour Chemists' Assoc.*, **29**, 214–21 (1946).
11. Letsky, B. M., "The Hot Lacquer Process Is Not So Hot," *Paint Manuf.*, **15** (2), 44, 53 (1945).
12. Nelson, H. H., "High Temperature Application of Nitrocellulose Lacquers," *Ind. Eng. Chem.*, **31**, 70–5 (1939).
13. Paasche, J. A., U.S. Patent 2,400,315, May 14, 1946, Coating Machine—Spray Heated Material with Heater Air.
14. Pitman, E. C., Canadian Patent 400,104, Oct. 21, 1941, Electrically Heated Hose for Heating Lacquer.
15. Smith, W. T., "Hot Lacquer and War Effort," *Wood Products,* **47** (124), 34 (1942); "Lacquer Developments Toward Heavier Coatings," *Org. Finishing,* **6** (8), 9–16 (1945).
16. Speicher, J. K., "High-Solid Metal Lacquers," *Can. Paint & Varnish Mag.*, **21** (6), 22–26, 55 (1947); *Can. Chem. Process Ind.*, **31**, 214–17 (1947).
17. Stedtefeld, D. J., "High Temperature Lacquering," *Metal Finishing, Org. Finishing Sect.*, **38**, 414–417 (1940).
18. Wampler, R. H., "Modern Organic Finishes," pp. 34, 78, 146, New York, Chemical Publishing Company, 1946.
19. Wiesel, J. B., "Increasing Total Solids of Nitrocellulose Lacquers," *Am. Paint J. (Convention-at-Home Daily)*, **29**, 32–4 (Oct. 31, 1944).
20. Wilson, S. P., "High Solid Lacquers," *Ind. Finishing*, 32–36 (May, 1948).
21. Yeager, J. R., "Recent Developments in Nitrocellulose Lacquers," *Am. Paint J.*, **31** (29), 26–34 (1947); *Paint, Oil, Chem. Rev.*, **110** (14), 22, 24, 38 (1947).
22. "Spraying Hot Lacquers," *Decorator*, 40–42 (Feb., 1944).
23. Bogin, Charles, U.S. Patent 2,150,096 (to Commercial Solvents Corp.), May 7, 1939. Process for Applying Cellulose Derivative Lacquers.
24. Commercial Solvents Corp., "The Application of Lacquers at Elevated Temperatures," Copyright 1939.
25. Commercial Solvents Corp., "Blistering of Lacquers Applied at Elevated Temperatures," Copyright 1940.
26. Hercules Powder Co., "High Solids Nitrocellulose Lacquers Formulation and Performance," Copyright 1945.
27. Hercules Powder Co., "High Solids Nitrocellulose Lacquers For Furniture Finishing," Copyright 1945.

13 : Fundamentals of Formulating Emulsion and Latex Paints

WILLIAM VON FISCHER

Case Institute of Technology
Cleveland, Ohio

In this chapter we are primarily interested in water-containing paints. Certainly the practice of using water in paint is not new, as some of the earliest organic protective coatings contained water. There are records available which show that the early Greeks and Egyptians used water solutions of casein from skim milk as a vehicle for pigmented coatings. Casein treated with slaked lime becomes liquid and can be emulsified with water. Pigments were dispersed in this emulsion system. Later, egg yolks and egg whites were used as the "binder" material. About the beginning of the present century various powder paints containing glues as binders were used for water-dispersible systems; fish glues as well as animal glues were used. These were the Kalsomines, which still are available. Now we have emulsion and latex paints. Before discussing the formulations of these systems the general theory of emulsion systems will be reviewed briefly.

General Theory of Emulsion Systems

An emulsion is a lyophobic colloidal system wherein the particles that make up the internal phase consist of globules of a liquid which is immiscible with the liquid of the external phase. If one liquid is water and the other is oil, obviously, two kinds of emulsions can exist—one in which the water constitutes the external phase and the other in which the oil constitutes this phase. If the surface tension of the oil is greater than that of the water, the oil will become the internal phase, and vice versa.

It is one thing to prepare an emulsion of either type and quite another to insure its stability. The emulsion can change by complete coalescence and separation of the two phases or by inversion, i.e., where the former external phase becomes the internal phase. To prevent such changes, an *emulsifying agent* is required. There are many theories regarding the mechanism of emulsifying agent activity, and probably no single theory fits all circumstances. In general, however, most of the theories presuppose the formation of oriented surface layers at the boundaries of the internal and external phases of the emulsion. This is analogous to the adsorption of surface agents on dispersed solids.

In principle, the manufacture of emulsions is simple: it consists of agitation (or colloid mill passage) of the external and internal phases and the emulsifying agent. The question of practical results, however, is affected considerably by the choice of emulsifying agents, the type and time of the agitation conditions (particle size), and the schedule of additions of one component to the other.

In concluding these introductory remarks on emulsions, let us consider the question of determining whether an emulsion is of the O/W or the W/O type. This is not always easy to establish, but it is very important. A tendency toward inversion is not only detrimental to the stability of paint, but it may indicate the possibility of this complicating phenomenon during film formation, which usually is undesirable for O/W emulsions. The principal methods of determining the type of emulsion can distinguish in the more positive cases. Where the situation is doubtful, the cumulative data of all the methods become helpful. The methods are as follows:

(1) **Dilution Test.** On a microscope slide (or in a glass graduate) add oil and water respectively to separate portions of the emulsion. One or the other will mix more readily with the emulsion. The diluent soluble in the external phase will tend to decrease the viscosity, whereas the other component tends to increase it. (This test can become confused if the dilution causes an inversion of the emulsion.)

(2) **Dye Method.** This test depends on the appearance of the emulsion when it is treated with a dye which is soluble in one of the phases and insoluble in the other. For example, an oil-soluble dye will dot an O/W emulsion with colored globules, whereas salts such as potassium permanganate will dot a W/O emulsion with colored globules. Some dyes will color the external phase, leaving the internal phase unaffected. Experience shows that different color effects are produced when the dye is occluded in the internal phase as compared to the external phase. This test can be developed by experience and may serve as a valuable rapid test in systems where inversion is possible.

(3) **Conductance Method.** The conductivity of an emulsion is greater when water is the external phase. Complete conductivity curves can be established for systems where phase inversion is possible. This provides a valuable test, since it not only distinguishes the state of the emulsion, but also gives some measure of the progress of the inversion process in instances where such a change occurs in preparing the stable emulsion desired as a final end product.

Properties of Emulsion Paints

Emulsion paints can be either of the O/W or W/O type; the former can be thinned with water and the latter with ordinary paint solvents. In either instance, the pigments can be dispersed in the oil or film-forming phase, although some hydrophilic pigments may be dispersed in the water phase. By "oil phase" is generally meant any water-insoluble paint vehicle, whether it actually is a drying oil, a varnish, an alkyd, or solutions of nonvolatile resins in volatile solvents. All dispersions represent nonequilibrium conditions and consequently are somewhat unstable. In the case of emulsion paint, we are concerned with all the pigment-vehicle stability problems of ordinary paints, as well as with the problems of emulsion stability. In view of this additional complication, it is difficult at times to show reason why emulsion paints should be used at all; however, they do fit some situations better than conventional types. The advantages and disadvantages of emulsion paints are as follows:

Advantages	*Disadvantages*
1. Water is a cheap diluent	1. Emulsifying agents are necessary and difficult to formulate properly
2. Solvent odors are eliminated in drying	2. Formulation more complicated to get good application properties
3. Minimum fire hazard	3. Inferior storage stability (heat or freezing unfavorable)
4. Fast drying	
5. Excellent for porous and moist surfaces	4. Somewhat inferior weathering resistance and washability (usually because of deleterious influence of emulsifying agents)
	5. Many paints contain dissolved protein, which is subject to bacterial decomposition

The first step of the drying process is the evaporation of water, which causes the oil phase to concentrate and finally coalesce. Next, other volatile components of the oil phase are vaporized and the normal process of oxidation proceeds, if the nonvolatile vehicle contains drying oil. If the paint is a synthetic resin type, the drying process is completed upon the loss of the volatile components of the oil phase. Here emulsion paints are favored for obvious reasons. Many synthetic resins, if used as ordinary solvent-type lacquers, need large quantities of expensive solvents to give a workable viscosity. In the case of water dispersions, only enough solvent plus plasticizer need be combined with the resin to permit emulsification and coalescence to a continuous film after evaporation of the water. It is possible to develop a higher nonvolatile resin content at workable viscosities in an emulsion paint than is practical in a lacquer. Air-dried films from drying-oil types of emulsion paints become hydrophobic i.e., no longer dispersible in water, and oxidative polymerization makes them less soluble in regular paint thinners. These films resemble conventional paint films except that the residual emulsifying agent in the film affects the water resistance more or less adversely. Synthetic resins (e.g., polyvinyl types) become water-resistant because either the solvent portion of the water-insoluble phase, or the emulsifying agent (e.g., volatile ammonia or amines), or both, is lost by evaporation.

Emulsion paints are most useful in coating porous and/or wet surfaces because emulsion particles tend to have less penetration than do solutions. Because of their fast-drying qualities, good application properties, and lesser odor, they have had quite a vogue in trade sales or maintenance paint for interior nonmetallic surfaces.

Manufacture of Emulsion Paints

The formulation of emulsion paints lacks some versatility because of the fact that many pigments cannot be used. It is necessary particularly to avoid pigments capable of forming soaps (e.g., pigments containing ZnO, $CaCO_3$, or $PbCO_3$) or pigments containing large proportions of water-soluble and acidic ions (e.g., Iron Blue). Some suitable pigments are:

White:	Titanium dioxide, zinc sulfide, barium sulfate, and extended pigments such as titanated lithopone and titanated barium sulfate
Yellow:	Iron Oxide Yellow, Cadmium Yellow
Green:	Chromium Oxide Green, Chromium Hydrate Green, Phthalocyanine Green
Blue:	Ultramarine; Phthalocyanine Blue
Red:	Iron Oxide Red, some organic reds
Black:	Iron Oxide Black, certain water-dispersible carbon blacks
Extenders:	China clay, mica, magnesium silicate, barium sulfate

The pigment can be introduced in various ways, either by dispersing into the water-insoluble phase before emulsification or by grinding the pigment into the emulsion. The procedure can be complex; for example, grind the pigment into a W/O emulsion, then by dilution, addition of emulsifying agents, agitation, etc., cause the emulsion to invert to an O/W type. Most of the favored procedures are regarded as practical trade secrets, and the eventual success of any particular one is dependent upon exact control of apparently minor details in the manufacturing process.

Before concluding this general discussion of emulsion paints, it is well to mention that, while the O/W type is the usual type, the W/O type is not without importance.

It has been a procedure of long standing to add water to conventional paint types in order to develop higher viscosity, thixotropy, or other consistency properties. The paints most favored by such practice already contain emulsifying agents in the form of aluminum stearate, calcium lineoleate, zinc oleate, or other salts, either added directly to serve this function or being formed by reaction of some pigments with drying oil fatty acids. If the water addition is not carried to extremes, the consistency produced favors stability by inhibiting the settling of the pigment. Trouble can be encountered, however, if the paint vehicle dries more rapidly than the water can escape. This is a particular danger in the less porous films produced within the semi-gloss to gloss range of the pigment/binder ratio. The more rapid the surface drying of the vehicle the greater is the chance of sealing in the water, which can influence a porous structure of the film, or, if it coalesces, causes an appearance of pinholing in the film.

Some Specific Details of the Formulation of Emulsions

As in all pigmented coatings, emulsion paints contain a pigment, binder, sometimes an organic thinner for the oil phase, and the other minor constituents essential to ordinary paints; for example, driers, antiskinning agents for oil paints, and light stabilizers in the case of some synthetic resins. In addition to these conventional coatings ingredients, the formulator need concern himself with agents specifically directed toward stabilizing the emulsion. Let us briefly examine the list of the raw materials with which the formulator may be concerned.

Binders:

Oil-base Emulsions
1. Processed drying oils: bodied oils, sulfonated oils, blown oils, maleic treated oils, etc.
2. Oleoresinous varnishes: ester-gum or other varnish resins.
3. Alkyd resins.

Lacquer Emulsions
4. Synthetic resins: which may contain plasticizers and/or solvents.

After an emulsion film forms, some finishes rely on normal air-oxidation mechanisms for setting and others, in the lacquer emulsion class, upon some solvent evaporation.

Pigments. These have already been discussed in general. It should be emphasized that they should be nonreactive with water, and be free of soluble salts which are detrimental to the stability of emulsions. Pigments of maximum hiding power, which can be used at the lowest possible pig-

ment volume concentration necessary for adequate hiding, are preferred
because this simplifies the problem of manufacture, storage, and application of water paints.

Emulsifying Agents. These ordinarily are large molecules of which
the greatest part of the molecule is nonpolar (for solubility in the oil
phase) and a smaller part is polar (for orientation and solubility into
the water phase). The most common of all such agents are fatty acids,
rosin acids, naphthenic acids, or salts of these acids which are designated
as soaps. Many synthetic emulsifying agents exist. A partial list is given
in Table 13.1.

TABLE 13.1. SYNTHETIC EMULSIFYING AGENTS*

Chemical Name	Type of Emulsion Favored	Trade Name	Source
2-amino-2-methyl-1-propanol	O/W	——	Commercial Solvents Corp.
Cetyl dimethyl benzyl ammonium chloride	O/W	"Triton K-60"	Rohm & Haas Co.
Diethylamino-ethyl-oleylamide acetate	O/W	"Sapamine A"	Ceba Co., Inc.
Diethylene glycol monolaurate	W/O	"Glaurin"	Glyco Products, Inc.
Diethylene imide oxide	O/W	"Morpholine"	Carbide & Carbon Chemicals Corp.
Dioctyl sodium sulfonsuccinate	O/W	"Aerosol OT"	American Cyanamid Co.
Pentaerythritol monooleate	W/O	"Pentamul 126"	Heyden Chemical Corp.
Polyoxyalkalene derivative of sorbitan laurate	O/W	"Tween 20"	Atlas Powder Co.
Sodium lauryl sulfate	O/W	"Duponol WA" also "Orvus WA"	du Pont Co. Procter & Gamble Co.
Sodium oleate	O/W	Soap	——
Sodium resinate	O/W	"Dresinate"	Hercules Powder Co.
Sodium salt of the oleyl derivative of taurine	O/W	"Arctic Syntex T" also "Igepon T"	Colgate Palmolive Peet Co. General Dyestuff Co.
Sorbiton monolaurate	W/O	"Span 20"	Atlas Powder Co.
Triethanolamine	O/W	——	Carbide & Carbon Chemicals Corp.

* From: Sutheim, "Emulsion Paints," *Chemical Industries* (June, 1947).

The emulsifying agents have other functions besides merely stabilizing
emulsions: they influence in subtle ways the viscosity and other consistency properties of emulsion paints. The selection of optimum combinations of surface-active agents is one of the critical formulation problems
in emulsion paints.

Stabilizers. These are frequently referred to as protective colloids. Ordinarily they are water-soluble polymers which increase the viscosity of the water phase. This, at least in part, produces greater emulsion stability by decreasing the mobility and collision frequency of the oil droplets. However, this is not the whole story, for many agents that increase the water phase viscosity do not stabilize emulsions. Some typical stabilizers are:

Casein	Zein
Soya proteins	Starches
Methyl cellulose	Bentonite
Sodium carboxyl methyl cellulose	Sodium salts of styrene-maleic
Alginates	copolymers

The stabilizers have some film-forming properties, purely by precipitation from solution as water evaporates. Most are somewhat incompatible with the major film-forming material and hence reduce the gloss and film strength of the basic coatings film. It is a constant formulation objective to reduce the quantity of stabilizer used to a minimum.

Preservatives. These are chemical poisons added to reduce bacterial decay of constituents such as casein and other proteins. There are many such agents and some have rather unpleasant odors. Among the common types are:

Bichloride of mercury	Phenol
Thymol and chloroisothymol	"Dowicide" A and G
Sodium trichlorophenate	"Santobrite"
Parachlorometacresol	"Borax"
Tribromophenol	Sodium and ammonium fluorides

Antifoaming Agents. These are extremely important in minimizing excessive foaming during the process of paint manufacture, and even more important in eliminating bubble formation in the paint when it is being brushed. Of all aspects of the formulation problem, foam control is one of the most elusive and most difficult to effect. Some agents which are effective as anti-foams in small amounts produce the reverse effect when optimum concentrations for foam control are exceeded. Frequently, two or more agents, each being very effective by themselves, greatly aggravate the reverse problem when used as mixtures. The contrary is also true at times. All that can be advised is to keep trying another composition or concentration if the one under test fails to work. No scientific rules exist regarding control of these phenomena. The problem is sufficiently critical so that some promising formulations of water paints have been discarded because no anti-foam agent could be found to reduce the foaming condition induced by other agents in the paint. Some agents that have at times served as anti-foam agents are:

> Dow Corning "Anti-Foam A" (silicone)
> "Foamex" (Glyco Products Co.)
> American Cyanamid "Anti-Foam H"
> Pine oil

This general description of formulation materials can best be illustrated by quoting some examples of emulsion paint formulation.

Example I is representative of one type of interior flat paint, now almost obsolete because more protein-free types are preferred which have less tendency to exhibit putrefaction trouble.

EXAMPLE I*

Pigmentation	Titanium dioxide	100	lb
	Lithopone	400	lb
	"Asbestine 5X"	250	lb
Oil phase	Pine oil	½	gal
	Ester gum-linseed varnish (50-gal length)	12½	gal
	Linseed fatty acids	¼	gal
	6% cobalt naphthenate	1/16	gal
	24% lead naphthenate	½	gal
Aqueous phase	Alginate	2	lb
	Fungicide	8.9	lb
	"Antifoam H"	3.7	lb
	Casein	35.75	lb
	Wetting agents	½	gal
	Ammonium hydroxide (26°Bé)	⅛	gal
	Water	56	gal
	Total	100	gal

* From: Matlack, *Offic. Dig.*, **303**, 283 (April 1950).

The formula of Example I is sometimes less desirable than is a protein-free type like the following:

EXAMPLE II*

Material	Lb
Rutile titanium dioxide pigment	75
Rutile titanium-calcium pigment	525
Diatomaceous silica	100
1. Linseed oil-ester gum varnish, 40-gal length (cold cut of ester gum in 9–12 acid value linseed)	185.7
2. Sulfonated castor oil, 75% solids (emulsifying agent for varnish)	30.8
3. Surface-active agent for pigment (polyethylene oxide condensates)	22.3

EXAMPLE II*—*Continued*

Material	Lb
4. 10% sodium hydroxide solution (to form soaps, and to preserve neutrality of emulsion which tends to break at low pH)	22.0
5. 3% methyl cellulose solution (protective colloid)	238.0
6. 24% lead naphthenate (drier for oil)	9.7
7. 6% cobalt naphthenate (drier for oil)	2.4
8. Water	100.0

Total 1310.9   lb
or 100 gal
of paint

* From: F. B. Steig, *Offic. Dig.*, **301**, 95 (Feb. 1950).

Both of the previous examples were for a flat paint, a type that is relatively easy to formulate. If gloss is desired, the formulation is more difficult but not impossible. Consider this example:

EXAMPLE III—GLOSS EMULSION PAINT*

Material	Lb
1. Rutile TiO_2	310
2. Ultramarine Blue	$\frac{1}{16}$
3. Dehydrated castor varnish, 10-gal length (ester gum dissolved in oil-viscosity Z-6 at 90% solids)†	338.0
4. Sulfonated castor oil, 75% solids (emulsifying agent for varnish)	17.4
5. Surface-active agent for pigment (polyethylene oxide condensate)	34.4
6. 10% NaOH solution	17.6
7. 10% starch solution (protective colloid)	212.6
8. 24% lead naphthenate	14.5
9. 6% cobalt naphthenate	4.0
10. Water	133.3

Total 1081.8   lb
or 100 gal

* From: Steig, *Offic. Dig.*, **301**, 98 (Feb. 1950).
† The varnish oil is made up of 6 gallons of Z-3 viscosity, blown dehydrated castor, 3 gallons G-H viscosity unbodied dehydrated castor and 1 gallon of distilled dehydrated castor fatty acids. (These will form soaps with NaOH.) This particular oil blend gave the best results with respect to gloss and package stability. In general, blown oils tend to promote gloss, bodied oils decrease gloss.

While alkyd resin emulsions offer some special complications, such emulsions have been offered from time to time by some resin manufacturers. Formulas for water paints based on emulsified alkyd resin solutions are reported in the literature; for example, as is shown in Example IV.

EXAMPLE IV—ALKYD-TYPE OF EMULSION PAINT*

Interior White	Lb
Titanium dioxide (water-dispersible)	200
Barium titanium pigment	200
Colloidal silica	150
Flake mica	50
Alkyd emulsion (50% solids)	200
Water	450

* From: Cheetham and Pearce, Chap. 17, Vol. III, of Mattiello, "Protective and Decorative Coatings" John Wiley & Sons, New York, 1943.

Lacquer Emulsions—Nitrocellulose Types

Nitrocellulose emulsions have long been used in leather and paper finishing. The procedure of preparing the emulsions is quite simple. The finished lacquer, preferably at high solids and high viscosity, clear or pigmented, is poured into an agitated solution of emulsifying agent in water. A number of commercial emulsifying agents of the cationic or nonionic type can be used, as well as agents such as casein, sodium oleate, gelatin, sodium algenate, and other proteins. Such lacquer emulsions were not too popular for general coatings work because of the extreme water sensitivity of the films (due to the residue of emulsifying agents) or because the films were dull and low in film strength and adhesion (as a result of incompatibility of the emulsifier with nitrocellulose). Also, the stability problem for the emulsions is severe.

Some development has occurred, mostly in Great Britain, on new resinous types of emulsifiers which are compatible with nitrocellulose in dry films, less water-sensitive in the film, and which also promote greater stability in the emulsions.

These polymeric emulsifiers are mixed esters prepared by reacting a low molecular weight polyvinyl acetate with polybasic acids such as phthalic, maleic, or citric at elevated temperatures. For example, such resins may consist of copolymers of polyvinyl acetate and 27 per cent vinyl phthalate (10 per cent vinyl citrate or 21 per cent vinyl maleate may be substituted for the vinyl phthalate). In addition, some of the polyvinyl acetate may be hydrolyzed further so that the effective copolymer is some mixture of vinyl acetate, vinyl alcohol, and vinyl phthalate (or maleate or citrate). These polymers are water-insoluble at pH 7, but can be water solubilized by forming the sodium salts with their residual acid groups. The details of preparation of these new agents are cited in British Patents 552,011 and 602,974.

Considerable data regarding the preparation and stability of nitro-cellulose lacquer emulsions are given by Simpson,* who investigated the

* *J. Oil and Colour Chemists' Assoc.,* **32,** 60, 72 (1948).

influence of different pigments, electrolytes, freezing temperatures, and other variables on emulsions stability.

A typical lacquer might be made as follows:

EXAMPLE V—COMPOSITION OF LACQUER BASE

Material	Parts by Weight
Clear nitrocellulose solution (1,075 parts of 70% nitrocellulose and 30% butanol; 960 parts ethyl acetate; 1,612 parts butyl acetate; 1,214 parts toluene)	200
Methyl cyclohexanone	40
Blown linseed oil (lacquer grade)	75
Blown castor oil	20
Butyl acetate	20

The pigments are dispersed with a roller mill into the minimum quantity of caster oil. The pigment paste is then mixed in proportions appropriate for that pigment with the nitrocellulose stock solution. The pigmented lacquer is poured slowly into a mildly agitated 0.5 to 6 per cent solution of the emulsifying agent resin (partially hydrolyzed polyvinyl acetate-phthalate or polyvinyl acetate-maleate resin salt are usually the preferred types). When emulsification is complete, a rather unstable emulsion exists (most emulsion particles have a diameter greater than 15 μ). To stabilize it, the agitation is increased to 2,000 rpm (for at least 3 minutes for pint to quart size batches). This time will vary proportionately for larger batches depending on the effectiveness of the agitation. After stabilization, most of the particles are in the range of 0.7 to 1.5 μ, and very few are greater than 15 μ. A good deal of the art of preparing stable emulsions depends on determining and accomplishing an optimum particle size distribution.

In general, organic pigments of the red and yellow type are poorer for stability than inorganic types; however, the phthalocyanines are superior to the inorganic blues and greens. The most stable are white pigments, particularly titanium and antimony oxides. Pigments that cause a lowering of the pH and hence precipitation of the emulsifier, are universally poor for stability. Salts in general are poor for stability, because they either precipitate the emulsifier by lowering the pH, form insoluble salts with the emulsifier, or promote the familiar salting-out effect. The latter effect is of course more gradual at low salt contents, and manifests itself by slow increase of viscosity, and gradual phase separation or inversion, or as creaming. The former effects are immediate, in that they break the emulsion quickly and in proportion to the quantity of added salt. It might be noted that some exceptions occur—occasionally, zinc, nickel, calcium, and magnesium salts, particularly in the presence of partially hydrolyzed polyvinyl-acetate-phthalate-salt emulsifier, actually promote stability. It is believed that a coherent film of insoluble resin salts of these metals may form a protective shell around the emulsion droplet if the conditions of precipitation are favorable. Ions such as aluminum, lead, silver, and iron cause breaking of the emulsion always; apparently here the precipitates formed are either not the right sort or are not formed so as to give favorable protective action. It was reported that these nitrocellulose emulsions are stable for nearly a year at temperatures as low as 0°C, but that they break immediately on actual freezing (about -6°C). The lower the volume-per cent of the dispersed emulsion phase, the better the stability. Practical ranges of volume-per cent dispersed phase are 32 to 75 per cent.

The volume use of nitrocellulose emulsions is not extensive; rather it is an interesting development which demonstrates how possibly any one of many synthetic resin lacquer emulsions, formerly believed to be impractical, can become of interest by virtue of discovery of some missing link, such as a better emulsifying agent. The development possibilities of lacquer emulsions based on cellulose ethers and esters still require much exploration.

Vinyl Emulsions for Coatings

Vinyl emulsions were extensively exploited as a coatings vehicle in wartime Germany. Presented here are some data given in the FIAT Report No. 681 by H. O. Farr, Jr. Paints made from these emulsions were used for coating wood, plaster, stone, and cement.

Three resin emulsions were commonly used:

(1) **"Mowilith D":** 50 per cent solids, emulsion-polymerized polyvinyl-acetate of high molecular weight. This deposits a very brittle film, and the resin is not extensively compatible with other resins or plasticizers. This emulsion is usually used in combination with resins that give softer films, such as the following.

(2) **"Mowilith D 32":** 58 per cent solids, composed of 38.7 per cent polyvinylacetate, 1.9 per cent polyvinylalcohol, 11.6 per cent tricresyl phosphate, 7.7 per cent dibutyl phthalate, 3.3 per cent methanol, and 36.8 per cent water.

(3) **"Mowilith D 300":** 50 per cent solids, made up of 38 per cent of a 70/30 vinylacetate-vinyl chloride copolymer, 11.6 per cent of tricresyl phosphate, 3 per cent methanol, and water. This emulsion was used unpigmented, generally where greater waterproofness was desired.

On this continent, polyvinyl acetate types of emulsions are manufactured by du Pont; Dewey and Almy; American Polymer Corp.; Shawinigan Chemicals Corp.; Carbide and Carbon Chemicals; and others. B. F.

Goodrich and the Dow Chemical Company also manufacture emulsions based on vinyl chloride or vinyl-vinylidene chloride copolymer which give more durable films and which can be used in a manner similar to the polyvinylacetate types. The same can be said of the acrylonitrile-vinyl chloride resin emulsions. However, since American development in the use of these resin-emulsions is just beginning, we will use as examples some typical German formulas based on the above-described commercial vehicles, remembering that similar systems can be developed for other resin-solution dispersions. In these examples, the polymers contain dissolved plasticizer and some solvent which make the emulsion droplets very viscous resin solutions—solutions that are unlikely to invert to a W/O emulsion. Here we are getting much closer to a latex type of dispersion than in the case of the nitrocellulose emulsions.

I. G. Farbenindustrie Formulas for Inside Exposure

EXAMPLE VI—GLOSS WHITE FOR PLASTER

	Per Cent
"Mowilith D 32"	15
"Mowilith D"	15
"Kaolin"	10
Lithopone (50% ZnS)	10
Talcum	5
Titanium-barium pigment (50/50 $TiO_2/BaSO_4$)	5
Water	40

EXAMPLE VII—FLAT WHITE FOR PLASTER

"Mowilith D 32"	15
Methyl cellulose	5
Chalk	15
Lithopone (50% ZnS)	30
Talcum	5
Water	30

EXAMPLE VIII—FOR OUTSIDE EXPOSURE; BROWN FOR WALLS

"Mowilith D 32"	20
Ochre, dark	20
Titanium-barium pigment (19% TiO_2, 25% ZnO, 56% $BaSO_4$)	8
Talcum	8
Umber, greenish	4
Water	40

In addition to the vinyl acetate polymer (or vinyl acetate-vinyl chloride copolymer) emulsions, the German technologists used resin emulsions derived from methyl, ethyl, or butyl acrylate polymers. Of particular interest to paint was I. G. Farbenindustrie "Acronol 500D" (a copolymer of 49 per cent vinyl acetate, 49 per cent butyl acrylate, and 2 per cent acrylic acid). The resin is neutralized with ammonia and an emulsion prepared. The neutralized emulsion takes pigmentation very well without increasing viscosity. This emulsion was used for exterior wood finishing where durability requirements could not be satisfied with less expensive emulsions made up of polyvinyl acetate alone.

An even higher quality emulsion could be made for the same purposes by emulsion polymerization of 50 per cent vinylisobutyl ether, 30 per cent methylacrylate, and 20 per cent acrylonitrile-butyl ether.

Another interesting emulsion polymer, that cannot be easily pigmented but which provides a good sealer undercoat for nitrocellulose films, is derived by copolymerizing 20 per cent acrylonitrile-butyl ether, 66 per cent ethyl acrylate, 12 per cent styrene, and 2 per cent acrylic acid. This emulsion, combined with rubber latex, can provide a primer or final coating for natural or synthetic rubber.

In most of these cases, the emulsion droplets are a solution of resin, residual monomers, plasticizers, and small quantities of solvent.

In the United States, Rohm and Haas is the only major producer of emulsions based on acrylate or methacrylate resins. They are marketed under the trade name "Rhoplexes." Because of their high cost their use has been limited. From the formulation point of view it should be remembered that such emulsions produce excellent cements and adhesives when compounded with synthetic rubber latices, particularly with neoprene latices. These mixtures possess improved adhesion to glass, rubber, and metals, and greater film strength.

Latex Paints

In recent years, the greatest emphasis in the formulation of water paints has been on attempts to use synthetic resin latices. It will be recalled that a latex differs from an emulsion in that a latex represents a dispersion of a resinous solid in water rather than an organic liquid. Film formation from an emulsion is relatively simple and consists largely in a separation of an oil (the film-forming phase) from the water as the water evaporates. If the oil phase in an emulsion is a drying oil, an oleoresinous varnish, or an alkyd, the resultant separated oil phase continues to form a film by oxidation, solvent evaporation, etc., in a manner normal to oil paints, or by solvent evaporation alone in the case of lacquer emulsions. Ordinarily, emulsion paints produce the type of continuous film characteristic of non-water-containing paints and lacquers. The main serious complications come largely from the possible entrapment of water if the process of emulsion phase separation is not complete, or if inversion occurs during the process of film formation. Naturally the entrapment of any emulsifying agents does make emulsion-deposited films less durable than normal oil, varnish, or lacquer films, but this is a difference only of *degree*, not of *kind*. In contrast, latices form a film by coagulation or flocculation of discrete particles. There is practically no chance for inversion of phases, and in this respect, film formation from latices is simpler than from emulsions. On the other hand, the process is considerably more complicated in that we are dealing with coagulation phenomena which in great part are electrical in nature and which are largely controlled by the concentration and types of dissolved electrolytes and of protective colloids and soaps (or other surface-active agents functionally similar to soaps). Changes in any of these variables affect the quality of the film that is formed. The film is essentially a close-packed mass of spherical particles, each individual particle more or less discrete. The film strength depends on the forces bonding the individual spheres; whether there are electrical forces or other types of cohesive forces, is yet uncertain. In extreme cases, the particles may have some tack, so that they can flow into and bond each other by a true diffusion and welding mechanism. This tends to give a film continuity approaching that obtained with lacquer emulsions. Whatever is the mechanism, the particle size distribution of the latex is an extremely important variable (more so than in emulsions where eventually all particles coalesce to a nearly continuous film). The questions have not been completely answered as to whether a high degree of uniformity of particle size distribution is more desirable than a high degree of heterogeneity. Present information indicates that it all depends on the viewpoint. From the viewpoint of the problems of stability and reproducibility of flow properties in the liquid paint, there are reasons to believe that these problems are decreased if the particles are nearly uniform in size and not too small. From the viewpoint of formation of films, where dense packing requires a maximum number of contact surfaces between particles, and a low ratio of volumes of voids/solid, the requirements are best served if there are not too many big particles and if there is a considerable variation in their size. These conditions which seem to promote best film properties make more difficult the formulation of the liquid latices for proper stability or application properties.

One might say that some of the same variables apply to the breaking of liquid emulsions into two phases. This is true only in a limited sense. The finest emulsions have an average particle size much larger than is common for the coarsest latices, the difference being tenfold or greater. As was pointed out before, the ideal in emulsions is the formation of a continuous liquid film whereas latex films are made up of more or less discrete solid particles associated by welding forces of yet undetermined nature. Practically speaking, this difference is not academic. Both latex and emulsion films contain residual soap and/or other emulsifying agents. This implies some reversibility of the emulsification phenomena when the film is attacked by water. For reasons yet to be discovered, the lacquer emulsion-deposited films are much more prone to attack by water than are latex films. In the latter, the exposure to water has much less effect in promoting a redispersion (or disintegration of the film); in fact, there is a marked tendency for water to leach out the water-sensitive agents, and there is a possibility for actually greater stabilization of the film when it is subject to water washing. This feature *above all others* has stimulated the popularity of latex formulations over emulsion types in water paints.

These comments apply to films containing latex particles as the sole film-forming constituent, and these advantages are preserved only to the extent that this restriction is made. For reasons shortly to be described, this objective has been attained only partly in existing formulations. In practice a film containing a latex as the sole binder would resemble a composition known as a "master-batch" in the rubber industry, where a mixture of pigments and extenders is dispersed into the water phase of a latex. When the latex is coagulated by adding electrolytes (or by other means) the rubber phase separates and drags down with it the cojointly suspended pigments. To consider the application of this phenomenon to paint, the master batch of rubber (or synthetic resin) and pigments would be coagulated when water evaporation raises the electrolyte concentration to a critical coagulation value and hence promotes the flocculation and intermediate gelation phenomena that are simulated in the coagulation of a master batch. If practical films of this sort could be deposited, very *washable* paints would be obtained. It is possible that such films might even be stabilized and rendered progressively less water sensitive as water washing leached out the residual soaps and emulsifiers.

Attempts have been made to use such films as a basis for paint, but thus far successful paints have not been produced for the following reasons:

(1) Such systems have very poor package stability.

(2) Such systems have very peculiar flow properties. In general, latex systems react unfavorably to crowding—application of pressure, as in pumping, milling, or brushing, causes coagulation in a nonuniform and usually unpredictable manner. This implies it would be difficult to codisperse therein pigments so that they are dispersed adequately for full hiding power; the undisturbed latex is too fluid, viscosity is low (pigment settling is rapid), and the brushing properties are poor. Either there is excessive sagging and running if the latex is excessively stabilized with

surface-active agents, or coagulation due to brush pressure leaves a streaked surface, if the latex is not overstabilized.

(3) If a latex has very uniform particle size and the particles are large, the above problems are minimized but then the quality of the films is poor.

(4) Adhesion of latex films to substrate is poor.

Hence, in practice, the trend of formulation has been in the direction of using modified latices, that is, adding some other film-former such as methyl cellulose, polyvinyl alcohol, gelatin, casein, or other water-soluble synthetic resin (e.g., the sodium salt of a partially esterified copolymer of styrene and maleic anhydride). The trick of this type of formulation is to add the least amount of such modifier (or protective colloid) as is necessary to assure package stability and application properties, and thereby to allow as much as possible of the actual film to be formed by latex coagulation. The result is a hybrid of the oldest type of water paint (water-soluble binder) and a latex paint. The finished paint may also contain constituents which are surface-active agents, which aid both the stability of the pigment suspension and change for the better the flow properties of the composition. If some of the agents are partially soluble in the latex particles, they tackify the resin particles and favor a true adhesive bond; i.e., in a limited degree, there is obtained some of the same sort of coalescence of particles to a continuous film as is found in lacquer emulsions. At the adhesion interface and in the voids between latex and pigment particles, is the deposited, water-soluble binder. This part can be leached out by water washing to the detriment of the film, but not as readily as if there were no latex film contiguous with it. A latex paint as it exists today represents quite a composite of types of water paint, e.g.:

(1) The most primitive type—a water soluble binder.

(2) At least in part—a true latex coagulum.

(3) At least in part—a coalesced resin binder of the character produced by lacquer emulsions.

No doubt, formulations can be devised that may superimpose even other types of film formation in the composite film. As a result, we have a compromise of both the *good* and of the *bad* properties that are characteristic of each of the different types of water paints. Hence we cannot suppose that we have achieved anywhere near the ultimate in the formulation of water paints. The ultimate would undoubtedly lie in the use of either a pure latex film-former or pure lacquer emulsion film-former, where the individual stability, application, and film-formation properties of the class have been solved without compromising the potential benefits of that mode of film formation. Whether it will be solved first for latex or for lacquer emulsions, we cannot know today. However, let us examine some type formulas of what are today classified as latex paints.

EXAMPLE IX — SATIN FINISH EMULSION PAINT*

	Pounds Non-vol.	Total Pounds	Gallons
"TITANOX RA 50"		225.0	6.4
China Clay		75.0	3.5
Casein solution[a]	19.0	147.0	17.0
"Dow Latex 529-K"[b]	65.2	145.5	17.0
"Dow Latex 512-K"[c]	134.8	299.5	35.0
Pine oil		3.0	0.4
Tributyl phosphate		10.0	1.2
Water		162.4	19.5
Total	219.0	1067.4	100.0

Pigment—28.1%   Vehicle —71.9%
P.V.C. —32.7%   Non-vol.—28.6%
Weight per gallon—10.7 pounds

[a] Casein Solution:

Casein	14.34 lb
Sodium hydroxide	0.61 lb
"Dowicide A"	4.10 lb
Water	128.00 lb

[b] For "Dow 529K", "Bakelite BKS-90" can be substituted. "Dow 529K" and "Bakelite BKS-90" should not be used in excess of 10 to 20 per cent of resin content, as they produce brittle films. These are used to harden films made up basically of softer resins.

[c] For "Dow 512K", it may be possible to substitute other commercial latices such as "Goodyear Chemigum 101", "Bakelite BKS-92", or "Dow 762K." When "Dow 762K" is used, ordinarily no other latex need be added to the formula.

* From: Titanium Pigments Corporation, Titanium Pigments Corp. Bull. No. MW-1655M12.

To prepare the casein solution, the casein is soaked in one-fourth of water at 140°F for 30 minutes. Sodium hydroxide is dissolved in another one-fourth of water and added to the casein. This is stirred continuously until all of the casein is in solution, and if necessary to complete the solution, the mix is heated to 160°F. The "Dowicide" dissolved in the remaining part of the water is then added.

In preparing the paint, the pigments are stirred into a mixture of the casein solution and enough of the latex to form a grinding paste. This paste is then passed through a loosely set roller mill. The remaining vehicle additions are then incorporated. Example X shows a somewhat different approach in details of formulation.

Comments Regarding the Constitution of Example X

(1) Wetting agent promotes easier milling and better dispersion, choice of agent depends on type of pigment (for above, isopropanol amine can be used).

(2) Tetrasodium pyrophosphate inhibits pigment flocculation and promotes latex stability.

EXAMPLE X—SEMI-GLOSS WHITE LATEX PAINT*

Production Breakdown of Formula	Lb/100 gal
1. Pigment Dispersion	
Use mixer, high-speed stone mill, or pebble mill	
Titanium dioxide (1)	225.81
Lithopone	64.52
Mica	32.26
Tetrasodium pyrophosphate	1.61
Wetting agent	0.75
Water	107.53
2. Soybean Protein Solution	
Part of (2) can be added to (1) if roller mill is used	
for pigment dispersion	
Soybean solution	20.43
Water	110.32
Ammonia (26°Bé)	2.04
Sodium pentachlorophenate	3.44
3. Thickener Solution	
Solution (3) and (2) are stocked separately	
Ammonium alginate	1.08
Water	52.37
Sodium pentachlorophenate	0.32
4. Latex	
"Chemigum 101" (55% solids)	351.61
5. Added water	
Water	101.18
Total lb/100 gal	1075.27

Summary (Complete Formula)

Material	Wt %
Titanium dioxide	21.00
Lithopone	6.00
Mica	3.00
Soybean protein	1.90
"Chemigum 101" (solids)	18.00
Sodium pentachlorophenate	0.07
Tetrasodium pyrophosphate	0.15
Ammonia (26°Bé)	0.19
Wetting agent	0.07
Ammonium alginate	0.10
Water	49.52
Total	100.00

* From: Burr and Matvey, "Latest Developments in Emulsion Paints," *Off. Dig.*, **304,** 347-358 May, 1950.)

(3) Sodium pentachlorophenate is a preservative against bacterial or mold decay of protein.

(4) Protein stabilizes the latex pigment mixture, acts as a thickening agent, improves brushing and adhesion, and hardens the film.

(5) Pigments should be selected which contain a minimum of water-soluble salts as impurities. Partial use of lithopone sometimes improves consistency of the paint and film strength. Mica serves as a flatting agent and as a reinforcing agent in the film.

Examples XI and XII quoted from the trade literature illustrate even further some of the variety of approaches to the formulation problem which can yield useful latex paints.

EXAMPLE XI—FORMULA FOR LATEX PAINT*

Material	Parts by Weight
Lithopone	60
Titanium dioxide	10
China clay	30
4% aqueous solution of 100 cps methocel	35
"Dow Latex 512" (50% solids)	40
"Dowicide G"	4.0
Monoethanolamine oleate	0.6
Ethyl alcohol	0.6
Pine oil	0.3
Tributyl phosphate	1.0
"Tergitol" wetting agent 4T	1.0

Note: Some formulas represent same composite of this and that illustrated in Example I.

* From: Dow Chemical Company Bulletin, "Dow Latex 512." See also Bulletin on "Dow Latex 762K.'

Most of the original latex paints of commercial importance utilized polystyrene or styrene-butadiene copolymers as the latex resin. Considerable experimental work, however, has been done with latices based on resins derived from polymers or copolymers of vinyl and/or vinylidine chloride, and from copolymers of styrene or vinyl chloride with acrylonitrile. The greatest part of the effort in these directions has been in the search for water paints for exterior application, such as replacements for house paint. These efforts have been, up to now, comparatively unsuccessful. Some promising results have been indicated where the vehicle is a combination of latex derived from vinyl-vinylidine chloride copolymers and emulsions made from oxidizing types of alkyds and oleoresinous varnishes.*

* Bulletin "Dow Latex 744-B," The Dow Chemical Company, Midland, Michigan, 1952.

EXAMPLE XII — FORMULAS FOR LATEX PAINT*

	Formula 1 Lb	Formula 1 Gal	Formula 2 Lb	Formula 2 Ga	Formula 3 Lb	Formula 3 Gal
1. "Rayox R-610"	25.00	0.73	25.00	0.73	25.00	0.73
2. "Lustrex 820" (alkali-soluble styrene-maleate copolymer)	3.00	0.36	3.00	0.36	3.00	0.36
3. Water	44.00	5.27	45.50	5.45	34.00	4.07
4. Ammonia (28% NH₃)	0.90	0.12	0.90	0.12	0.90	0.12
5. "Santicizer 160" (expensive plasticizer)	8.00	0.96	—	—	—	—
6. "HB-40" (low-cost plasticizer)	—	—	9.0	1.08	—	—
7. "Lustrex 601-2" (polystyrene emulsion, 50% solids)	18.00	2.14	16.0	1.90	—	—
8. "Aerosol OT"	0.04	—	0.04	—	0.04	—
9. "Methocel," 100 cps	0.50	0.06	.50	0.06	0.50	0.06
10. Copolymer resin (styrene butadiene type, 45% solids)	—	—	—	—	—	4.50

Note: Formulas 1 and 2 are plasticized polystyrene latices. Formula 3 is based on a styrene-butadiene copolymer latex such as "Dow 512K" or Goodyear "Chemigum 101." Note that these formulas do not use protein. Some practical formulas may represent a composite of the type examples above and such as are illustrated in Examples 1 and 2.

* From: Monsanto Lustrex Latices in Emulsion Paints Bulletin, Monsanto Chemical Company, Springfield, Mass.

Gloss Paints Based on Latex

There are a number of approaches to the problem of gloss-water paints. One of these is through the use of vehicles in the new class of styrene-oil or styrenated-alkyd interploymers in combination with latex as in Example XIII.

Comments on Example XIII

This is an interesting example, since it involves film formation by

(1) Air-drying mechanism of the drying oil (oil phase).
(2) Coagulation and coadhesion of the latex particles (latex phase).
(3) Precipitation of the styrene polymer or copolymer (lacquer phase) from the organic phase.
(4) Separation of soluble methocel from aqueous phase (water solution phase).

Another type of coating exists which resembles a latex, but which does not produce a coherent film solely by room-temperature evaporation of water. These are the vinyl resin water dispersions, presently not used for air-drying paints, but which give excellent films when the dried films

EXAMPLE XIII—GLOSS TYPE WATER PAINT CONTAINING LATEX

Material	Parts by Weight
1. Interpolymer, 45/55 styrene-dehydrated castor oil	100
2. "Solvesso 2"	25
3. Driers (0.02% cobalt, 0.5% lead, based on copolymer)	
4. Linseed oil fatty acids	4.1
5. 10% NaOH solution	4.1
6. 10% 15cps "Methocel" solution	5.4
7. "Ponolith EL"	59.5
8. "Ti Pure R-110"	180
9. "Dow 512K Latex" (50% Solids)	200

Procedure

(a) Combine and mix 1, 2, 3, 4, and 5.

(b) Prepare a paste of above solution and 7 and 8, on a roller mill. Then add 6 to paste on the rolls.

(c) Reduce paste by stirring 9 in slowly.

(d) Adjust viscosity by dilution with water.

are baked at high enough temperatures to fuse the individual resin particles into a continuous film.

While presently such formulas as Example XIV are only of theoretical interest insofar as paints are concerned, it is possible that in the future this approach may represent one of the directions for adapting water paints for baking-types of production finishes for wood, plastics, etc.

EXAMPLE XIV—COATING FROM VINYL TYPE DISPERSION RESIN*

Material	Parts by Weight
"Vinylite NV-4" (vinylchloride-vinylacetate copolymer)	200
"Tipure R-510"	30
"Surfex"	60
Dioctyl phthalate	130
"Triton X-155"	2
"Superla" wax	3
Water	200
3% solution sodium carboxymethyl cellulose	30

Note: Premix dry resin, pigment, and filler. Dissolve "Triton" and "Superla" wax in plasticizer, and mix into the resin solid mixture. Add some water and thickening agent and mill on a 3-roll mill. Adjust to 65% solids with water. Apply film, air-dry, and bake for 3 to 5 minutes at 350 to 375°F.

* From: Bakelite Bulletin, Technical Release No. 10 "Vinylite Resin NV-4" for Water Dispersions.

An interesting development similar in principle to Example XIV has been reported by the du Pont Company.† Here a series of pigmented coat-

† New Product Technical Bulletin No. 1, Fabric and Finishes Dept., Teflon Finishes (Nov. 15, 1949).

ings based on water dispersions of "Teflon" resins (polytetrafluoroethylene) are applied to metal and baked to a coherent film at 750°F, either by oven-baking or by use of a blow torch. A water quenching of the hot coating is essential so as to produce a high-strength film of low crystallinity. This example has been mentioned to indicate at least one contradiction of the current prejudice that water paints cannot be used for metal because corrosion presents a serious adhesion problem. Here is one instance where the near ultimate in an anticorrosive film is produced starting with a water paint.

The range of theoretical types of water paints extends from the simplest, which use water-soluble binders, to the other extreme of completely water-insoluble resin dispersions as represented by Example XIV. In between are all shades of complexity represented by the emulsions and latices. Modern water paints depend frequently on two or more different mechanisms of film formation, and this explains some of the complexity of the formulation problem. Only rarely are we certain which complication of the system is the source of difficulty. Obviously, to guide formulation practice we need more precise scientific data regarding the physical properties of emulsions and latices. Such fundamental studies are in progress and information is accumulating slowly regarding such critical questions as to the causes of instability, the factors that control flow properties, and the mechanism of film formation.

Bibliography

1. Burr, W. W., Matvey, P. R., "Latest Developments in Emulsion Paints," *Offic. Dig. Federation Paint & Varnish Production Clubs, 304,* 347 (May, 1950).
2. Ryden, L. L., Britt, N. G., and Visger, R. D., "Emulsion Paints from Butadiene-Styrene Emulsion Polymer," *ibid., 303,* 292 (April, 1950).
3. Steig, F. B., "Emulsion Paints," *ibid., 301,* 94 (Feb. 1950).
4. Payne, Henry F., "Emulsion Paints—Theory, Practice and Literature Survey," *ibid., 302,* 212 (March, 1950).
5. Hahn, F. J., "Variables Affecting Post Plasticized Polystyrene Water Paints," *ibid., 329,* 386 (June, 1952).
6. Westgate, M., *et al.,* "Latex Paints—A Round Table Discussion," *ibid., 335,* 888 (Dec. 1952).
7. Peterson, N. R., and Hensen, W. A., "Formulation of Latex Paints," *ibid., 337,* 543 (Aug. 1952).
8. Am. Chem. Soc. Symposium, Atlantic City Meeting, Sept. 1952, "Emulsion Polymers and Emulsion Paints," Pub. in Preprint Booklet, by Division of Paint, Varnish and Plastics Chemistry, American Chemical Society, 1952.

14 : Metal Protection with Synthetic Resin Coatings

E. E. McSWEENEY

*Battelle Memorial Institute
Columbus, Ohio*

Four general factors affect the ability of an organic coating to protect metal from corrosion: (1) chemical resistance of the coating; (2) proper application of the coating; (3) good adhesion to the metal; and (4) minimum permeability to water, salts, or other corrosive materials.

In the following discussion, each of these factors will be considered with particular reference to its influence on the formulation, application, and performance of protective coatings. Some consideration will then be given to the mechanism of film failure, particularly as influenced by the above four factors. Finally, the general types of synthetic resins which are suitable for corrosion protection will be discussed.

Chemical Resistance

Good chemical resistance is probably the first property considered, but also one of the easiest properties to build into a synthetic resin coating. From the wide range of resins available, it is quite easy to select one that is resistant to almost any particular environment. Outstanding examples are polyvinyl chloride and related copolymers; phenolic resin baking finishes; phenolic resin-tung oil varnishes; epichlorhydrin-bisphenol resins; butadiene-styrene copolymers; polytetrafluorethylene; polytrifluorochloroethylene; furfural-furfuryl alcohol resins; and bituminous materials, such as asphalts, gilsonite, and coal tar pitches.

Chemical resistance is not the only problem—in fact, it is possibly the least important because it can be readily determined and predicted. If it were the paramount factor, polyethylene and polystyrene should be expected to make good coatings for protection of steel from water. This, however, is decidedly not the case, probably because they are too permeable to water and lack adhesion to steel.

Moreover, when a sufficiently resistant resin is used as the base for a coating, considerable care must be taken that its resistance is not impaired by other ingredients of the coating. Two specific examples of this may be cited as typical. In searching for a coating with good adhesion to aluminum, lead, and tin, and with sufficient adhesion and flexibility to withstand the deformation of a collapsible tube, a polyvinyl chloride copolymer ("Vinylite" VMCH) was used. Initially, several plasticizers were used with it to improve flexibility and adhesion. It was soon found, however, that even small amounts of plasticizer lowered the resistance to soap and essential oils so that the coating failed rapidly. The unmodified resin, however, gave satisfactory resistance, as well as adequate flexibility and adhesion. In another case, a coating based on a butadiene-styrene resin was developed as an air-dry or force-dry water-resistant finish for a metal article. Initially, the system was quite serviceable; then, a marked lessening of its ability to protect metal from moisture vapor was noted. Some time was spent looking for formulation errors or changes in raw material before it was discovered that replacement of about 10 per cent of the xylene used as solvent by a less volatile aromatic to improve application properties had seriously impaired chemical resistance. Hindsight, of course, made it obvious that, under the mild force dry used, the heavy ends of the solvent were not removed, and apparently increased the permeability of the coating to the point of rapid failure in service. A switch to a more carefully fractionated high-boiling solvent immediately corrected the trouble.

Some of the difficulties with the early zinc chromate primers caused by minute amounts of soluble sulfates or chlorides is another example of the weakening of an otherwise good coating by a trace ingredient.

Therefore, every ingredient of a corrosion-resistant coating should be selected with great care. The base resin may be more than adequate for a given purpose, but the coating ruined by another ingredient not normally considered significant.

Application of the Coating

Although it may seem redundant to state that no coating is better than its method of application, probably more premature coating failures result from improper application than for any other reason.

Obviously, a coating must be nonporous, and to achieve this, a minimum of two coats should be applied while three to five coats are no more than adequate for some applications. In general, two thin coats are better than one thick coat, since this minimizes possibility of voids. Film thickness will also vary widely, but normally will be in the range of 1 to 5 mils, although for some applications, such as can coatings, as little as 0.2 mil is often used.

Dust which is either on the metal or settles on the film before it sets will usually result in a void in the film and will assure early attack on the substrate. This can be especially serious if the area beneath the void is or soon becomes anodic, since rapid perforation of the metal can then occur, especially where light-weight metal is used, as in can stock.

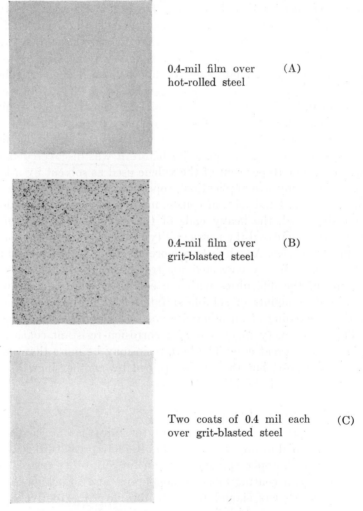

0.4-mil film over   (A)
hot-rolled steel

0.4-mil film over   (B)
grit-blasted steel

Two coats of 0.4 mil each   (C)
over grit-blasted steel

Figure 14.1.   Electrographic prints showing porosity of unpigmented phenolic coating over various steel surfaces.

Surface prepartion is important in any coatings application; it is doubly so where good corrosion resistance is sought. In general, it is important to have clean metal, free of scale or corrosion. The conse-

Figure 14.2. Electrographic prints showing porosity of 0.4-mil phenolic coating over normal grit-blasted surface (left) and "smooth"-blasted surface (right).

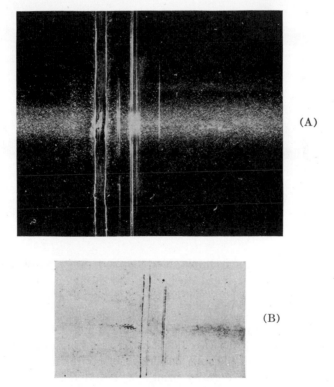

(A)

(B)

Figure 14.3. (A) Photograph of weld section of steel drum. (B) Electrograph print of porosity at weld section.

quences of such a minor contamination as a finger print will be noted below. Sand or grit blasting is one of the preferred methods of cleaning and may be followed by a passivating treatment, such as phosphating or a chromic acid rinse. In blasting, care should be taken to avoid excess roughening of the film, since this will necessitate heavier coating weights

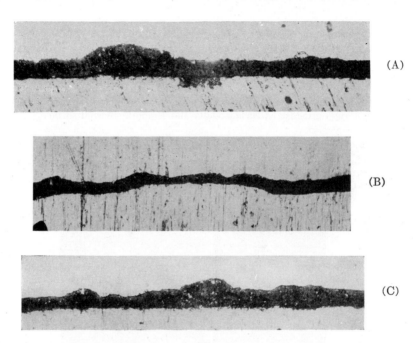

Figure 14.4. (A) Cross section at top of rolling hoop; minimum film thickness—0.4 mil. (B) Cross section at side of rolling hoop; minimum film thickness—0.15 mil. (C) Cross section at bottom of rolling hoop; minimum film thickness—0.3 mil.

to avoid porosity. For example, it was found that a vinyl coating, when applied to normal hot-rolled steel sheet and the same sheet after a normal grit blasting, required 25 per cent greater coating weight on the grit-blasted sheet to obtain a coating thickness of one mil as measured by a General Electric Type A Film-Thickness Gauge.

Figure 14.1 shows the effect of normal grit blasting on the porosity[1] of a one-coat film of phenolic baking resin approximately 0.4 mil thick. Figure 14.1a shows a porosity print[1] of a coated hot-rolled steel panel, while Figure 14.1b shows the tremendous increase in porosity caused by the rough surface. (The black areas correspond in size and number to pores in the film.) In Figure 14.1c, it is seen that adequate coverage is again obtained by multiple coat applications.

Improved coverage can also be obtained by using finer sand or grit. Figure 14.2 shows the porosity in a normal medium-rough-blasted surface (about 160 microinches) in contrast to a smooth-blasted surface of 35–50 microinches.

Design is likewise extremely important.[2] It is virtually impossible to coat a sharp edge such as a screw thread or an improperly prepared weld line. Figure 14.3 shows the exposed metal in a photograph of the weld

Figure 14.5.   Cross section through rolling hoop of steel drum. Dark gray film is scale. Light gray film is coating.

section of a coated steel drum, as well as a porosity print of the same area. Such defects can readily be corrected by smoothing such areas by wire brushing or similar treatments.

Other illustrations of application difficulties are given in Figures 14.4 and 14.5. These are photomicrographs (500X) of a cross section of a film. They were prepared by pouring babbitt metal over a phenolic coating, and then sectioning, polishing, and photographing by normal metallographic techniques. Figure 14.4 illustrates the variation in film thickness in the rolling hoop of a steel drum coated by moving a spray gun at a uniform rate of speed perpendicular to the surface being coated. At position A, corresponding to the top shoulder of the rolling hoop, a normal film thickness of about 0.5 mil was obtained. At Position B, along the side of the indentation, film thicknesses as low as 0.15 mil were observed, while in the bottom of the indentation (Position C), the coating is somewhat thicker but still less than on the flat.

Figure 14.5 illustrates the virtual absence of coating on one side of a rolling hoop when the spray gun was held at an angle. (In this photograph, the light-gray film is scale on the hot-rolled sheet. The organic

coating is the darker gray area). A porosity print through this same
area is shown in Figure 14.6. The upper half of the print corresponds

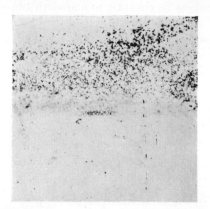

Figure 14.6.   Electrographic print showing porosity at rolling hoop.

to the thin area and shows a large amount of porosity, while the lower
part of the print shows the relative freedom from porosity where the
coating was thicker.

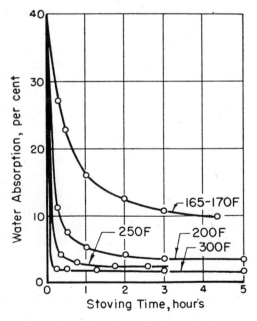

Figure 14.7.   Water absorption as function of baking schedule (Duntley and Earp [3]).

Allowing necessary drying time between coats and before placing the coated article in service is very important for maximum serviceability. Where possible, the coating should be baked to assure maximum adhesion and density of the film. For example, Figure 14.7 shows the effect of baking time and temperature on the water absorption of a urea-alkyd enamel.[3] Obviously, an underbaked coating is much more susceptible to water than a properly cured one.

Adhesion

Good adhesion of the coating to metal is essential to good coatings performance. The poor performance of polystyrene and polyethylene noted above is undoubtedly a result of poor adhesion. Although highly resistant to water, these resins are permeable. When water is transmitted through the film, it easily displaces the resin from the metal interface and rusting soon follows.

Two types of adhesion are generally considered. One is mechanical and is influenced by degree and type of surface roughness. A phenolic baking resin will readily be flaked off a smooth surface by striking a blow on the uncoated side of the panel. However, when applied over a grit-blasted surface, this does not occur, although the coating will be cracked through the metal as can be noted by microscopic examination or porosity measurements.

How this mechanical adherence is achieved can readily be seen in Figure 14.8. These are photomicrographs of cold-rolled steel with various pretreatments. They were obtained by plating nickel over the surface and then sectioning at an angle to magnify the vertical dimension. The extremely rough and under-cut nature of the grit-blasted surface is readily apparent.

Far more important, however, is so-called specific adhesion, which depends on polarity of the resin to form a relatively strong bond to the metal by Van der Waals forces.

Permeability

Since most coating failures result from permeation by water or other corrosive material through the film in one way or another, corrosion-resistant coatings must be as impermeable as possible.[4] The problem of permeability to moisture has been studied by many workers. Obviously, a relatively impermeable resin should be selected as the base for a corrosion-resistant coating, and care should be taken in formulating to further decrease rather than increase permeability. Let us therefore examine some of the factors which influence permeability to water vapor.

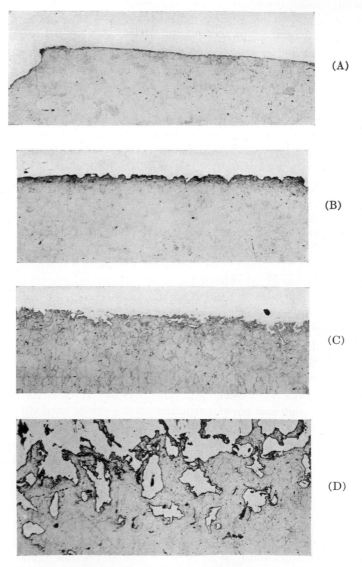

Figure 14.8. Taper sections of cold-rolled steel with various pretreatments. (A) As received; profilometer, 4.5–22 microinches. (B) Phosphate treated; profilometer, 14–20 microinches. (C) Phosphoric acid treated; profilometer, 14–26 microinches. (D) Grit-blasted; profilometer, 160–220 microinches.

The permeability of a film is given by the equation

$$Q = \frac{Pat\,\Delta p}{l}$$

where Q = quantity of water vapor transmitted; a = area of film; l = thickness of film; t = time; Δp = vapor pressure difference; and P = the permeability constant. The latter, which is characteristic of different materials, is usually expressed as g/hr/sq cm/cm/cm Hg. Table 14.1 gives this permeability constant (x 10^8) for a number of common resins.[5]

TABLE 14.1. PERMEABILITY CONSTANTS OF COMMON RESINS (Deeg[5])

Resin	Constant (X 10^8)
Alcohol-soluble phenolic	0.1
Polyethylene	.2
Polyvinyl chloride	.5
Polyvinyl chloride-acetate 95/5	.8
Polyvinyl chloride-acetate 87/13	1.0
Polystyrene	3.5
Polyvinyl acetate	30.0
Ethyl cellulose	77.0
Cellulose acetate	114.0

From these data, it is apparent that phenolics, PVC's, and polyethylene should make fairly satisfactory coatings if permeability were the sole criterion. However, as pointed out above, polyethylene is deficient in adhesion. The data indicate that phenolic baking varnishes should be outstanding as they are, and that the vinyls should also be good. Furthermore, these data show why polyvinyl acetate, ethyl cellulose, and cellulose acetate are not too satisfactory as corrosion-resistant coatings. Polystyrene is not so outstanding a protective coating as would be predicted. However, as Mayne[6] has pointed out, sufficient water and oxygen would diffuse through a clear polystyrene film for ten times the normal corrosion rate of uncoated steel. He further points out that the limiting factor is the transfer of iron and sodium ions through the film.

The difference noted above in permeability of phenolic and polyvinyl chloride films would indicate that the phenolics should be somewhat superior. This is borne out by the fact that the vinyls are almost always pigmented when used as corrosion-resistant finishes. One good reason for this is the decrease in permeability of pigmented films.

The influence of various pigments on permeability of paint films has been shown by Elm and Kittelberger,[7] who studied the effect of a number of pigments on linseed oil, alkyd, and phenolic resin films. The data in Table 14.2, with the permeability of the unpigmented film taken as one,

TABLE 14.2. MOISTURE-PERMEABILITY FACTORS FOR SEVERAL PIGMENTS
AT 30 PER CENT PVC (Elm[7]).

Pigment	Permeability Factor
ZTO chromate	0.343
Red lead	.419
Zinc oxide: iron oxide	.403
Zinc oxide	.428
Zinc dust: zinc oxide	.476
Blue lead	.466
Scarlet basic lead chromate	.524
Iron oxide	.556
Zinc yellow	.609
Chrome yellow	.695
Silica	.896
Unpigmented vehicle	1.000

show that pigments in general greatly reduce the permeability of a film
and also indicate that some pigments are much more efficient than others.
For instance, silica causes relatively little change, while ZTO chromate

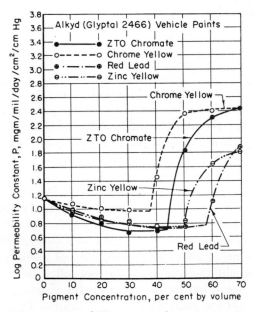

Figure 14.9. Moisture permeability versus pigment concentration (Elm[7]).

reduces the permeability to approximately one-third that of the vehicle.
The relative order of the effect of different pigments is nearly the same
in all three types of vehicles.

Elm[7] reports that the permeability of paint films depends also on the pigment volume concentration. Some typical data for four pigments in one alkyd vehicle are plotted in Figure 14.9, on a log permeability scale. These data show that the permeability decreases with increasing pigment volume up to a minimum point, known as the critical pigment volume, after which a very rapid increase in permeability is noted. This undoubtedly results from insufficient vehicle to fill the voids between the pigment particles. It is interesting to note that the so-called critical pigment volume is characteristic of each pigment and varies from 36 to 70 per cent (Table 14.3).

TABLE 14.3. APPROXIMATE CRITICAL PIGMENT-CONCENTRATION VALUES IN PER CENT PIGMENT BY VOLUME, AS CALCULATED FROM MOISTURE-PERMEABILITY DATA (Elm[7]).

| Pigment | Critical Pigment Concentration | | |
	Linseed Oil Vehicle	Alkyd Vehicle	Phenolic Vehicle
Chrome yellow	45	38	38
ZTO chromate	45	45	52
Zinc yellow	55	50	48
Red lead	65	58	68
Zinc oxide (XX-50)	55	50	—
Zinc dust	70	70	—
TiO$_2$ (anatase)	50	46	—
TiO$_2$ (rutile)	50	47	—
Aluminum powder	45	45	—

Leafing-type pigments, particularly aluminum, are, of course, very effective in increasing the resistance of a coating to transmission of water.

Not all pigments decrease permeability. As pointed out by Deeg,[5] hydrophilic pigments, such as wood flour, considerably increase permeability.

Permeability to ions is also an extremely important characteristic of coatings, especially those in contact with water containing any quantity of electrolyte. Kittelberger and Elm[8] have reported the rates of diffusion of sodium chloride through linseed, alkyd resin, phenolic varnish, and polyvinyl butyral films pigmented with a variety of materials. As would be expected, the resin films were much less permeable than the oil film. Pigments may either increase or decrease ionic permeability, as noted in Table 14.4.

Kittelberger and Elm further point out that ionic diffusion is directly related to the electrical resistance of the film.

Pigments, of course, play other roles than that of decreasing permeability. For many years, red lead has been recognized as a superior pigment for the protection of steel. The chromates are also noted as inhibitive pigments, and zinc and aluminum are used because they may afford some measure of galvanic protection by being anodic to the steel substrate.

TABLE 14.4.   THE DIFFUSION OF SALT THROUGH VARIOUS PAINT COATINGS
(Kittelberger and Elm[8])

		Rate of Sodium Chloride Diffusion in Moles/Day/Cm^2 x 10^{10}		
Pigment	Bodied Linseed Oil	Alkyd Resin Vehicle	Phenolic Resin Varnish	Polyvinyl Butyral Solution
Chrome yellow	1,335*	5	22	2,415
Zinc yellow	1,419	1,098	20,900	13,412
ZTO chromate	120	1	351	42
Red lead	132	30	104	2
Zinc oxide XX-50	187	10	134	331
Iron oxide	19,039	594	576	7,155
85/15-Iron oxide/Zinc oxide	2,167	392	—	9,575
Aluminum	7,971	9	116	17
Zinc dust	492	—	—	18
Silica	1,315	3,748	64	388
Unpigmented	946	18	2	1

* This value must be viewed with some suspicion, because it was obtained with a film only one-half mil thick.

Deeg[5] has also shown the effect of various plasticizers on permeability of a 95-5 polyvinyl chloride-acetate copolymer. These data (Figure 14.10) indicate quite clearly why the addition of a plasticizer decreases

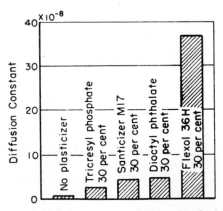

Figure 14.10.   Effect of plasticizers on permeability of polyvinyl chloride (Deeg[5]).

the corrosion protection of a vinyl film by increasing the amount of water transferred through the film, in addition to decreasing resistance to alkali, which would be expected to slowly saponify the plasticizer. On the other hand, some plasticizers may decrease permeability.[4]

Mechanism of Film Failure

That corrosion of metals is an electrochemical process is now fairly well recognized.[9] However, until the recent work of Kittelberger and Elm, the role of water or water vapor in this process was not fully appreciated. These authors pointed out that water passes through a paint film under the influence of two forces, osmosis and electroendosmosis.[7]

Osmosis is the passage of water through a semipermeable membrane under the influence of a solute concentration gradient, while electroendosmosis is the transfer of water through a membrane under the influence of a potential gradient. For the former, water-soluble material in or *under* a paint film may cause osmosis through the film which is the semipermeable membrane. Eventually, sufficient water should be driven through the film to create enough pressure to cause blistering. To test this hypothesis, Kittelberger and Elm exposed a series of panels on various substrates to distilled water and to salt solutions with osmotic pressures up to 30 atmospheres, which is about that of sea water. As predicted, blistering was found to be more severe in distilled water, regardless of substrate, and decreased with increasing salt concentration.

With this factor in mind, it is readily seen why some of the earlier zinc chromates with relatively high concentration of soluble chlorides or sulfates or why a finger print left on otherwise clean steel will cause rapid rusting and blistering. This has been graphically illustrated by Munger,[10] as shown in Figure 14.11.

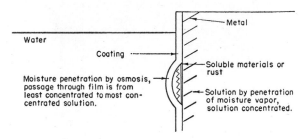

Figure 14.11. Mechanism of coating failure by osmosis (Munger[10]).

It should be noted that immersion in water is not necessary for this process, since moisture vapor in the air can cause the same process to take place at a slower rate.

Let us now consider what can happen when a potential is applied across the coating so that electroendosmosis, which is the passage of a liquid through a membrane under force of an applied current, occurs. This can and does happen when there is a break in the paint film so that corrosion can start and thus set up a potential difference across the coating. The direction of movement of the water will depend on the charge on the film, but since this is usually negative, water moves toward the cathode[10] (see Figure 14.12).

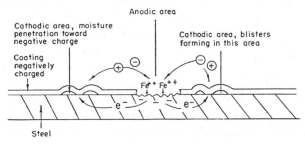

Figure 14.12. Mechanism of film failure by electroendosmosis (Munger[10]).

The blisters which form at cathodic areas are normally alkaline and often tend to spread by undercutting.[11] Furthermore, when the blisters finally rupture, the new exposed metal becomes anodic and another series of blisters forms. This accounts for the symmetrical rows of corroded areas formed when a scribed panel is exposed in seawater, as shown in Figure 14.13.

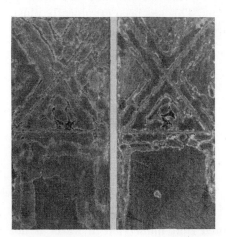

Figure 14.13. Corrosion pattern developed by immersion of scribed panel in seawater (O'Driscoll[11]).

According to Elm and Kittelberger, over 90 per cent of the water absorbed by painted panels coupled to unpainted panels results from electroendosmosis.

Type Formulations

Having considered some of the fundamental aspects of corrosion-resistant coatings, let us now consider some typical types of resin coatings.

Where baking is permitted, the so-called 100 per cent phenolic, which is a relatively low-stage phenolic resin in alcohol, can be used. When cured, a film which is extremely resistant to most chemicals except alkalis is obtained. Adhesion to clean steel is excellent, but flexibility is poor. In a recent series of tests on coatings for resistance to a chlorinated paint remover, this 100 per cent phenolic was the only type of resin found satisfactory. Other uses of this type of coating are linings for tanks and pipes, water heaters, and shipping containers.[12]

In the past several years, a new series[13] of resins related to the phenolics has been developed. These are polymeric phenol ethers, such as the epichlorhydrin-bisphenol resins:

$$CH_2CHCH_2O\underset{O}{\overset{}{\diagdown\diagup}}\left[C_6H_4-\underset{CH_3}{\overset{CH_3}{\underset{|}{\overset{|}{C}}}}-C_6H_4-OCH_2\underset{OH}{\overset{}{CHCH_2O}}\right]_x C_6H_4-\underset{CH_3}{\overset{CH_3}{\underset{|}{\overset{|}{C}}}}-C_6H_4-OCH_2CHCH_2\underset{O}{\overset{}{\diagdown\diagup}}$$

They may be cured with catalysts such as triethylene tetramine or urea, melamine, or phenolic resins. Such cured films have much of the chemical resistance of the 100 per cent phenolics and, in addition, are quite flexible and also are resistant to alkalis.

They can also be used as polyols and esterified with fatty acids:

$$H_3C-\underset{\underset{R}{\overset{|}{\underset{|}{C=O}}}}{\overset{|}{\underset{|}{O}}}{CHCH_2O}\left[C_6H_4-\underset{CH_3}{\overset{CH_3}{\underset{|}{\overset{|}{C}}}}-C_6H_4-OCH_2CHCH_2O\right]_x C_6H_4-\underset{CH_3}{\overset{CH_3}{\underset{|}{\overset{|}{C}}}}-C_6H_4-OCH_2CHCH_3$$

These esters have excellent adhesion, flexibility, color, and color retention, and very good soap resistance—far superior to that of melamine alkyds. They can also be used as air-dry coatings.

The vinyl resin systems need little further comment here since they are discussed in Chapter 9. Suffice it to say that they are outstanding for corrosion-resistant coatings, especially in air-dry systems.

Varnishes made from oil-soluble 100 per cent phenolic, e.g., *p*-phenylphenol types, and tung oil are also outstanding. When pigmented with zinc and zinc oxide, they have given years of service in underwater exposure such as on lock gates on the Ohio and Mississippi Rivers.

Although polystyrene, as noted above, is not, per se, a good coating resin, copolymers of styrene with butadiene have good adhesion and flexibility and low permeability. They are therefore finding considerable application in air-dry corrosion-resistant coatings.

Chlorinated rubber is also widely used in air-dry corrosion-resistant finishes.[14]

Where good heat resistance and fair chemical resistance are required, the silicones or silicone-alkyds are especially suitable. Still better chemical resistance, as well as excellent heat resistance, is also characteristic of polytetrafluoroethylene ("Teflon") and polytrifluorochloroethylene.

References

1. Shaw and Moore, "Pore Size in Protective Film by Electrographic Printing," *Ind. Eng. Chem., Anal. Ed.* **19,** 777 (1947).
2. Scott, J. B., *Chem. Eng.,* **58,** 135 (April, 1951).
3. Duntley and Earp, *J. Oil & Colour Chemists' Assoc.,* **30,** 413 (1947).
4. Singleton, W. F., and Johnson, W. C., "Moisture Resistant Coatings for Metal," *Ind. Eng. Chem.,* **41,** 749 (1949).
5. Deeg, *Bell Lab. Record,* **25,** 227 (1947).
6. Mayne, *J. Oil & Colour Chemists' Assoc.,* **32,** 481 (1949).
7. Elm, *Official Digest Federation Paint & Varnish Production Clubs,* No. 267, 197 (April, 1947); Kittelberger and Elm *Ind. Eng. Chem.,* **38,** 695 (1946); *Ind. Eng. Chem.,* **39,** 876 (1947).
8. Kittelberger, *J. Phys. & Colloid Chem.,* **53,** 392 (1949); Kittelberger and Elm *Ind. Eng. Chem.,* **44,** 326 (1952).
9. Eickhoff and Shaw, *Corrosion,* **4,** 463 (1948).
10. Munger, *Corrosion,* **4,** 557 (1948).
11. O'Driscoll, W. G., "Blistering Phenomena of Paints in Marine Environments," *J. Iron Steel Inst.,* **167,** 353 (1951).
12. Waters, Chap. XI, "Phenolic Resins in Protective Coatings," in von Fischer, "Paint and Varnish Technology," Reinhold Publishing Corporation, 1948.
13. Ott, G. H., *Bull. Assoc. Swiss Paint & Varnish Chemists,* 3rd Special Issue, Nov., 1949, pp. 55–63; *Paint Oil Chem. Rev.,* **113,** 175 (1950).
14. Martin, J. B., *Org. Finishing,* **9,** 10 (Feb., 1948).

15 : Organic Coatings for Electrical Insulation

A. J. SHERBURNE

General Electric Company
Laminated and Insulating Products Division
Coshocton, Ohio

Electrical insulating materials have a very necessary and important role in the development, design, and service of electrical machinery and in the transmission and use of electrical power. Although mathematical calculations frequently determine electrical design, no such exact treatment is possible for the design and use of insulating materials. This is partly because most insulating materials are organic in nature and often are applied in an intermediate or uncured state; the process used to complete the cure determines in large measure their ultimate worth as insulation.

Although there are numerous theoretical articles and publications on dielectrics and their behavior, there is surprisingly little literature available to the electrical engineer or the interested chemist on the more practical considerations regarding electrical and physical properties, insofar as these influence the choice and use of insulating materials by the electrical industry. There are publications, service specifications, and engineering instructions for their use which are usually the result of cut and try methods and shop experience. For many years the development and use of electrical insulating materials were not guided by sound engineering principles, as was the case, for example, for other materials such as iron and copper. The manufacture of electrical insulation is recognized as a highly specialized industry and the use of such materials is still considered a specialized form of industrial art that is governed by very few universal rules of engineering practice.

This accounts for the fact that the small number of manufacturers of insulating varnishes, varnished cloth, mica products, and industrial papers and laminates are usually specialists in particular types of insulating materials, rather than manufacturers of general lines of paints, varnishes, and industrial finishes. Some of the larger manufacturers of coatings have entered the insulation field of late, partly because a resin, varnish, or coating developed for other use has incidently proved to be of value in the field of insulation.

This chapter will discuss the major uses of insulating materials, and the properties required for each; the composition of some typical useful materials will be noted, and the problems involved in their development and application will be reviewed.

Electrical insulation may involve the use of one or more of the following materials:

(1) Cellulose materials, such as cotton, silk, paper, wood, both untreated and varnish-(or resin-) impregnated, or coated.
(2) Resins, resin solutions, and varnishes, based on both natural and synthetic materials.
(3) Plastics, both laminates and molded parts, including rubber.
(4) "Fiberglas" and asbestos in sheets and tapes.
(5) Mica-pasted splittings in sheets, tapes, and molded forms.
(6) Glass, porcelain, and other rigid ceramics.
(7) Liquid dielectrics, such as oil and askarels.
(8) Waxes and similar materials.

Although all these materials will be included in this discussion, emphasis will be laid on the resins and varnishes used to treat, fill, and coat other materials, many of which are merely carriers for the varnish film.

Electrical insulating materials are used by five large classes of industry:

(1) Manufacturers of electrical machinery and equipment-rotating machinery and control.
(2) Utilities—power installations and distribution.
(3) Service and repair shops, both general and captive, such as the several railroad shops and steel mill shops which do their own repair service and rebuilding.
(4) Wire and cable manufacturers.
(5) Electronic apparatus.
(6) A few special contributing industries, such as the magnetic sheet steel manufacturers, and the magnet wire manufacturers.

The problems of each of these users differ greatly, however all have the following general objectives:

(1) Greater durability or improved service of their equipment or installation under normal load.
(2) More overload capacity and greater reliability under stress.
(3) Better space factor; reduction in weight.

(4) Improved quality as measured by life under practical service conditions.

(5) Lower cost.

Insulating materials are the most important determinants of the life expectancy and service efficiency of electrical apparatus. Their quality establishes the quality of the apparatus. Although the quality of the insulating materials is so important to the design of the apparatus, it is the one feature most difficult to predict or control. Insulating materials are subject to deterioration by heat, by oxidation, by moisture, and by chemical attack, and their durability is affected significantly by conditions of temperature, humidity, and their mechanical limitations.

PROPERTIES OF INSULATION

The important properties of insulation can be classified in four major categories—electrical, thermal, chemical, and mechanical. The major categories permit the following subclassifications:

Electrical Properties
  Dielectric strength
  Insulation resistance
  Surface conductivity
  Power factor and dielectric loss
  Ionization loss or corona
  Arc resistance
  Voltage endurance
Thermal Properties
  Aging under heat
  Softening under heat (thermoplasticity)
  Thermal conductivity
  Thermal expansion and contraction
  Flammability
Mechanical Properties
  Bonding or adhesive strength
  Penetration and filling properties
  Abrasion resistance
  Adhesion
  Impact strength
  Elongation and tensile strength
  Hardness
  Toughness
  Flexibility

Resistance to breakdown under conditions of vibration at certain stresses and frequencies.

Chemical Properties

Water resistance (either to diffusion of liquid or vapor)

Resistance to acids and alkalies or other chemicals that can be encountered under special service conditions.

Resistance to solvents (such as oils) or to corrosive vapors.

Resistance to deterioration by metallic dusts or other contaminants of similar electrical properties.

Standard evaluation tests have been developed for measuring most of the properties and for predicting the utility of an insulating material for various service conditions. These tests are imperfect and need be applied with caution and with many reservations in all attempts to evaluate real service properties. Such tests are valuable as a guide to the selection of materials, but performance in service use is the only conclusive test.

The titles of most of the properties listed in our classification are self-explanatory. The methods of testing are for the most part those described in the ASTM standards for insulating materials. A few of the properties listed may need further definition, particularly the electrical properties, which are not commonly required for ordinary coatings.

Dielectric strength is the voltage gradient at which electrical failure or breakdown occurs. It is represented as the voltage required to puncture the insulation, divided by the thickness of the sample; hence the units are volts per mil. The numerical test values for a particular material can vary with thickness, with the form and size of the test electrodes, and with the time of application of the voltage. The frequency and wave shape of the voltage as well as the temperature and the character of the surrounding medium are also important.

Power factor is the ratio of that part of the input energy in watts which is lost as heat through the dielectric to the total input. It becomes more and more important as the voltage stress is increased. Dielectric loss is also of importance in selecting material for high-frequency applications. Low power factor materials are essential in these applications. Power factor is affected principally by frequency, temperature, and moisture.

Dielectric constant is a measure of the relative capacity of a material to store electrostatic energy. The dielectric constant is used to calculate the loss factor and also is of primary importance to a common type of calculation which evaluates the voltage stress across several different insulating materials in series.

Loss factor is the product of the power factor and the dielectric constant and may be defined as the relative tendency of a material to absorb energy when used as a dielectric in an electrical field alternating at a specific frequency.

Volume resistivity is the resistance offered by a material to the passage of electric current if passage of the current over its surface layer were prevented. It is expressed in ohms/cm.[3]

Arc resistance is the ability of a material to withstand the discharge across its surface of a specified intermittent and then continuous arc of high voltage and low current. It is a rough evaluation of the ability of materials to withstand arcing across their surface.

There are many methods of determining moisture and water absorption and much work has been done on determining the behavior of insulating materials under different humidity conditions. The behavior of insulating materials when immersed in water may be quite different from that observed in high humidity atmospheres.

The electrical properties of greatest importance are the dielectric strength or the measure of the voltage which a unit thickness (per mil) of insulation will stand without puncture; measurements of insulation resistance provide indications of deterioration or lack of stability. Because an insulation is not perfect, a certain percentage of the input power is lost through the dielectric as heat—this percentage is the power factor. It is of most importance in high voltage machines or cables where high power losses may develop a runaway condition of overheating and burn out the insulation and short the conductor.

The mechanical properties of insulating materials are important in the design, manufacture, and use of electrical machinery. Mechanical abuse during winding and assembly may be very severe, involving conditions of abrasion, stretchings, and poundings. The insulation must be sufficiently tough to withstand these severe conditions of mechanical stress during the manufacture of the electrical apparatus, and still retain adequate mechanical properties to satisfy the service conditions of the equipment.

Vibration and unequal expansion and contraction are important causes of deterioration, as are also thermally produced effects, such as enbrittlement and shrinkage.

Centrifugal forces are large in high-speed or large-diameter electrical machines; hence bonding strength of insulating materials is important. Varnishes vary greatly in this property, and in nearly all instances the bonding strength changes with temperature. Small very high-speed drill motors, vacuum cleaner motors, etc. require the utmost in rigidity in the rotating part of the motor, even at temperatures up to 150°C.

Thermal deterioration depends on the temperature, the time of exposure at high heat, and the nature of the organic components of the insulation. Cotton deteriorates rapidly at 110°C as indicated by its loss of strength and discoloration; however, when varnish treated, it may resist deterioration for short periods of time at temperatures 50°C in excess of what is damaging to untreated cotton.

This feature provides an important reason for varnish treatments which fill and impregnate coils and windings. Improvement of thermal conductivity is another. Other things being equal, the use of varnish fillers allows

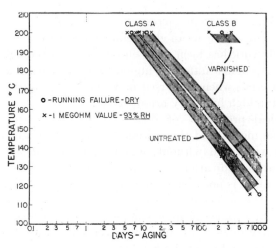

Figure 15.1. Temperature-life under operating conditions at ¼ hp-motor stators. with and without varnish treatment of cloth insulation. (From J. J. Smith and J. Ascott, *AIEE Trans.,* **58,** Sept. 1939 and **61,** July 1942.)

continuous operation at about 10°C higher temperature without shortening service life as compared to untreated windings (Figure 15.1). In the presence of moisture, thermal deterioration effects are aggravated, and hence the extent of damage due to overheating is difficult to valuate in a quantitative manner.

A most important variable which is difficult to measure as a determinant of the life of insulation is the film continuity, or the ability of the varnish or sealing coat to form a continuous protective film over the irregular conductors and windings. Pinholes or discontinuities may entirely invalidate a good varnish for effective insulation.

Ordinarily, the particular conditions of use of a particular motor cannot be predicted by the manufacturer; hence, a general level of quality must be achieved to give reasonable service in all but the most severe conditions.

Fortunately all of these properties are never required at their maximum in one material or one application. Intelligent choice of materials to meet the job is of prime importance. Knowledge of the properties of the materials is only part of the information upon which the choice should be based. As much as possible of their behavior in combinations as they are used in completed or assembled apparatus, both on test and in service, is most desirable in providing data to guide the best choice of materials for new designs, or for improvement of standard lines.

The fundamental purpose of electrical insulation is to keep the electrical current in its proper path and to mechanically separate one conductor from another and from the magnetic iron core and ground. An insulated structure is an assembly of several components, each with a function to perform. A surface coating is not usually sufficient alone to satisfy all requirements of insulation. There are many instances where the electrical requirements are overshadowed by demands for better mechanical or thermal properties. The electrical designer must know his temperature limits, the centrifugal forces to be involved, and other critical conditions, and must be able to match to these conditions a material that adequately satisfies all requirements.

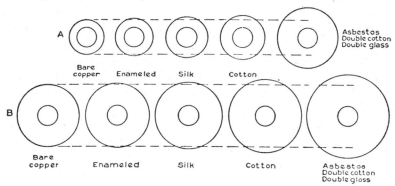

Figure 15.2. Relative diameter of one-half-inch coil wound with 1,000 feet of wire on a one-inch core; (A) with 0.010-inch wire; (B) with 0.020-inch wire.

The ideal insulating material would have the greatest possible electrical strength in the thinnest possible layer or smallest space. The approach to this ideal is measured in part by what we call space factor.

If a solid copper bar is taken at 100 per cent, the possible lay of round bare copper conductors in the same space would be about 90 per cent and, in the so-called square-lay, about 80 per cent; however conductors must be insulated, which increases bulk. The first insulations were very bulky, but great improvements in this respect were effected through the use of enameled wire. The dependence of the space factor on the choice of insulation is shown schematically in Figure 15.2.

Insulating materials have been classified as to composition and temperature resistance by AIEE* in "Classification of Insulating Materials."

Temperature limits are established by the AIEE standards. The values of "hottest spot" temperatures established under this classification are:

For Class O	90°C
For Class A	105°C
For Class B	130°C
For Class C	No limit
For Class H	180°C

The limiting ambient temperature is 40°C. Allowable temperature rise is obtained by subtracting 40°C from the above values.

These classifications are described as follows:

Class O—Consists of cotton, silk, paper, and similar organic materials when neither impregnated nor immersed in a liquid dielectric.

Class A—Consists of (1) cotton, silk, paper, and similar organic materials when either impregnated or immersed in a liquid dielectric; (2) molded and laminated materials with cellulose filler, phenolic resins, and other resins of similar properties; (3) films and sheets of cellulose acetate and other cellulose derivatives of similar properties; (4) varnishes (enamel) as applied to conductors.

Class B—Consists of mica, asbestos, "Fiberglas," and similar inorganic materials in built-up form with organic binding substances. A small proportion of Class A materials may be used for structural purposes only.

Class C—Consists entirely of mica, porcelain, glass, quartz, or similar inorganic materials.

Class H—Consists of (1) mica, asbestos, "Fiberglas," and similar materials in built-up form with binding substances composed of silicone compounds or materials with equivalent properties; (2) silicone compounds, not rubbery or resinous in form, or materials with equivalent properties. A minute proportion of Class A material may be allowed only where essential for structural purposes during manufacture. The electrical and mechanical properties must not be impaired by the application of the temperature permitted for Class H materials. (The word "impaired" is here used in the sense of causing any change which would disqualify the insulating material for continuous service.)

These values are, for the most part, very conservative using many modern synthetic materials. The trend has been away from cellulose materials and oxidizing varnishes as thermal and moisture resistance requirements have become more severe.

The development of insulating materials with improved properties to meet the objectives noted above has gone hand-in-hand with the develop-

* American Institute of Electrical Engineers.

ment of the use of electricity in industry and with the increasing requirements for better service, longer life, reliability, and other special needs
of our economy. The development of the machine tool industry during
World War I stimulated important improvements in insulating materials,
and further advances have proceeded continuously since that time.

The early electrical machines—generators and motors and transmission
cable—were crudely wound with cotton or linen rags or bandages, bonded
with drying oil or natural resins. If more insulation was needed, more
bandages or more tapings were applied. Considering their low-power output, these early machines were excessively bulky and heavy. Their ratings
as to temperature and load were modest; however, service conditions were
not severe, by present standards.

The cotton, wood, and paper used as the early insulations were treated
with natural resins and oils as binders, impregnants, or coatings. Because
copal, shellac, and other gums with linseed oil were common materials in
the paint and varnish trade of the late 19th and early 20th centuries,
they were naturally the first to be used for insulation. Voltages were low
and chemical and thermal requirements were very moderate. At an early
date, asphalts were found to be superior to the clear gums in electrical
properties and to have improved moisture resistance; hence such materials became standard for use in insulating varnishes and compounds.
Low cost favored their universal acceptance. The use of tung oil established further improvements in some important characteristics of insulating varnishes, principally chemical resistance and mechanical properties.

INSULATING VARNISHES

Varnishes are used extensively in electrical insulation for the filling of
spaces in porous insulation and the interstices between coils and windings
in transformers and all forms of electrical rotating apparatus. In addition they are used to build up film insulation on wires, coils, and coil
assemblies.

In many instances varnishes serve both for filling and coating as in
the production of varnished cloth and other sheet insulation in which
the pores are first filled and a surface coat applied to build up the necessary degree of insulation. Varnishes are also used to bond coils, windings,
and other insulations.

Insulating varnishes may be classified as follows with relation to their
end-use:

(1) Filling and insulating coils and coil assemblies.
(2) Protective insulating coatings.
(3) Pasting or cementing of insulation before or after assembly.

(4) Coating magnet wire and core plates.

(5) Treating of cloth and paper.

To explain further:

(1) The principal use of insulating varnishes is in the treatment of coils and windings, either before the coil is wound or after it is assembled in place. Next to filling, its most important function is bonding.

(2) When a protective surface coat or a sealing and finishing film is needed over the filled and bonded coils, an application of a pigmented alkyd enamel is common practice. It provides a hard, tough, smooth, continuous film which is highly resistant to moisture, chemicals, oils, and other surface contaminants. Also it provides improved arc resistance and possesses good dielectric strength. Field experience has demonstrated the value of this material in protecting and prolonging the life of electrical windings, and the superiority of the dual system over additional clear varnish treatments is well established. After prolonged aging even at temperatures much above the Class A limits, such protective films remain intact without cracking. Satisfactory performance for as long as eight months at 150°C have been established for test coils containing cotton tapes (Figure 15.3).

(3) Pasting or cementing varnishes can be classed as auxiliary insulating materials since they are used primarily to facilitate the assembly of other insulation and contribute very little directly toward improvement of insulation properties. In the cementing of mica flakes, for example, it is the high insulation value of the mica that is wanted; however, the binder must have some of the mechanical, moisture-resistance and thermal-resistance properties of the better insulations if high-quality performance and long life are to be expected.

(4) The demand for an insulating material with the best possible space factor led to the development of a group of high-grade insulating varnishes for coating directly on the bare copper conductor. These wire enamels, as they were called, were a major advance in the insulation of magnet coils and motor coils and windings. The conventional wire enamels were largely drying oil-resin combinations capable of being baked at very high temperatures to produce thin coats of a hightly flexible film on copper wire. These oleoresinous enamels had many deficiencies. They required considerable care in handling during assembly of coils in the apparatus; however, as compared to fabric windings, they allowed for a great gain in the space factor.

The second important advance was the development of "Formvar" enamel which solved many of the deficiencies of the conventional enamels. Since 1937 this type of coating has been used extensively for the insulation of conductors in most small and medium size apparatus. It is now possible to eliminate cotton covering in a large number of applications without incurring some of the problems that arise when oleoresinous varnishes are used in a similar manner; principally, the problem of mechanical failures of the insulation under the drastic production conditions of high-speed winding of coils, or, subsequently, during assembly of parts of electrical apparatus.

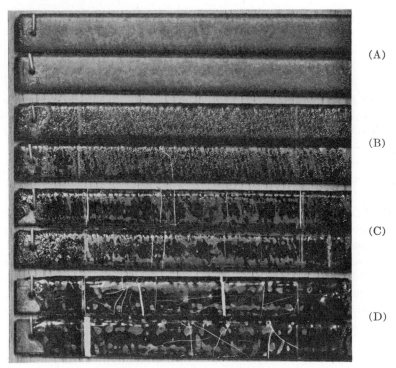

(A)

(B)

(C)

(D)

Figure 15.3. Samples of varnish-treated cotton insulation on copper bars, aged 237 days at 150°C for systems where finishing materials are (A) red pigmented alkyd; (B) short-oil alkyd; (C) oil-modified phenolic; (D) asphalt type varnish.

Enamels are also used on the magnetic steel laminations which make up the iron or magnetic circuit of a motor, generator, or transformer. These are called core plates. The very thin enamel coating prevents eddy currents and heat losses. The core plate enamels are usually baked on the laminations at high temperature and may have an inert filler such as "Zonolite" or silica gel.

(5) In the manufacture of coil and cable insulations, the use of varnish-coated fabrics and papers enables the varnish to be used in otherwise difficult applications. Treated fabrics, because of their high degree of

flexibility and high mechanical strength, may be wound tightly into place on cables, leads, coils, etc. Both cloths and papers are used for wrappers and mechanical protection.

Methods of Application

The chief methods of applying varnish to windings are:

(1) Dipping
    (a) Without prebake
    (b) With prebake
(2) Vacuum filling
(3) Pressure filling
(4) Combinations of (2) and (3)
(5) Brushing or coating as coil is wound
(6) Use of pretreated materials

Dipping is the oldest and simplest method of applying varnish. In most applications, as on small motors, where baking temperatures from 125 to 150°C are used, prebaking is unnecessary, as all moisture in the insulation system is effectively removed during the baking cycle. In some instances, however, as in the treatment of coils of large cross section, it may be desirable to prebake the insulated coil or winding before dipping. This will facilitate varnish penetration. It is very desirable to prebake, when using infrared baking and treating cycles, to facilitate solvent removal and rapid cure.

Best results are obtained by using dipping varnishes of as high a non-volatile content as possible, but which will still be sufficiently fluid to permit adequate penetration and filling. When the varnish is baked and the thinner evaporates, there will then be a sufficient amount of varnish left to do a good job of insulating.

A varnish cannot be dried or hardened if it is allowed to stew in its own solvent vapors. In this connection, vacuum baking has proved most useful for promoting complete drying in large coils; the process is not necessary for small motor windings.

Baking

Baking not only removes all traces of solvent and moisture, but, by promoting permanent chemical and physical changes, also improves substantially the properties of an insulating varnish. Most insulating varnishes require baking for best performance.

Air-drying varnishes are, however, useful for the quick treatment of porous insulation for which the highest dielectric value and bonding strength are not needed, or for the finishing coat of relatively large pieces of apparatus which can not conveniently be placed in ovens, but remain on the shop floors for sufficient intervals to allow an adequate air-drying period.

Baking temperatures and periods are largely dependent upon and sometimes limited by the design and materials of the coils or assemblies to which the varnish is applied. The total period of baking must be sufficient to bring the temperature of the varnish itself to the full heat of the oven and keep it there until the varnish has been properly cured. Conditions of baking must be determined by a pilot production run for each type of coil or piece of apparatus involved.

When treating coils that are wound with unannealed "Formex" wire, a baking temperature of 150°C is desirable in order to quickly heal any crazing in the film that may have occurred when the formed coil was subjected to the liquid varnish. The coils may be pre-annealed for five minutes at 150°C prior to a more extended period at lower temperatures.

Insulating systems containing cellulose materials in the form of cloth, tape, twine, paper, etc., when treated with modern varnishes, can be safely subjected to baking temperatures of 125 to 150°C for short periods of time.

Electric or steam ovens should be used of a design that provides for uniform temperatures; ventilation should be provided for the removal of solvent vapors. If the process is correct, baking removes the last traces of solvents and moisture. With synthetic resin varnishes of the thermo-setting type, baking promotes the conversion of the resin to a more desirable state than can be obtained by air-drying and oxidation. The ideal is to use the highest temperature and shortest possible time to establish the best electrical, mechanical, and chemical properties. The use of driers is not to be recommended as they accelerate aging and deterioration in service.

The hardening process is complex. Any insulating process must take into account the chemistry of the materials to make sure that the following are accomplished:

(1) Complete penetration and filling.
(2) Complete removal of solvent.
(3) Polymerization of the varnish to a hard gel having favorable physical properties.
(4) Removal of oxidation or other reaction products before surface setting takes place.
(5) Retention of maximum solids in the windings.
(6) Minimum injury to insulation already on the wires.

These all involve considerations of varnish viscosities, temperature, curing characteristics, oven conditions, ventilation, heat capacity, and other process factors.

TYPES OF VARNISHES

A varnish consists essentially of a film-forming base and a solvent or thinner. The base may be a natural or synthetic resin blended or chemically combined with a drying oil. Drying oils commonly used are linseed, chinawood, soya, and castor oils. Modern varnish bases may be of synthetic resins, with or without a drying oil. The synthetic resins are usually of the alkyd and phenolic types. They may dry or harden by oxidation, by thermally induced polymerization, or by various combinations of different types of curing reactions.

The present trend is toward varnishes of these types. Less generally used today are the bases of the oleoresinous type, using natural resins and asphalts blended with the drying oils.

Varnishes may be clear or black, the former being generally of the synthetic type and the latter of the oleo-asphaltic type which are of lower cost but inferior in over-all properties. Because of the asphaltic ingredient usually contained in black varnishes, they are generally less oil-resistant but of greater acid- and alkali-resistance than most clear varnishes. Black varnishes are preferred for cables since they are usually of higher dielectric strength and lower power or loss factor.

In choosing the most suitable varnish, the designing engineer must first list the requirements in the order of importance, such as dielectric strength, moisture resistance, heat resistance, bonding strength, etc., and then select the varnish most suitable in accordance therewith.

SYNTHETIC RESIN VARNISHES

The synthetic resin age, in which we are now so firmly established, began for insulation with the partial substitution of shellac with "Bakelite" and other phenolic resins. The rapid development of other synthetics brought the insulating varnish and compound art out of its alchemy age of trade secrecy to the state of an advanced technology founded on scientific principles.

Synthetic resin chemistry and recently established knowledge of the physical properties of high polymers have made it possible to custom-build insulation to fit particular needs and to predict or choose, with more assurance, the properties and the materials best suited for particularl applications. Today, synthetics have substantially displaced the older oxidizing types of varnishes and protective coatings in the electrical insulation field to about the same degree as they have in the general protective coating industry. A partial listing of the types of synthetic resins used in insulation, and the approximate time of their development, are given in Table 15.1.

TABLE 15.1. USE OF RESINS IN ELECTRICAL INSULATION LISTED IN THE CHRONOLOGICAL ORDER OF THEIR DEVELOPMENT

1870	Cellulose nitrate (first synthetic)
1895	(Shellac—in insulating materials)
1909	Bitumens and asphalts
1910–12	*Phenol formaldehyde resins* (first synthetic widely used)
1922	Phenol-furfural
1926	*Alkyd resins*
1927	Cellulose acetate
1928	Phenol-urea formaldehyde casting
1929	Vinyl esters (chloride-acetate)
1930	Styrene
1931	Acrylic resins
1932	Cellulose aceto-butyrate
1935	Ethyl cellulose
1936	Methyl methacrylate casting
1937	*Vinyl acetals*—"Butvar," "Formvar"
1938	Polystyrene
	Synthetic rubbers
1939	Vinylidene chloride
	Nylon
1940	Methyl cellulose
	Melamines
1942	Allyls and polyester resins
1943	Polyethylenes
	Silicones
	Polyfluroethylenes
1947	Ethoxylines or epoxy resins

Both the alkyd and phenolic types of varnishes are now used for filling, filming, and fastening, and for providing good dielectric strength, flexibility, heat resistance, water resistance, tenacious adherence, and non-shrinkage. Where aging and flexibility, as well as surface sealing and protection, are very important, the alkyds are preferred.

The phenolic-resin varnishes excel in quick baking, through-curing, and bonding strength; thus they impart strength and rigidity to the finished windings. Phenolic-resin varnishes are usually less arc-resistant than other types, and if used, where exposed to arcing, they should be coated with a pigmented alkyd-enamel such as General Electric Co. "Glyptal" Red 1201. A combination of a phenolic for bonding and dielectric

strength and a finishing coat of alkyd enamel gives superior performance as a coil treatment.

Phenol-Formaldehyde Resins

The oldest historically (1909) among synthetic resins used in quantity
in electrical insulation are the phenol-formaldehyde resins. Their properties of heat and fire resistance, dielectric strength, hardness, chemical
resistance, mechanical strength, durability, and abrasion resistance
favored their use in electrical apparatus where arc resistance was not
of prime importance. They are still widely used today because of the
over-all excellence of their properties, and because of their relatively low
cost and ease of application. As varnishes, the 100 per cent phenolics have
limited but important uses in insulation where bonding and rigidity of
coils or mechanical strength are of paramount interest, such as rotating
field coils.

The first phenolic resins found important uses as substitutes for shellac
in coatings and molding materials. The more soluble types of phenolic
resins can be dissolved in drying oils at high temperatures to give the
more ordinary type of insulating varnish. Some phenolic resin-varnishes
are known in which drying oils are not blended but are combined chemically with the resin. Such insulating varnishes are outstanding with
respect to their speed of cure, even in thick sections, and provide improved bonding strength, excellent electrical and physical properties, and
superior resistance to moisture and chemical deterioration. Thermosetting phenolic-oil modified varnishes of this new type are widely used for
high-quality treatment of small motors, random wound motors, and
generator coil insulation.

The Alkyds (1926)

Glyceryl phthalate resins were first proposed as competitors to phenolics for molding and casting resins, but they failed to find their major
use in the field of moldings or laminates. They cure more slowly. Although the arc resistance is better, the power factor is inferior as compared to ordinary types of phenolics. Because of their flexibility retained
at elevated temperatures, excellent durability, oil resistance, and weather
resistance, some alkyds have been used as insulation varnishes for many
years, even though such are frequently inferior to phenolic varnishes in
their curing characteristics. Developments in the last decade have greatly
improved their chemical and moisture resistance, dielectric strength, and
curing characteristics; consequently, the alkyds are becoming increasingly important as insulating varnishes for coil treating and finishing, for
electrical windings, and for the protection of the metal frame.

In combination with other plastics, alkyds are becoming more important in the casting and laminating field than they have ever been before. Combinations of some alkyds with phenolics have also been used extensively as insulating varnishes.

Urea-Formaldehyde Resins (1929) are largely used in molded form for all types of electrical sockets, plugs, switches, etc., but find little use as insulation on electrical windings.

Melamine-Formaldehyde Resins (1939) can be cured more rapidly at higher temperatures than ureas to obtain coatings of better hardness, strength and toughness, and improved dielectric strength. The higher cost of melamine resins tends to discourage their wider use, although the properties show some promise.

Vinyls (1929–1945)

These are thermoplastic resins of a wide variety of properties and uses. Straight vinyl acetates are used for adhesives, paper coatings for layer insulation, core plate enamels, and heat and pressure bonds for steel laminations. Extruded coatings of plasticized vinyl chloride are used on wire and cable. Vinyl copolymers find similar applications as layer insulation in coils, windings, transformers, and capacitors, and as wire coverings and enamels; they are also used for sleeving, tubing etc.

The toughest resins of the polyvinyl formal or polyvinylbutyral class, such as "Formvar" and "Butvar," both alone and in combination with other synthetic resins, are widely used for wire enamels, wire coatings, adhesives and surface films, and for laminates.

In general most vinyl coatings are tough, and highly resistant to water and chemicals.

The acrylic resins (1931–1937) have been used for wire enamels. In general their use has been limited by the faults of excessive thermoplasticity and other physical deficiencies as compared to some other less costly plastics.

Nylon (1938)

Nylon has found some use as a wire enamel and as an insulating textile covering over other insulation. Polyamides other than the now commonly known nylon polymers may find even greater insulation uses in the future.

Polyester Resins (1942–   )

These new materials which are creating interest in the field of insulation are a group of thermosetting and room-temperature polymerizing liquids. They are peroxide-catalyzed, liquid mixtures which cure by what is called addition polymerization to a solid infusible condition. A wide variety of these resins are available as low-pressure laminating and casting resins, but certain species of this class, such as the "General

Electric Permafils," have been developed primarily for electrical insulation. During the last ten years, certain varieties have proved of great value in high-voltage and high-frequency insulation of many important wartime devices, including magnetos, transformers, solenoid and relay coils, aircraft ignition systems, collector rings, commutators, mica substitutes, core lamination bonding, and potting and sealing compounds. Recently, these resins have been used for cloth coating and flexible sleeving, and for high-speed armature treatments. A wide variety are available ranging in properties from soft gels to hard rock-like solids, including tough and rubbery elastomers. Because these resin compositions cure without releasing a large volume of volatiles, it becomes possible to fill coils completely with nearly void free coatings. This feature is essential in some types of high-voltage applications. Oxygen is not required to promote curing.

Silicone Resins (1943–   )

Almost all insulating materials with the exception of mica, glass, asbestos, and porcelain are organic and tend to decompose when subject to heat and oxidation. Moisture usually accelerates this decomposition. Even mica, glass, asbestos, and porcelain have certain physical handicaps in their use as insulating materials. The first three have to be used with a varnish or plastic binder or filler.

Silicone resins are condensation polymers made up of alternate linkages of silicon and oxygen atoms, where each silicon atom is attached to one or two aryl or alkyl radicals through a silicon-carbon bond. The silicone resins provide high-temperature-resistant resins which may last for years at 200°C. They thus are an improvement on Class B materials. Motors of a variety of sizes have been constructed using silicones which have had remarkable life not only under conditions of dry heat, but even in the presence of moisture. With present-day silicones properly applied on apparatus designed to equal or exceed the life of the best organic varnish treated apparatus, it can be estimated conservatively that the service temperature may reach 180°C with hot spots to 200°C. The AIEE has recently revised temperature limits for electric apparatus to include Class H insulation which allows a 180°C hot spot. For use at this temperature, silicone coatings are available which will allow an anticipated service life for an apparatus that is at least as long as is obtained with Class B materials at 130°C.

Epoxy Resins (1947–   )

One of the newest classes of plastics used in insulation and coatings contains reactive ethylene oxide functional groups. The resins are condensation products of epichlorohydrin and bisphenol A, and can be cured by baking at high temperatures, usually in the presence of coupling agents such as amino-resins, polyfunctional amines, or phthalic anhydride. Modified resins can be obtained by reacting the epoxy resin with fatty acids such as are linseed oil acids. Most of these products are characterized by low shrinkage on curing, excellent adhesion, and superior mechanical, chemical, and electrical properties.

APPLICATIONS OF INSULATING MATERIALS

One of the fundamental units of all electrical apparatus is the electrical conductor—a wire carrying a current. We are especially interested here in the conductor in motors, generators, transformers, and control equipment. The prime function of a conductor insulation is to keep the current in its proper path. The best coating for such a conductor is a continuous film such as a wire enamel. A wire enamel is a special type of varnish made from resins and drying oils, or from a combination of synthetic resins, which, when applied in several thin coats to wire, and baked at high temperature, gives a continuous dielectric, and physically strong insulating film on the conductor.

One of the outstanding advances in the electrical art was the development of enameled wire. By depositing a more or less uniform insulating film on the conductor, less space was needed for the required insulation. Early machines were large and heavy for their output, and the problem of higher voltages or greater currents was met with more and more bandages, tapes, or wrappings of cotton bonded with linseed oil or shellac or some other spirit varnish solution of a natural gum in alcohol.

The oleoresinous enamel on wire had the deficiencies of inferior physical properties which had to be tolerated for years until the General Electric Company developed "Formvar" enamel and "Formex" wire.

"Formex" wire has remarkable mechanical properties. It offers no advantage electrically or spatially over bare enamel of the same thickness but bare enamel could seldom be used—it had to be associated with a protective covering of cotton or paper to allow it to withstand the mechanical abuse of assembly and service. "Formex" permitted the elimination of cotton and improvement of the space factor; in fact, many compact, light-weight designs of electrical aircraft parts, and other important war devices were possible only because "Formex" wire was available.

While "Formex" wire enamel can not satisfy all conditions, it can be used as the conductor insulation on Class A machines (with a hot spot temperature of 105°C) and on some Class B applications at temperatures of 125°C (sometimes up to 150°C). Ordinarily, Class B insulation makes use of asbestos or glass bonded to the conductor with a varnish applied in several coats in a tower. "Silicones-with-glass" offer an even higher temperature limit or longer life at the same temperature, but to date silicone resins are so inferior *mechanically* to "Formex" wire enamel and to ordinary enamels that no satisfactory silicone wire enamel has yet been developed.

Now let us consider one of the more important uses of an insulated conductor, namely, in an electric motor, in order to demonstrate some of the more important problems of selection of a considerable variety of

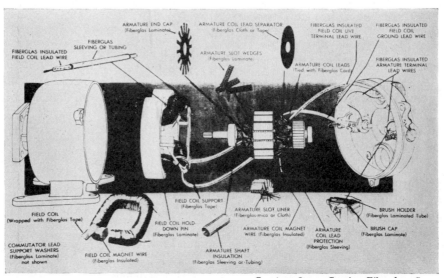

Courtesy Owens-Corning Fiberglass Corp.

Figure 15.4.   Insulating materials used on the component parts of an electric motor. Class H design of insulation is illustrated.

insulating materials. An over-all picture of the component parts of a simple motor is shown in Figure 15.4. Diagrammatic sketches of some representative armature coil and field winding assemblies are illustrated in Figures 15.5 and 15.6.

From the electrical insulation standpoint we are most interested in what is called the stator (the part that stays still) and the rotor (the part that rotates). A motor or generator has both a magnetic and an electrical circuit. To generate electricity only two things are necessary: a magnetic field and a conducting wire moving through it.

Conductors in both rotor and stator may use enameled wire, or, depending upon conditions, bonded glass or asbestos wire. These conductors are wound into coils of so many turns of a particular size of wire, or they may be placed in the slots in definite groups according to the ultimate function of the type motor it is to be, the number of poles, the horsepower rating, and other factors involved in electrical engineering.

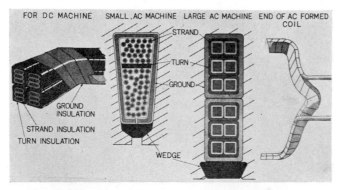

Figure 15.5. Some representative armature coil insulating systems.

But those coils, when placed in the slots in the magnetic or iron part of the device, must be insulated from that iron and from ground; hence some insulating material must first be inserted in each slot. This material may be paper, varnished paper, varnished cloth, cellulose acetate, or

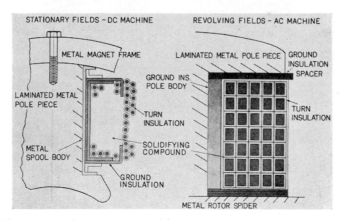

Figure 15.6. Some representative field winding insulation systems.

combinations of these with flexible mica or glass. The greater the voltage, the higher the operating temperatures, and the bigger the machine, the more complicated need become these insulators.

The slot armor or tube is inserted, and the coils are wound into the slot or are placed in after winding (Figure 15.7). In many cases such as this, there must be another insulating spacer between this set of coils and another set called a start winding which functions (when the switch is turned on) to start the rotor and to prevent burn-out. When both sets of coils are in place, they must be held firmly against movement, abrasion, or unbalance by the use of a slot wedge which may be hard fiber, hard wood, phenolic laminate, glass melamine, or silicone glass accord-

Figure 15.7.   This illustrates the manner of placing coils into the slots of a stator for a motor.

ing to requirements. Soldering fluxes are used in the connection of coils, and, if there is a commutator, the bars are soldered to the proper coil leads.

Then follow, in most cases, one or more treatments of varnish which bond the conductors, dampen vibration, and give better aging characteristics and better moisture protection. In some cases further protection of the end windings—those that stick out of the slot—is needed; here alkyd resin, putty-like compounds or viscous, pigmented alkyd enamels may be applied and baked. Baking varnishes are used almost exclusively because of their superior electrical, thermal, and mechanical properties. Air-drying varnishes are applied only to allow temporary operation or to make quick repairs.

In polyphase stators, coils belonging to separate phases may find themselves adjacent or in the same slot; thus varnish cloth or paper strips may be inserted for additional dielectric strength. The voltage per turn is usually very low, but the full voltage may occur between phases. Leads must be provided and connections made which involve the use of varnish-cloth-wrapped or vinyl-extruded lead wire, with varnished sleeving over the connections and cross-overs.

The switch mechanism and the starting mechanism call for various molded or laminated plastics.

There is just one insulating material of interest in the magnetic circuit—that is the core plate enamel. The armature or field core is not made of solid, magnetic steel. It is made of layers (or laminations) of thin sheets of a high-silicon steel of strong magnetic properties to provide a strong magnetic field under the poles. These steel punchings are pressed together, bonded, bolted, or clamped by end plates. This core plate assembly must be aligned perfectly and must have a thin film of insulation between laminations.

There are eddy currents formed in the iron which, if allowed to flow uninterruptedly as they would in a solid steel core, would overheat and burn out the adjacent coils and even melt the iron in extreme cases. A core plate enamel is applied to the sheet metal either before or after punching. This high-temperature-baked enamel, while thin, provides the resistance required to protect the punching by controlling these eddy currents.

It is always best to speak of the stator or rotor rather than fields or armatures, because in some machines, especially large generators or synchronous motors, the field rotates and the armature remains static.

As we move on to larger and larger machines with more subtle changes in design, we note a very definite change to what is called the open-slot construction. The smaller motors all have partially closed slots and the windings are called random, being placed in the slot as they happen to fall. This major change in the design of the larger machines is that the coils are constructed and formed into shape and are completely insulated before they are placed in the slots. These are called "form" or "formed" windings (Figure 15.8).

Rectangular wire is used ordinarily for the sake of space economy. The insulating material may be enamel, "Formex" wire enamel, cotton, glass, or asbestos. Since a tight fit is required, the size of slot must be regulated to the size of winding required plus the thickness of insulation needed to protect it. The coils are first wound in loops or long bars for the really big machines. The wire may be varnish-treated before winding, and it may get one or more coats of varnish after being wound. Bond strips—paper coated with a thermosetting or thermoplastic adhesive—

are placed between layers or on the outside of the straight or slot portion of the coil. The coil is then molded to size and the turns are bonded sufficiently to allow for the subsequent pulling out to a hexagonal shape and to hold position in subsequent high-temperature varnish treatments.

The insulation is then built up by tapings and varnish treatment, using untreated cotton tapes, varnish cloth tapes, or mica or glass tape, according to the requirements; subsequently the coil may receive a

Figure 15.8. Formed insulated coils being placed in stator for large A-C motor.

special wrap of varnished cloth around the slot portion, which is either cemented with a "special sticker" or a gutta-percha backed tape, or wrapped on. Some limited use has been made of synthetic tapes—cellulose acetate, vinyl, and "Formvar," as well as polyethylene—and more use may be made of such materials in the future.

The coils are then assembled, using slot armor and wedges and spacers as before. The assembled stator or rotor may then receive spray or dip coats of an air-dry or baking varnish. This is practically the only place where air-drying varnishes are used, other than in taping operations. For best electrical, chemical, and mechanical properties, baking (or thermosetting) varnishes are preferred.

While synthetic resins are almost universally used today for random wound apparatus, reliance is still put upon asphalt varnishes for treating the larger machines, using synthetic resins only in the finishing operation in order to obtain added oil and chemical resistance. Developments using polyester resins have been announced and further progress along that line surely is to be expected.

For high-voltage machines, mica tapes are used. Compounding by a vacuum-pressure process is required to produce a dense, corona-resisting coil for high voltages.

In the construction of a commutator, use is made of molded and cut mica parts called segments, to insulate each copper bar. The commutator may also be insulated from the shaft and the windings by what are called side and ring mica parts.

Magnet coils are used as relay or control coils, usually wound on a spool body of many turns of enameled wire in layers with paper, acetate, or other separating insulation. Examples of important insulating materials used in this type of coil are the treating varnish; lead insulation; sheet insulation to wrap around the spool and the outside of the coil; pasted mica sheet under and around the connections to the leads; insulating papers; varnish-cloth wraps, etc. Some coils require as complete a filling as possible; in others it is sufficient to seal the surface. Moisture resistance, heat transfer, stability under vibration, surface sealing, and lead-corrosion are service requirements that may be encountered, and for which proper insulation need be designed.

Field coils may be of large size and usually such are wound with a compound of a thermosetting phenolic varnish plus a filler mixed on the job and brushed on each layer as it is wound. The coil is wound on a spool which requires ground insulation of hard fiber, varnished cloth, or mica, and which fits over the pole clamped to the assembly so as to withstand shock and rotation. The electrical requirements are not exacting but the coils must be rigid and strong.

Besides the hot-melt, vacuum-pressure, treating compounds just mentioned, other compounds used are putties applied to end windings, to pockets between coils, and to surfaces for mechanical protection. They are used also to promote better heat transfer. Such coatings ordinarily are tough and hard, and possess considerable heat resistance.

Potting or filling compounds are usually hot melt waxes or asphalts that are poured around transformers, into cases, into cable joint enclosures and pot-heads, and over or into bolt heads, screw holes, and bushings.

The largest use of varnished cloth is in cable construction. It has a potential competitor in various new synthetics such as polyethylene and butyl rubber which may be applied by extrusion. Varnished cloth requires special impregnating cloth varnishes with good electrical properties, penetration, flexibility, and aging. Cloth is manufactured as 36-inch master rolls which are later cut into tapes. The use of varnished cloth, papers, and fibers in motors, in generators, and in transformers, and their use as spacers and coil wrappers, have been mentioned. They have similar applications on coils and leads, and bushings.

Mica, like glass, is an inorganic material, and it has the highest electrical and thermal resistance of the common insulating materials. It is used in small pieces for washers, spacers, and for capacitor insulation. Like glass, its limited mechanical properties require that it be combined with a binder. Until recently these binders have always been organic and this has limited the thermal and electrical properties of mica insulation. Built-up mica consists of pasted mica in sheets called plates, or cut into tapes. The sheets may be laminated, molded, or cut to form commutator segments, cones, or side mica ground insulation for commutators. Commutator segments and heater plate must be hard and rigid; the others may be flexible or thermoplastic.

Alkyds, shellac, copal, and asphaltic varnishes are used as binders for mica parts. Alkyd binders have been preferred to date because of their superior arc resistance, bonding strength, and good oil resistance. Flexible mica tapes are employed in winding splittings, well lapped and faced on both sides with thin paper, cloth, or coil. An important use of mica is in composite insulation used in slots and ground insulation—there are combination sandwiches of mica with paper pressboard, cloth, glass cloth, rawhide fiber, etc. Round mica tubing is also manufactured for bushings, brush-holders, and rheostat rods, for high-temperature use. With the coming of silicones, a better high-temperature binder is now available for mica products.

Besides tubing or sleeving, cords and twines are used for tying down coils, connections, and leads and as binding and protection over armature lead-ins to the commutator. These are sometimes impregnated with coatings to improve their insulation properties or thermal resistance.

References

1. American Society for Testing Materials Standards on Electrical Insulating Materials, ASTM Committee D9 in Electrical Insulating Materials.
2. Conference on Electrical Insulation—Annual Reports National Research Council.
3. Ellis, Carleton, "Handbook of Plastics," D. Van Nostrand Co., Inc., New York, 1943.
4. Gibson, D. L., and Braithwaite, C. H., Jr., "Control of Electrical Insulating Varnishes," *Trans. Am. Inst. Elec. Engrs.,* **14** (1945).
5. Leihinger, Faucett-Houpes, "A Survey of Electrical Insulation Practices," *Univ. Illinois Bull. 47, No. 23* (1949).
6. Mathes, K. N., "Evaluating Insulating Varnishes," *Gen. Elec. Rev.* (May 1945).

7. Miner, D. F., "Insulation of Electrical Apparatus," McGraw-Hill Book Co., New York, 1941.
8. Moses, G. L., "Electrical Insulation," McGraw-Hill Book Co., New York, 1951.
9. Moses, G. L., "Heat Setting Varnishes," *Partway Electrical Eng.* (Dec. 1942).
10. National Electrical Manufacturers of America Standards.
11. Richardson, H. M., and Wilson, J. W., "Fundamentals of Plastics," McGraw-Hill Book Co., New York, 1946.
12. Smith, J. J., and Scott, J. A., "Temperature-Aging Characteristics of Class A Insulation," *Trans. Am. Inst. Elec. Engrs.*, **58** (Sept. 1939); **61** (July 1942).
13. Whitehead, S., "Dielectric Phenomena," Vol. 1, D. Van Nostrand Co., Inc., New York, 1927.

16 : Silicone Resins in Heat-Resistant Paints

MYRON KIN

Dow Corning Corporation
Midland, Michigan

About a hundred years ago, the only silicon-containing compounds that contributed much to human welfare were the mineral silicates and the natural forms of silica. These were used in glass and ceramic products and as components in the formulation of adhesives. The organic derivatives of silicon were unknown. Probably the study of organic silicon compounds was delayed by the fact that neither free silicon nor organic compounds of silicon occur in nature. These compounds had to be synthesized before they could be studied.

Friedel, Crafts, and Ladenburg[1,2] prepared the first organic compounds of silicon during the latter half of the nineteenth century. A description of the Grignard reaction was published[3] toward the turn of the century, and shortly after, Kipping[4] began his study of organosilicon compounds. Because the Grignard synthesis proved to be a very convenient and versatile method for attaching hydrocarbon groups to the silicon atom, Kipping and his co-workers were able to prepare a great number of organosilicon compounds. The results of this research described in over fifty papers laid the foundation for our present knowledge in this new field of chemistry.

In 1930 interest in organosilicon chemistry spread to this country and gained added impetus when Hyde[5] developed the first flexible silicone resin in his search for a heat-stable binder for glass cloth. Other equally interesting and potentially useful silicone polymers were synthesized. The production of silicones on a commercial scale began in 1943[6,7] and quickly expanded as new products were developed and perfected. Silicones now include a wide variety of products in the form of liquids, compounds, greases, resins, and rubbery materials.

Chemistry of Silicones

Silicones possess some unusual combinations of properties. A look at the chemical make-up and a brief review of the chemistry involved will disclose why the physical and chemical characteristics of silicones are different from their hydrocarbon counterparts. Silicones are semi-inorganic materials and possess much of the stability and the good dielectric properties associated with glass, quartz, and the mineral silicates. They acquire flexibility, solvent solubility, ease of handling, and water repellency through the synthesis of organic groups.

Silicones and hydrocarbons behave as differently as silicon and carbon. Although these two elements are in the same group in the periodic table and both of them are tetravalent, they react quite differently with other elements, especially chlorine, oxygen, and carbon itself, the three elements that are at present most important in silicone chemistry. For example, carbon dioxide is a gas while silicon dioxide is a very heat-stable solid. Carbon tetrachloride is relatively stable in presence of water while silicon tetrachloride hydrolyzes instantly to form silica and hydrochloric acid.

The two linkages which are most important in silicone chemistry are the silicon-to-oxygen and the silicon-to-carbon bonds. Silicones are built on a molecular skeleton of silicon-oxygen atoms just as hydrocarbons are built on a skeleton of carbon-to-carbon atoms. The bond energy of Si-O linkage, however, is about one and one-half times as great as the bond energy of the C-C linkage.[8] Furthermore, the Si-C linkage is strong and relatively heat-stable, especially when the organic group is small and compact.

Silicones are made by two general methods: by substitution and by direct synthesis. In the substitution methods, a silicon compound such as silicon tetrachloride or tetraethylorthosilicate is used. The halide or ester group is replaced by organic groups through a single or multiple reaction step. In the direct method, silicon is reacted directly with a hydrocarbon halide such as methyl chloride to form the organochlorosilanes. Of the several substitution methods known, the Grignard method has been the most important thus far. The basic chemical reactions of both these two methods can be summarized as follows:

(1) *Grignard Reaction*

$$RMgCl + SiCl_4 \longrightarrow \begin{matrix} RSiCl_3 \\ R_2SiCl_2 + MgCl_2 \\ R_3SiCl \end{matrix}$$

(2) *Direct Synthesis*

$$RCl + Si \xrightarrow[\text{heat}]{\text{Catalyst}} \begin{matrix} RSiCl_3 \\ R_2SiCl_2 \\ R_3SiCl \end{matrix}$$

organochlorosilanes

The organochlorosilanes can be prepared by either method and separated by distillation into the various intermediate products. From this point on the process is the same, namely that of hydrolysis and condensation.

(3) *Hydrolysis*

$$\begin{matrix} RSiCl_3 \\ R_2SiCl_2 \\ R_3SiCl \end{matrix} + XH_2O \longrightarrow \begin{matrix} RSi(OH)_3 \\ R_2Si(OH)_2 \\ R_3SiOH \end{matrix} + XHCl$$

organosilanols

(4) *Condensation*

$$\begin{matrix} RSi(OH)_3 \\ R_2Si(OH)_2 \\ R_3SiOH \end{matrix} \xrightarrow{-H_2O}$$

The physical form and the properties of the finished material are determined by the organic radicals involved and by the degree of substitution. The degree of substitution or R/Si ratio depends on the choice of the organochlorosilane intermediates. For example, when an organodichlorosilane (R_2SiCl_2 with R a methyl group) is hydrolyzed and condensed, a liquid polymer is formed either in a linear or cyclic form.

The R/Si ratio is 2.0 with two methyl groups attached to each silicon atom. A monofunctional unit such as the trimethylmonochlorosilane can be introduced into the polymer as a chain stopper to control viscosity. The products made from the mono- and difunctional intermediates are liquids and noncuring because they are not cross-bridged. The cross-linking that occurs in resinous structures can be accomplished, however, by producing polymers containing trifunctional or tetrafunctional units. By varying the organic radicals and the R/Si ratio it is possible to obtain resins ranging from very flexible and slow-curing materials to hard, brittle and fast-curing bodies.

General Properties of Silicones

Silicone products regardless of whether they are fluids, resins, or rubbery materials possess a number of common basic properties.[9] The first common quality is their stability to a wide temperature range. They have the special ability to withstand not only high temperatures, but also extremely low temperatures. At high temperatures silicones have given satisfactory service at 100 to 200°F above the limits of comparable organic materials. These same heat-stable materials retain a large share of their properties at low temperatures—in some cases as low as —125°F.

The second property common to all silicones is their moisture resistance. This is understandable when one considers their structure. The silicon-oxygen-silicon chain surrounded by nonpolar hydrocarbon units just naturally repels water.

In addition, silicones are resistant to chemicals and oxidation. The lack of any unsatured bonds contributes to this ability to withstand contact with oxidizing solutions, mineral acids, alkalis, and salts.

Finally, the dielectric properties of most silicones are very good. The dielectric strength of cured silicone resins is of the order of 1,500 to 2,000 volts per mil on thin sections. On arc flashovers silicones do not track or carbonize.

Nonresinous Silicones in Protective Coating Industry

A number of nonresinous silicone products have proved their usefulness in the protective coating industry. The dimethyl fluids are widely used to prevent flooding and silking in pigmented finishes.[10] Concentrations of only 1 to 100 ppm are used. Why such low concentrations are effective has not been completely explained. Undoubtedly, the low surface tension of the silicones is a contributory factor, It has also been established that the phenyl-containing fluids are less effective than the dimethyl fluids. Some care must be exercised in establishing the minimum concentrations since excessive amounts can lead to undesirable surface effects such as cratering or crawling. A methyl silicone resin has recently been found to be quite effective without having too critical a concentration. Figure 16.1 compares the effect of the methyl- and the phenyl-containing silicone fluids with the methyl silicone resin at a concentration of 3 parts per 10,000 parts enamel.

These fluids are also being used to improve leveling in organic finishes. The dimethyl silicone fluids are incompatible with most organic film formers. The phenyl-containing fluids, on the other hand, are more compatible and so are sometimes used to impart mar resistance in conventional enamels.

A silicone compound is widely used as a defoamer in both solvent and aqueous systems. Here again the effective concentrations are very low, of the order of 1 to 100 ppm.

Figure 16.1. The effect of a phenyl methyl, a dimethyl fluid, and a methyl silicone resin on pigment floating of a conventional enamel. Reading from left to right: control; phenyl methyl polysiloxane, 3 parts per 10,000 enamel; dimethyl polysiloxane, 3 parts per 10,000 enamel; methyl silicone resin, 3 parts per 10,000 enamel.

Silicone Resins

The resins are of primary interest to the paint industry because of their potential use as a paint vehicle. Silicone resins are used in the electrical industry primarily as clear varnishes for coating and bonding purposes.[11] In this use they can be classified as a type of protective coating although somewhat specialized. Their development for these applications has progressed so rapidly that the electrical industry uses the major volume of silicone resins produced. A number of silicone varnishes and resins have been developed specifically for the electrical industry. The adoption of silicone insulation makes it possible to increase the life and wet insulation resistance of electrical equipment tenfold. By proper design, it is possible to double the power per pound ratio in electrical machines such as motors, transformers, generators, and coils.

Another successful, but also specialized use for silicone resins is as a coating to eliminate the need for greasing pans used in the commercial baking of bread.[12] The bread pans are glazed with a very thin coat of a special silicone product. When properly applied and cured by baking, this silicone coating gives easy release of bread for several hundred bakes before it has to be renewed. Saving of grease and time as well as improved cleanliness are realized by this process.

A number of silicone resins have been made available to the paint chemist for formulating heat-resistant finishes. Some are relatively slow curing and very flexible. They require 1 to 3 hours at 482°F to produce tack-free coatings.[13] Others are faster curing and more thermosetting. In general, these silicone resins are compatible with each other. Coatings with a wide range of flexibility and hardness can, therefore, be produced by altering the percentage of each type of resin. Silicone resins are readily soluble in aromatic solvents and can tolerate a large proportion of the aliphatic solvents. They are very light in color and do not discolor upon aging. Since there is no need to take into consideration darkening of the paint vehicle, the silicone resins can be used in white and light-colored enamels at a much lower pigment-to-binder ratio.

Paints and enamels based on these silicone resins are no different in appearance than those based on conventional resins. They can be brushed, sprayed, dipped, silk-screened, or roller coated. Silicone enamels are outstanding for their heat, chemical, moisture, and weather resistance, as well as for their color and gloss retention. More about these properties later.

Silicone resins have a number of limitations that have retarded their widespread use in protective coatings. These are (1) high cost, (2) relative incompatibility with the more common organic resins, (3) low intrinsic viscosity, (4) only fair toughness and abrasion resistance, (5) relatively poor solvent resistance, and (6) slow curing rates. No attempt is made to list these limitations in any order since they are so interdependent. For example, if their compatibility with other film-forming materials were increased, it would be possible to formulate finishes that would be not only cheaper, but also tougher, faster curing, and more solvent-resistant.

Various types of silicone paints are on the market today.[14,15] These include paints with straight silicone resins and those containing blends of silicones and various organic materials, more commonly referred to as modified silicones. Another method of remedying the drawbacks involved in the use of silicone resins has been the study of copolymers of silicone and organic materials. This attack seems to be more promising because the copolymers overcome some of the disadvantages without sacrificing too much of the stability inherent in the silicone resins.

Silicone-Alkyds

The silicone-alkyd copolymers have been investigated to a greater extent than other combinations.[16,17,18,19] Work to date indicates that the film properties can be improved at only a slight sacrifice in heat and chemical stability. These copolymers are faster curing and more thermosetting, and they have much improved adhesion to metals.

The use of saturated fatty acid in the silicone-alkyd copolymer permits greater color retention and stability at elevated temperatures. However, intermediates containing unsaturated fatty acids have been made and should prove useful in formulating fairly heat-stable air-drying finishes, but with some loss in color and heat stability.

Properties of Silicone Resins and Silicone-Alkyd Copolymers

Heat Stability. The outstanding property of silicone resins is retention of film integrity after long exposure to temperatures of 500°F and above. At such temperatures, practically all commercial organic resins quickly darken and decompose. Unmodified silicone resins do not discolor or

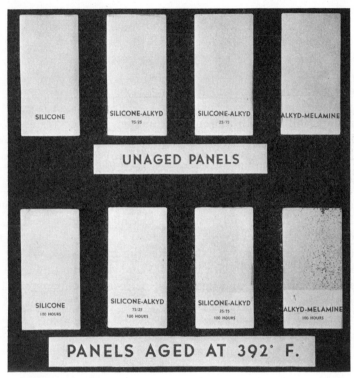

Figure 16.2. The heat resistance and color retention of silicone, silicone-alkyd, and an alkyd-melamine heat-resistant white stove enamel aged at 392°F.

darken even after thousands of hours at 480°F. Weight loss is only 5 to 10 per cent. Test panels coated with various silicone resins, each pigmented with two pounds of aluminum paste per gallon, were aged at 480°F. The least flexible of the resins tested did not show surface checking until after 700 hours A flexible type resin was still intact after more than 7,000 hours. By blending 20 per cent of the flexible silicone resin with the more thermosetting type of resin, the life of the coating was extended to more than 7,000 hours.

Several years ago, the Houston (Texas) Paint and Varnish Production Club[20] in their survey of heat-resistant paints found that an aluminum paint with a flexible silicone resin as the binder was still intact after more than 40 hours of exposure at 1,000°F. The relative heat stability of the vehicle shows up very quickly in a white enamel. Figure 16.2 indicates the relative heat resistance of white enamels made with silicone, silicone-alkyd, and alkyd-melamine resins. The formulations of all the enamels

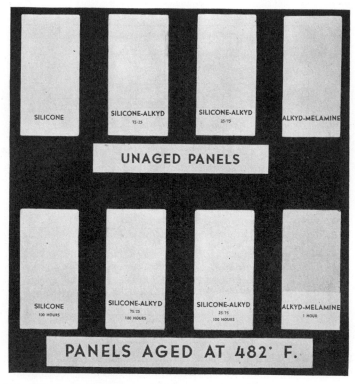

Figure 16.3. The heat resistance and color retention of silicone, silicone-alkyd, and an alkyd-melamine heat-resistant white stove enamel aged at 482°F.

were the same except for the vehicle. The silicone resin was one of the more thermosetting types. Of the two silicone-alkyd resins, one had a ratio of 75/25 silicone-alkyd and the other, a ratio of 25/75. These silicone-alkyd resins were copolymers and not cold blends. The alkyd-melamine resins were physical mixtures. This particular formulation was recommended as a heat-resistant white stove enamel. The silicone enamel exhibited no discoloration after 100 hours at 390°F. The 75/25 silicone-alkyd was almost equally good. The 25/75 silicone-alkyd had darkened, but was still intact as compared with the alkyd-melamine coating which was badly crazed.

Figure 16.3 is even more conclusive proof of the unusual heat stability and color retention of silicone and silicone-alkyd enamels. These panels were aged at 480°F. The silicone and 75/25 silicone-alkyd panels had darkened only slightly in 100 hours while the alkyd-melamine not only discolored, but had begun to craze and peel after an exposure of only one hour.

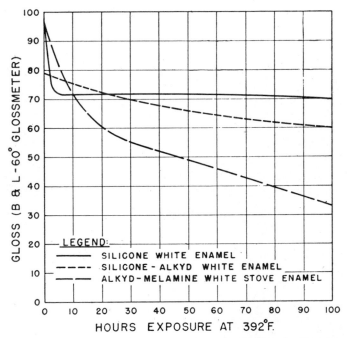

Figure 16.4. Gloss retention after heating at 392°F of silicone, silicone-alkyd, and alkyd-melamine white enamels.

Gloss Retention. Silicones are noted for their gloss retention even after continued heating at high temperatures. The gloss retention of silicone, silicone-alkyd, and alkyd-melamine white enamels upon exposure to 392 and 482°F is compared in Figures 16.4 and 16.5, respectively. The straight silicone, after an initial drop, leveled off at about the same value at both temperatures. At the higher temperature, the silicone-alkyd showed a greater loss in gloss while the alkyd-melamine disintegrated in a few hours.

Compatibility. In some applications, a coating must have all of the heat resistance, color, and gloss retention offered by the silicone enamels. There are other applications where some heat resistance can be sacrificed to obtain better adhesion and better solvent and abrasion resistance. For such applications, organic modified silicone paints have been developed.

The compatibility of silicone resins with some of the common organic film-forming materials is indicated in Table 16.1. Silicone resins are compatible in all proportions with a few organic materials, such as non-reactive phenolics, acrylates, and chlorinated diphenyl and ethyl cellu-

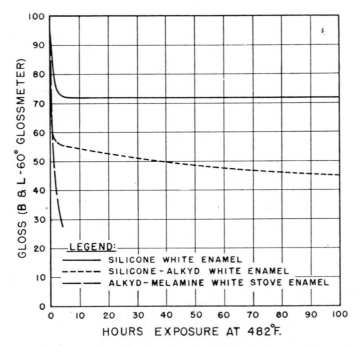

Figure 16.5. Gloss retention after heating at 482°F of silicone, silicone-alkyd, and alkyd-melamine white enamels.

lose. They have limited compatibility with a greater number of materials. A small percentage of these compatible organics can be added to hasten the curing rate or to improve adhesion without too great a sacrifice in heat stability or color retention.

Silicone resins with methyl as the major organic constituent are generally incompatible with organic film-forming materials. As the phenyl content of the silicone polymer is increased, compatibility increases.

As would be expected, silicone-alkyds are much more compatible with organic materials (Table 16.1). This is obviously due to the alkyd portion of the copolymer. The silicone-alkyds, especially those with higher silicone content, are compatible with the straight silicone resins. Compatibility decreases as the alkyd ratio is increased. The silicone-alkyd copolymers are generally quite compatible with each other.

Moisture and Weather Resistance. Silicone resins are unusually water-repellent. Cured resin patties absorb about 0.2 per cent after 7 days' immersion in water. Water repellency and low moisture absorption are combined in silicone finishes with resistance to heat, oxidation, and sunlight to give excellent weather resistance.

TABLE 16.1. COMPATIBILITY OF SILICONE AND SILICONE-ALKYD RESINS* WITH SOME ORGANIC FILM-FORMING MATERIALS

	Silicone		Silicone-Alkyd	
	803	804	XR-379	XR-398
Alkyd-nondrying	I	I	C	C
Alkyd-oxidizing	I	PC	PC	C
Alkyd-styrenated	PC	PC	PC	I
Phenolic-reactive	PC	C	C	C
Phenolic-nonreactive	C	C	C	C
Acrylates	C	C	PC	I
Urea-formaldehyde	I	PC	C	C
Melamine-formaldehyde	I	C	PC	PC
Urea-melamine-formaldehyde	I	PC	PC	PC
Triazine formaldehyde	I	PC	C	C
Coumarone indene	PC	I	C	I
Ester gum	C	PC	C	PC
Tung oil	PC	C	I	I
Linseed oil	I	C	I	PC
Chlorinated diphenyl	C	C	C	PC
Nitrocellulose	PC	PC	C	C
Ethylcellulose	C	C	C	I
Cellulose Acetate	I	I	I	PC
Vinyl chloride-acetate	PC	PC	PC	PC
Vinyl acetate	I	I	I	PC
Vinyl butyrate	I	PC	PC	I

C = Compatible   PC = Partially Compatible   I = Incompatible

*Dow Corning.

Steel and aluminum test panels coated with clear and pigmented silicone enamels have been exposed to outdoor weathering in Midland, Michigan, where chemical fumes accelerate the deterioration of protective coatings. After 4½ years of such exposure, many of the properly cured silicone finishes show no sign of failure due to chalking, yellowing, checking, or peeling.

The weather resistance of three silicone primer formulations has also been compared. Steel panels coated with each primer were all given an initial cure of 6 hours at 300°F. These panels were then given an additional cure of 48 hours at either 77, 300, 390, 425, or 480°F.

The primer formulations were as follows:

Primer A	*Primer B*	*Primer C*
67% $\begin{cases} 10\% \text{ zinc oxide} \\ 10\% \text{ asbestine} \\ 10\% \text{ chrome orange} \\ 70\% \text{ iron oxide} \end{cases}$	70% $\begin{cases} 58\% \text{ chrome orange} \\ 22\% \text{ leaded zinc oxide} \\ 20\% \text{ asbestine} \end{cases}$	67% $\begin{cases} 55\% \text{ zinc yellow} \\ 20\% \text{ Impedex AID*} \\ 10\% \text{ iron oxide} \\ 15\% \text{ asbestine} \end{cases}$
33% Dow Corning 801	30% Dow Corning 801	33% Dow Corning 801

*E. I. DuPont de Nemours & Co., Inc., Pigments Dept.

The panels were rated on a 10–0 scale with 10 indicating no evidence of corrosion and 0 complete failure due to corrosion. The results are summarized in Table 16.2.

TABLE 16.2. EFFECT OF CURING TIME AND PIGMENTATION ON CORROSION RESISTANCE

After Final Cure for 48 hr at °F	Rating of Primer A after Weathering for			Rating of Primer B after Weathering for			Rating of Primer C after Weathering for		
	1 yr	2 yr	4½ yr	1 yr	2 yr	4½ yr	1 yr	2 yr	4½ yr
77	10	9	9	10	9	8	10	10	10
300	10	10	9	10	9	8	10	10	10
390	7	5	4	10	9	8	10	10	10
425	3	3	2	10	8	7	10	10	9
480	3	3	1	9	8	5	9	7	3

These results indicate that the choice of pigments and their concentrations as well as curing times are important in formulating heat- and weather-resistant silicone finishes.

In another series of similar exposure tests, a silicone-aluminum finish coat was applied over a similar set of primed panels. In this case, none of the panels showed any evidence of corrosion after 4½ years. Differences in the primers were nullified by the silicone-aluminum topcoat.

The effect of cure upon weathering properties was investigated with an enamel containing a chalking grade of anatase titanium pigment with a flexible silicone resin as the vehicle. The curing schedules compared were 2 hours at 280°F, 4 hours at 280°F, 1 hour at 390°F, and 1 hour at 480°F. After 4 years' exposure, all coatings were still intact with no evidence of chalking, checking, peeling, or yellowing. It was interesting to note that the coatings cured at the lower temperature were soft and picked up dirt during the first six months of exposure. However, as time went by, their hardness increased, probably due to the catalytic action of ultraviolet radiation from sunlight. Coatings cured at the higher temperatures were quite hard initially and after 4 years were in excellent condition and still retained a high percentage of gloss.

Chemical Resistance. Silicone resins are resistant to dilute and to most concentrated acids and alkalis.[21] Exceptions are concentrated sulfuric, nitric, and glacial acetic acids. Resistance to aromatic hydrocarbons and chlorinated solvents is poor. Aliphatic solvents soften the film, but most of the original hardness is recovered if the solvent is evaporated. Table 16.3 indicates the chemical resistance of a white silicone enamel.

TABLE 16.3. CHEMICAL RESISTANCE OF A SILICONE COATING CONTAINING 60% DC 804 AND 40% DC 802 PIGMENTED WITH TiO_2

Chemical Reagent	Rating After Immersion at 70°F for			Rating After Immersion at 100°F for		
	3 hr	20 hr	100 hr	3 hr	20 hr	100 hr
Acetic acid 2%	E	E	E	E	E	E
Acetic acid 100%	G	O	O	O	O	O
Hydrochloric acid 2%	E	E	E	E	G	G
Hydrochloric acid 10%	E	E	E	E	G	F
Nitric acid 2%	E	E	E	E	G	O
Nitric acid 10%	E	E	E	E	G	O
Phosphoric acid 2%	E	E	E	E	E	E
Phosphoric acid 10%	E	E	E	E	E	E
Sulfuric acid 2%	E	E	E	E	G	G
Sulfuric acid 10%	E	E	E	E	E	O
Sodium hydroxide 2%	E	E	G	E	E	O
Sodium hydroxide 10%	E	E-x	E-x	E-x	E-x	O
Butyl alcohol	E	E	E	E	E	E
Kerosene	E	E	E	E	E-x	E-x
Methyl ethyl ketone	O	O	O	Not	Tested	
Turpentine	P	O	O	Not	Tested	
Sodium chloride 2%	E	E	E	E	E	E
Sodium chloride 10%	E	E	E	E	E	E
Sodium polysulfide 2%	E	E	G	E	G	P
Sodium polysulfide 10%	E	O	O	Not	Tested	
Linseed oil	E	E	E	E	E	E
Oil SAE 30	E	E	E	E	E	E
Petroleum grease	E	E	E	E	E	E
Clorox	E	E	E	E	E	P
Distilled water	E	E	E	E	E	E
Hydrogen peroxide	E	E	E	E	E	E

E = Excellent; G = Good; F = Fair; P = Poor; O = Failure
E-x = Panel attacked at edge, but film intact.

The unusual chemical resistance of the silicones as well as their resistance to staining suggests their use in finishes for many household appliances and industrial equipment.

The resistance of silicone-alkyd resins to most chemicals is almost equivalent to that of the straight silicones. Certain of the silicone-alkyd copolymers have improved solvent resistance.

Pigments for Silicone Finishes

A pigmented coating is required in practically all applications where heat resistance is the major problem. Pigments must be thermally stable and relatively inactive.

For maximum heat resistance and protection, aluminum powder is undoubtedly the best and most widely used because of its singular property of adhering to the base metal even after the vehicle has completely volatilized. Aluminum powder leafs very well in silicone vehicles because of the low acid number (less than 0.2) of these resins. The ability to leaf is retained even after storage for several years. Zinc dust, flaked stainless steel, and cadmium and mica powders are also suitable for finishes resistant to extreme temperatures.

Titanium dioxide, antimony and zinc oxide, lithopone, and asbestine are satisfactory for formulating white silicone and silicone-alkyd paints and enamels. The usual carbon pigments are satisfactory for formulating most black and grey finishes that will not be exposed to above 600°F for long periods of time. Cobalt, copper, and manganese oxides are recommended for black enamels for temperatures above 600°F. Stable reds and yellows may be obtained with cadmium selenides and sulfides as well as with iron oxides, the choice depending on the shade and brilliance of color desired. Blues and greens can be made with the copper phthalocyanines. Although these pigments are largely organic in nature, they are quite stable at 500°F with silicone vehicles.

Lead-, calcium-, and chromium-containing pigments must be checked individually because of the danger of livering the paint and reducing the life of the finish at high temperatures.

Catalysts to Promote Curing

In general, the driers used to accelerate the curing of organic finishes can also be used with silicone finishes. The solvent soluble metal salts are the most practical. Of these, cobalt, copper, manganese, iron, and zinc exert a catalytic effect. Lead, tin, calcium, and chromium are also very active with silicones, but they cannot be used because they limit the storage life. For the same reason, storage of silicone resins and finishes in metal containers with soldered seams should be avoided.

Zinc is the most satisfactory catalyst since it does not discolor or impair the flexibility or heat resistance of the finish. Iron is more effective, especially in top hardness, but it tends to embrittle the resin at high temperatures. Optimum concentration is 0.1 to 0.2 per cent metal based on silicone resin solids.

Although some of the clear and pigmented silicone finishes will air-dry to form tack-free and fairly hard coatings, silicone resins remain thermoplastic and will not develop optimum chemical and physical properties without baking. Even with the addition of catalysts, silicone finishes should be baked at least 30 to 60 minutes at 400°F.

Uses of Silicone Finishes

Silicone finishes are most commonly used where superior heat or weather resistance or a combination of heat and weather resistance is required. They are being used as protective coatings on hot metal sur-

Figure 16.6. Diesel exhaust mufflers. The one on the left is coated with a silicone aluminum paint; the one on the right with conventional aluminum. Exposure—18 months at 510°F in a corrosive atmosphere.

faces including stacks, flues, boilers, furnaces, heating ducts, exhaust mufflers, engine blocks, and space heaters. In such applications where heat is the major problem and color is secondary, aluminum pigmented finishes are most satisfactory.

Figure 16.6 shows two diesel exhaust mufflers located in the Midland plant of The Dow Chemical Company. They were coated the same day, the one on the left with a silicone aluminum paint, the other with a conventional heat-resistant paint. The photo was taken after 18 months exposure to temperatures of approximately 500°F in an atmosphere heavy with moisture and chemical fumes.

Figure. 16.7.   A furnace stack coated with a silicone aluminum paint after one year's exposure to top operating temperature of 1,000°F and corrosive atmosphere.

Figure 16.7 shows a stack from an ethylene furnace in the Dow Midland plant coated with a silicone aluminum paint. Top operating temperature was 1,000°F in a corrosive atmosphere. The illustration shows the condition after one year of exposure.

Ivory and brown modified silicone enamels have been adopted for finishing space heaters. These finishes have to withstand 485°F continuously without appreciable discoloration or softening.

Silicone finishes are also being used on glass and ceramic surfaces. These include resistors, television tubes, light bulbs, electronic tubes, and welding rods.

The use of silicones in the protective coating industry has shown a slow but steady growth as the knowledge of their virtues and limitations has increased. The interest stimulated by the potentialities of this new field of chemistry may result in new and better resins to help solve many problems in the field of protective coatings.

References

1. Friedel, C., and Crafts, J. M., *Ann.*, **127**, 28 (1863).
2. Friedel, C., and Ladenburg, A., *Compt. rend.*, **66**, 816 (1868).
3. Grignard, V., *Ann. chim. et phys.*, **24**, 437 (1901).
4. Kipping, F. S., *Proc. Chem. Soc.*, **20**, 15 (1904).
5. Hyde, J. F., U. S. Patent 2,371,050 (1945).
6. Hyde, J. F., *Chem. Eng. News*, **22**, 1134 (1944).
7. Collings, W. R., *Chem. Eng. News*, **23**, 1616 (1945).
8. Doede, C. M., and Panagrossi, A., *Ind. Eng. Chem.*, **39**, 1372 (1947).
9. Bass, S. L., Hyde, J. F., Britton, E. C., and McGregor, R. R., *Modern Plastics*, (Nov. 28, 1944).
10. New York Paint and Varnish Production Club, *Paint, Oil, Chem. Rev.*, **59** (Nov. 8, 1951).
11. Kauppi, T. A., Grant, G., Moses, G. L., and Hovell, R. F., *Westinghouse Engr.*, **5**, 135 (1945).
12. Kauppi, T. A., *Food Industries*, **194**, 44 (Jan. 1951).
13. Pedersen, W. W., *Offic. Dig. Federation Paint & Varnish Production Clubs*, **282**, 529 (July, 1948).
14. Glaser, M. A., *Product Eng.* (Feb. 1950).
15. Glaser, M. A., and Miller, E., *Product Eng.* (March, 1953).
16. Bowman, A., and Evans, E. M., British Patent 583754 (1946).
17. Goodwin, J. T., and Hunter, M. J., U. S. Patents 2,584,340, –341, –342, –343, –344 (1952).
18. Hunter, M. J., and Rauner, L. A., U. S. Patent 2,584,351 (1952).
19. Doyle, C. D., and Nelson, H. C., U. S. Patent 2,587,295 (1952).
20. Houston Paint and Varnish Production Club—*Offic. Dig. Federation Paint & Varnish Production Clubs, No. 275*, **721** (1947).
21. McHard, J. A., *Chem. Eng.*, **55**, 228 (1948).

Index

Color matches, 45, 46, 120
  calculation of, 133–145
  choice of pigments for, 45, 46, 133–140
    and wavelengths, 140–143
    "metameric," 133
Colors, dye, in luminescent pigments, 115–118
"Compreg," 257
Consistency. *See also* Viscosity
  effect of particle size on, 69–70
Constants
  of pigments, 119
    changes in, causes of, 145
    colored, calculation of, 129–133
    white, calculation of, 126–129
Copal, as binder for mica, 346
Copper, as stabilizer, 196–197
  for black enamels, 361
Copper ferrocyanide, 159
Copper phthalocyanine blue, 166
Copper phthalocyanine colors, 166, 361
  chemical structure of, 165
  crystallization of, 166
  light-fastness of, 159
  properties of, 165–166
  uses of, 166
Copper phthalocyanine green, 166
Corrosion
  causes of, 64–65
  control, defined, 4
  damage in U. S., annual, 61
  defined, 61
  inhibition, mechanism of, 66–67
  mechanism of, 61–65
    alkaline theory, 62–63
    electrochemical theory, 63–65
    oxygen attack theory, 62
    peroxide theory, 62
  of dissimilar metals, 64
  resistance
    effect of curing time on, 359–360
    effect of pigments on, 33, 61–80, 359
    effect of zinc yellow on, 67, 158
  seawater, tests for, 79
  vs. exposure, 74
  vs. surface condition, 74
  vs. vehicle composition, 73
Corrosion-resistant coatings, 182, 183, 304–320
  adhesion of, 311
  air-dry, 320

application of, 305–311
chemical resistance of, 304–305
effect of curing on, 359–360
effect of pigmentation, 359
failure of, mechanisms, 317–318
for metals, factors affecting, 304–318
permeability of, 311–317
resins in, 170, 180–181, 320
surface preparation for, 70–71, 75–77, 306–309, 312
types of formulations for, 319–320
Cost
  of coatings, 42–44
    sprayed, 38
  of colored pigments, 38
  of enamels, 42
  of raw materials, 37
  of silicone resins, 38
Cost index of coatings, 42–44
Curing
  aminoplast resins, 212–215
  effect on corrosion resistance of, 359–360
  of amino resins, 212–215
  of epoxy resins, 339
  of films, 23, 319
Cyclohexanone, 173, 175

D

Deflocculation, 48–52, 56
  effect on flow, 49, 51
  effect on gloss, 59
  effect on mixing, 50
  effect on settling, 59
  effect on yield value, 54
DeVilbiss-type steam unit, 264
Dibenzanthrone violet
  in automotive finishes, 165
  properties of, 165
Di-2-ethylhexyl phthalate, 176–177, 180
Diisobutyl ketone, 187
Dilatancy, 55–57
Diluents. *See also* Thinners
  aromatic hydrocarbon as, 173, 187
  ratio to dispersant, 186–187
    effect on viscosity, 188
Dilution ratio, of "Vinylite" resin, 172–173
Dimethyl silicones, 351–352